In The
Of The Wind

AN EXPERIMENT WITH DEATH

James Christie

For Chris
y para la gente y el duende de Jimena de la Frontera

Author's Note

This is a true story. The events narrated actually occurred in Jimena de La Frontera between December 8th and December 29th 2003. For reasons that will become clear the names of five people have been changed, and in two cases, their identities have been thoroughly disguised. La Casa Blanca does exist, but not *quite* where I have placed it in the story. This book is dedicated to the memory of Anthony Zander, and also to Elizabeth Hammond and Julian Boyd. With Elizabeth and Julian's kind understanding, it is also dedicated to my wife Joanna, who suffered me in my pursuit of this quest.

MAGE PUBLISHING:
27 Clifford Moor Road, Boston Spa, Wetherby LS23 6NU
Fax: 01937 845660

ISBN: 0-9527109-3-5
© James Christie - Mage Publishing
Printed by TJ International Ltd. Padstow, Cornwall.

Part One

The Love That Is Held In The Heart

Extract from a taped interview with Anthony Zander
10th December 2003, Spain

"Whether you live in Bournemouth, Bermuda or Beijing, and no matter whether you are Christian, Moslem or Jew, regardless of your cast, colour and tradition, be you rich or be you poor, you are a member of the human race and as such you have one thing in common with every living thing on this planet. You are going to die! There is no escape. One day, for whatever reason, your heart will stop beating and that will be the end of it.

"This life, the only life you have ever known, will be over – and then the mystery begins. Do you fall into the black void of forgetfulness – a permanent hole of dreamless sleep, a scenario where your life spark is snuffed out for ever and everything you have done with that life, the triumphs, the disasters, the successes, the failures, the lessons, the loving, the myriad experiences that have formed your thoughts, beliefs and actions – do they all count for nothing? Are they meaningless and without point? Or is there something else? And if there is something else, what is it? Where is it and how does it work, and will that 'something else' be the same for all of us or will there be variations depending upon our faith and creed?

"Many people from a variety of different cultures believe that Death is not the end of the story but merely a gateway of transition from one life to another. A better life lived on a different plane of existence. This place, called Heaven in many languages, and appropriately enough derived from the word 'haven' is supposedly the place of peace and personal enlightenment, of spiritual grace and tranquillity where all inequalities are equalled, all wounds and hurts are healed, and we all, in our different ways, come closer to the source energy that created us. Furthermore, as an added bonus, we are reunited with our loved ones and ancestors who have gone before.

"Sounds divine, doesn't it? So why is that even the most hard pressed of us, from the lowliest untouchable in the back streets of

New Delhi to the loneliest drug addict in the back streets of New York, does not want to die – and fights tooth and nail to hang on to the last vestiges of life, no matter how awful and untenable that life might be? Why is it that our most enlightened spiritual pundits from Arch Bishops to Imams, New Age Angelics to evangelists of any creed, are not in any great hurry to go to this other 'better' life?

"And yet there is an even more fundamental question to be asked. Given that death is such an intrinsic part of our lives and always has been, given that we all, as it were, are in the same boat, and given its absolute inevitability, why do we fear it so much? And make no mistake, despite all religious faiths and platitudes, we are terrified witless by the thought of dying – and if not in our intellectual conversations with our fellow men, then certainly within the recesses of our private imaginings, we rail and recoil against the concept. Someone else's death we can deal with, albeit not always easily, but dealing with the prospect of our own death is a different matter entirely. It causes some of us to dismiss the idea completely, others it impales upon the crutch of religion, while others still find their salvation by spending their lives in preparation for the event.

"For me the event we're talking about is just around the corner, and although I most certainly have not spent my whole life in preparation for it, I have invested a couple of years in the project – and in round figures, about three million dollars."

I am in love with Spain. Therefore when the letter from Anthony Zander arrived on November 11th it was immediately noticeable in the pile of junk mail and bills because of the Spanish stamps and postmark. Filled with curiosity I opened the envelope, and along with a single sheet of very expensive notepaper there was a cheque made out to me for $10,000.

I looked at the cheque – yes $10,000 made out to James Christie, and drawn on The Chase Manhattan Bank of New York. It was signed in an indecipherable flourish over a neat black logo line that said "Anthony Zander Executive Admin. Account." Puzzled and just a little bit excited, but at the same time extremely suspicious that this was just another spam scam – "This $10,000 cheque could be yours if you sign up to twenty seven years subscription for Time Life Magazine" – I turned to the letter. Thick cream velum paper, hand written in an immaculate script, and an address that almost leapt off the page: *La Casa Blanca, Camino Hozgarganta, Jimena de la Frontera, Provincia de Cadiz.* I wasn't quite sure where the White House was, but I could remember the Camino Hozgarganta well enough, and as for Jimena de la Frontera, I knew it better than I knew the streets of my own home town. Back in the 80's and 90's I had lived in the village for a while and over the intervening years I had frequently returned for holidays and sabbaticals. Jimena was and always would be a special place for me and insidiously it had become my spiritual home.

I read the letter, then looked at the cheque again. I felt a buzz of genuine excitement begin to tingle through my veins. To all intents and purposes this was a genuine cheque for an awful lot of money: everything seemed to be on the level. There did not appear to be any hooks. So very very carefully, digesting every word, I read the letter again.

"Dear Mr Christie –

I am writing in compliance with the instructions of Anthony Zander to ask if you might be interested in attending a most unusual series of experiments that are scheduled to take place at the above address between December 8th and December 29th of this year. The experiments are designed to prove once and for all that there is life after death and that it is possible to have two-way

7

communication between this life and the next. Three of the worlds top international clairvoyant mediums will be in attendance, and on the strength of your two books "Light In The Darkness" and "Out Of This World" Mr Zander is extremely keen to have you on the team to objectively observe and record events as they happen and then to write a publishable account thereafter.

The enclosed cheque for $10,000 will not affect any further fees and royalties you might receive from anything you might write and subsequently publish, and represents a single one-off payment for your time and expenses in the period 8th – 29th December. We are prepared to provide food and accommodation, but duly note that you have independent links with the village of Jimena de la Frontera, and quite understand if you would prefer to make your own arrangements.

We are aware that this is being presented to you at rather short notice, but the other aspects of the experiment have only come "on-line" within the last few days. I would be most grateful if you could telephone me at the number given at the top of the page upon receipt of this letter, at which point in time I can provide you with more details. If you are not available to take part in Mr Zander's experiment kindly destroy the cheque or return it to the above address – but I really would appreciate a telephone call as soon as possible either way so that I may keep Mr Zander informed.
Yours most sincerely

Elizabeth Hammond pp Anthony Zander"

Of course I knew in an instant that I would go. Yes it was a knee jerk reaction, but also on a psychic level, it felt right and well timed. Justifying it to my wife and business partner might, I realised, take just a little more time and effort.

I began to process by going over the letter for a third time. There were some interesting aspects to it. They (whoever they were) had read my two books and therefore "they" knew of my work with spiritualism and clairvoyance and of my long association with some of Britain's leading psychics and clairvoyants.They assumed that I could write an accurate and objective report, and, if through no other source than my second book "Out Of This World" they knew of my personal links with Jimena. They *might* have talked to mutual acquaintances in the village – I wouldn't know until I got there and did some research of my own – but either way they were prepared to pay me $10,000 (about £6,000) for less than a month's work, and although it wasn't a fortune, right now, in what was essentially a very quiet time of the year, it would come in very handy indeed. A couple of things hooked themselves into my mind; "three of the world's leading clairvoyant mediums" the letter had said – Well, apart from anything else, I'd be more than interested to find out who *they* were. And then there was that magical little line about "two-way communication between this life and the next" – no one had to work hard at convincing me about the feasibility of *one-way* communication, but to my satisfaction and based on all my research to date, a *two-way* link had yet to be proven. I suppose it might depend on what they meant by *two-way*, but I knew what I meant by it, and my professional interest was aroused. And then there was that *other* little bit, wasn't there... The bit that mentioned "further fees and royalties". Oh yes, they had me with that line. Spiritual I may be in part, but there's another, not very nice side to my nature which could best be described as mercenary money grabbing little North Yorkshireman.

And on that very dark note I started to take stock of my surroundings.

The cottage, our home and office from where my wife and I ran our small promotions and publishing company, had always been at least two rooms too small, and on this cold grey November morning it seemed particularly dark and cluttered. I had yet to lay a fire and hadn't even started on coffee and breakfast. We'd had a very late night and the pile of dirty plates and dishes waited accusingly on the draining board. Empty wine bottles and stained wine glasses covered most of the work surfaces, the Marshall amp. and my guitars dominated the floor space of the lounge area and there was a small dead bird on the kitchen floor; an offering from either Merlin or Morgana – Morgana probably, as she was the hunter of our pair of coal black cats who dominated our cottage with claw and paw.

The computer table was littered with papers, bills, accounts and book orders and the hard driving November rain rattled against the window pain in a miserable cacophony of a discordant English winter concerto. The light outside was dismal, dark and lowering and my SAD syndrome inched a couple of notches up the scale of desperation.

SAD, or to give it its full title, "seasonal adjustment deficiency" is a bit like piles, and gout, tennis elbow and housemaid's knee. It seems a bit feeble and funny, the butt of many jokes and misunderstandings, but talk to someone with housemaid's knee, and believe me, they are not laughing! Bursitis, or inflammation of the kneecap, can be excruciatingly painful. Gout can be so crippling that the sufferer cannot walk and will frequently break out into a cold sweat whenever anyone gets within an eighteen inch radius of their swollen feet. Tennis elbow, well that's not much to worry about, is it? Well mate, you try holding a pen or a cup and saucer when you can't move your arm more than ten degrees in any direction without lances of pain ricocheting from your wrist to the shoulder and back again!

A bit like ME, seasonal adjustment deficiency doesn't exist until you've actually got it, and living with SAD has its own set of challenges. Believe me it isn't just a case of feeling a bit fed up about the weather. The lack of light and the perpetual bloody grey depresses the spirit into some unusual caverns of the soul and let's loose a torrent of rage and frustration that makes you want to walk into Marks and Spencers and shout "Woolworths!" at the very top of your voice. The cynic might say this is a load of old bunkum, but suggest to my wife that her arachnophobia is bunkum and she'll soon give you short shift with the lashing of an indignant tongue!

Any given Tuesday morning at nine o'clock during the dark days of an English winter! God, just the thought of three weeks in Spain – almost the better part of month, and time that I was to actually be *paid* for, was enough to lift my spirits.

It had been a busy year – a very busy three years actually, and my wife and I had worked and lived together in close proximity, eighteen hours a day, seven days a week to establish our small business. There was never enough space, never enough *personal* space, hardly any leisure time, and we seldom had a conversation that didn't have something to do with our work. For the past couple of months we'd been getting in each other's way and on each other's nerves, arguing about silly things and on my part, letting principles get in the way of common sense. I loved my wife dearly and I knew that her love for me was as strong and as constant as ever, but God knew we could do with a short break from each other and maybe a few weeks apart might be just enough to remind us of what our relationship was supposed to be about. Whether she would see eye to eye with me on this remained to be seen, but I'd cross that bridge when I got to it.

Next I looked in the diary. Our workload promoting "Britain's most gifted medium" and selling his books had been extremely heavy during 2003 but now towards the end of the year, things were lightening up somewhat. We had two more shows to put on, the last being on December 4th at The Kenton Theatre in Henley-on-Thames, and I had a personal commitment to do a TV recording with my poet friend Adrian Spendlow on December 1st – after that there was nothing in the book until the end of January. Nothing that is, except my 11th wedding anniversary, a little thing called Christmas, New Year's Eve and my wife's birthday on January 2nd. I suddenly realised that this projected trip to Spain might be as popular with some people as a fart at a perfumery convention in Paris.

Gritting my teeth I set about tidying up the cottage. My wife, who'd been up a lot later than I had the night before, came down while I was half way through. Neither of us are what you might call morning people but I bit the bullet, and showed her the letter. As I had imagined, she was not particularly happy about it, but she could see that I was determined to go, and at the end of a disgruntled argument, the $10,000 fee (with the promise of more goodies to come) won the day. But she did have some valid questions:

'Just what exactly are you supposed to do for all this money?'

'Well according to this letter, observe and record some experiments with these three top mediums and then write about it afterwards.'

'Yes but write what, exactly?'

'Er, not quite sure...'

'And who is this Anthony Zander?'

'Again I'm not sure who he is, but his name *does* ring a bit of a bell.'

'Who's this Elizabeth Hammond?'

'Dunno... His secretary or PA I suppose...'

'And what exactly is this experiment?'

'You've read the letter, so right now you know about as much as I do.'

'Well don't you think you should telephone and find out a bit more before you commit yourself one way or the other?'

11

'Yes, I'll do that right now...'

So I picked up the phone and put a call through to Spain. When the connection was made with the usual Spanish *Dija* I asked for Elizabeth Hammond and was told in perfect English that this was she speaking. I explained who I was, and that I had received her letter – and cheque – and was calling now to see if I could glean some further details.

Her voice was very crisp and professional, nicely modulated. She seemed very pleased to hear from me so quickly but she certainly wasn't giving much away.

'In some ways,' she said, 'this is very awkward and I dare say from your point of view, somewhat frustrating. By the very nature of the experiment that Mr Zander is conducting I can't divulge too much information otherwise there would be a breach of integrity and confidence. Suffice to say that this is a very important, and we feel, ground breaking experiment, which if it works, will provide incontrovertible and public proof that there is life after death and that it is possible to communicate between the two worlds... And Mr Christie, I am not talking about circumstantial evidence here but hard tangible proof. The experiments will be recorded both on audio and video tape, but Mr Zander is hoping that you will be here to make a personal, but never-the-less objective recording of events that can be published in some form in the New Year.'

'Fair enough. Can you tell me who your three mediums are?'

She had a nice laugh. 'No I most certainly can't. That would be a major breach of security!'

'Can you give me any clue as to the precise nature of the experiments that Mr Zander will be conducting?'

'Again, no Mr Christie, I'm afraid I can't. But I do assure you that Mr Zander will brief you in person should you decide to accept our offer.'

This was reminding me a bit of Mission Impossible.

'Okay, well can you at least tell me why you have extended this invitation to me?' I asked.

'Mr Zander has read both of your books and he is very impressed by your approach to the subject. Obviously your work has been geared towards the publicising the mediums you work with in the UK but despite that he feels that you are the man for the job. The fact that you have knowledge of a number of different aspects of the paranormal makes you a fine catch for us, and of course we are aware of your links with this part of the world. Therefore, we feel that you would not only be in sympathy with what we are trying to do down here in Spain, you would also be very sympathetic to the environment. We feel that there is a strong element of synchronicity here.'

She talked for at least another five minutes, but said nothing new. This was a clever lady and I wondered how much experience she might have had in the direct sales industry. In the end I told her that I'd be there some time on the 8th December and would phone nearer the time with a flight number and airport. She promised that I would be met, and I terminated the call with an afterthought – telling her that if it was okay with them, I would prefer to arrange my own accommodation in the village. I had good reasons for doing that, but she didn't need to know what they were.

I turned round to my wife who had been listening over my shoulder. 'Well one thing's for sure, love, they know a damn sight more about me than I know about them!'

She nodded. 'I'll make just one suggestion,' she said, 'and that is bank the cheque first and wait 'till it clears before you start making any hard arrangements.'

Needless to say the cheque cleared without a problem and I started organising the trip: an easy flight into Gibraltar and a phone call to an estate agent friend of mine called Jan Miles in Jimena to try and sort out a short term rental in the village. She told me to dream on... There was nothing, as far as she knew, available that close to Christmas. I asked her if she knew anything about the people living at La Casa Blanca down on Camino Hozgarganta – she said that she didn't (which surprised me because Mrs Miles was an old Spanish hand and had been in business in the village for twenty four years, and what she didn't know about what was going on wasn't worth knowing) but she did promise to make some enquiries.

'Very discreetly,' I requested.

'As quiet as a mouse,' she confirmed.

Next I 'phoned another old acquaintance who ran a super little hotel called "El Anon" right in the heart of the village to see whether or not she had a room spare for the required period.

'James we're pretty full, but if it's just for yourself and you don't mind climbing a few stairs, I can squeeze you into one of the small balcony rooms... Would that be okay?'

13

I thanked Suzana Odell profusely, told her that would be fine, and asked if she knew anything about someone called Anthony Zander living down on the Hozgarganta.

'Sorry James, no I don't. There are so many new people in the village these days, and unless they use the hotel, they're just like so many ships that pass in the night.'

In the scheme of things I also spoke to a handful of my clairvoyant friends and asked them if *they* had ever heard of anyone called Anthony Zander. No one had, but at least these phone calls led to a long overdue reunion with an American friend called Harry Andrews who was on a whistle stop promotional tour of the North of England. Harry is a journalist who specialises in the paranormal: he lives in Los Angeles, and gets into the UK once every two or three years. He was on route from Manchester to Hull and I caught up with him for a brief meeting at the Ferrybridge services on the M62. I wanted to give him a few copies of my latest book in the hope that he might test the waters for an American publishing deal, but apart from that, Harry and I had been close friends for a long time and I wanted to see him again for his own sake. It may have been an odd place for a rendezvous, but both of our schedules were very tight and after all, Ferrybridge was only a dozen miles down the road

Propelled by a merciless east wind that blew directly across the North Sea from the Russian steppes, the icy Yorkshire rain lanced down viciously at an acute and unremitting forty five degrees, turning the service area car park into an opaque flood.

The SAD syndrome that, in its most wicked form creates a rage of psychological imbalance and destroys rationale, kicked in with a gleeful vengeance causing waves of madness and intolerance to reverberate and richochet throughout my psyche like a mad bullet hellbent on a trail of suicidal self destruction and as I ran the one hundred yards from my parking bay to the steamed up windows of the cafeteria (getting soaked to the skin in the process) the SAD dragon uncoiled from within my solar plexus and bellowed its roar of hot protest across the soon to be flooded Ferrybridge car park.

Somewhere in the background the huge concave towers of the Ferrybridge power station spewed filth an pollution into the lowering sky, intensifying the bruised and brooding cloud base that caused headaches, depression, aggression, ignorance and arrogance and no small degree of apathy in the hive mind of the indigenous population.

Okay, so we needed the electricity but did we need it *that* much and at such an incredibly high price?

Looking at the filthy grey industrial landscape that stretched across the compass of the horizon, I wanted to vomit with disgust and despair! That people lived (or pretended to live) in this environment caused me to question the mentality of the human race – and if not the human race in general then certainly that percentage of it that resided in these uninspiring wastelands of Northern England. And yet there were people who professed to *like* it up here and who were proud of their heritage and inheritance!

Why?

Despite the ubiquitous power stations this land was cold and dead! Satanically dark and dismal, over populated, seriously polluted, dingy, mingey, mean and parochial. Did these people not know about blue uncontaminated skies, fresh water rivers, clean oceans, white sand and verdant green palm trees? Were these same folk not aware of just how much they were over governed, overtaxed and forced into a soviet-like conformity by the ever present force of the big brother state that *demanded* conformity from the population so that the select and self elected few could remain in their ivory tower positions of influence and all consuming power? And yet, one of the greatest British mediums of all time, my mentor and friend Ossie Rae, had spent his last years in Ferrybridge and he had positively loved the place. Maybe it had something to do with him being a Geordie from Bishop Auckland. At the end of the day all things are relative.

But it did cross my mind that if Britain's politicians got all that they deserved from an uninterested and unenlightened electorate, then that electorate got all that it deserved from the pathetic grey men who professed to be in politics for the benefit of the nation and its people. George Orwell got his dates wrong. 1984 was a none-event but in 2004 he would be nearer his nihilistic truth, and by 2084, if our world continued to turn around its dying sun, he'd be all the way there! Beyond and gone!

Totally depressed and crying with anger within the prison of my own making, I tried to repair my fractured mentality and marched into The Little Chef section of the services and found Harry, calm and serene, waiting for me in a window seat. He'd seen me running

15

through the puddles. Had already ordered me some coffee and had already lit me a cigarette.

The rain drenched down the plate glass as I slipped into the seat opposite him. I picked up the Marlboro, inhaled deeply, and told him that he was a star – which, of course, in his own universe, he was. When I was still a very young man I'd gone to Harry looking for answers but instead of giving me those answers he had only provoked the asking of deeper and more relevant questions. A practising medium himself he had proven beyond all shadow of a doubt that it was possible to receive communications from the world of spirit – but as I'd always believed that anyway, he had been preaching to the converted. My problem was that I wanted to know so much more. How did it happen? What was life like on the other side? Were there angels? Was there a God? My list of questions had been endless but no answers had been forthcoming – at least, not from Harry they hadn't. It wasn't that he was being secretive or nurturing mystery, but that he simply did not have the answers to give me. Even when on more than one occasions I had pushed him, he had refused to speculate, and once when I had almost lost my temper, saying something like *"For God's sake, you're probably the best bloody medium in the world, so if you don't know, who the hell does?"* he'd given me that wise old smile, had twiddled with the extremities of his handle bar moustache and had told me quite simply that, in his opinion, no one knew, and any one who said that they did was projecting theory as fact.

That had been back in the 1970's when I was still only in my twenties. Since then I'd researched and written hundreds of articles on spiritualism and clairvoyance, I'd attended thousands of séances and clairvoyant demonstrations, and had, by most peoples' assessment, written two quite authorative biographies on one of the UK's top young clairaudient psychics... But I still had none of the answers. Certainly I could tell you what it is like to be on the receiving end of a clairvoyant message and I could even tell what it is like to be the medium giving that message; I could tell what it means to be clairvoyant in the 21st century and I could entertain you with hundreds of anecdotes about clairvoyants and their various gifts – but as for trying to figure out how it all actually worked, what the nuts and bolts and mechanics were – I hadn't even got close and more to the point none of the clairvoyants and mediums I'd met over the years had been in a position to give me any hard answers. Oh sure, they may have had theories and they may have been able to speculate, but theory and speculation were no longer good enough for me. They never had been good enough for me.

Interesting synchronicity.

I had planned to deal with some of these aspects in the third part of the trilogy of biographies I'd been writing, but then for some reason best be known to himself, my subject had felt that it wasn't the right time to start work on book three, and so the project had been put on hold for a couple of years, which left me conveniently free to take up the Spanish offer.

Over two cups of coffee I showed Harry the letter and told him about the mysterious invitation to go to Spain. Harry thought for a minute and then said that he'd never heard of Anthony Zander...

'But,' he suggested, 'you could always try Eric Hatton at Stourbridge. He might know something. In fact...' Harry keyed in Eric's number on the mobile and put a call through for me there and then... 'Sorry James, Eric's never heard of the man either.' He paused. 'Have you got any idea who the three top international mediums are going to be?'

'Haven't got a clue,' I admitted, 'but as soon as I find out, I'll let you know. For a minute I did think one of them might be you.'

Harry looked at me laconically. 'James, my lad, I have to look in my diary just to figure out when I can take a bath so the idea of buggering off to Spain for a few weeks is the biggest joke I've heard all year. But apart from that, I haven't been asked, and I'm sorry, but I don't know anything about this Zander chappie at all. Having said that, I do get a good feeling about all of this, so if I were you I'd tend to go with the flow, follow it through and see what happens... Especially,' he added, scanning the letter from Elizabeth Hammond pp Anthony Zander, 'if you can get a book out of it.'

'That's a point,' I acknowledged, 'but it would help a lot if I knew what I was supposed to be writing the book about!'

'Well James, I dare say you'll find out when you get there.'

We talked a bit more about our up and coming plans for the future, then we parted company and I slogged the old red Volvo back up the A1. At the back of my mind the name of Anthony Zander tickled away with quiet irritation. I knew I'd never knowingly met anyone by that name, but there was something about the name which jangled a distant tinkling bell of familiarity. I tried and wanted to remember but memory denied access. So we'd *vamos a ver* and as Harry had said, we'd find out when we got there.

Two: *Gibraltar – Jimena, Monday 8th December*

The Monarch flight from Manchester landed in Gibraltar exactly on schedule. It had been an uneventful journey, but not an altogether happy one. The aircraft had been full to the gunnels with Gibraltarians returning to their fortress for the Christmas break, boozy British ex-pats dashing back to their costa bolt holes thankful to be getting out of the awful English weather, and there'd been the usual ubiquitous happy holiday makers revelling at the idea of having their Christmas vacations in the sun.

Frankly the Gibraltarians were the worse, jabbering away in their Spanglish patois and complaining, as they were frequently inclined to do, about everything British. And here's a little known truth – Gibraltarians hate the British only slightly less than they hate the Spanish and anyone who thinks that Gibraltar *is* British has obviously never spent very much time there.

If I ruled the world one of the first orders of the day would be the return Gibraltar to the governing hands of Madrid, and if you think that's a bit draconian, think of how we Brits might feel if Spain owned Penzance and Lands End!

Once upon a time I'd spent many hours a week commuting between Manchester, Majorca and Barcelona. In those days the wine had been young and had travelled quite well, but now, rather like an over aged Rioja, I'd become slow and thick with tannin and didn't respond well to being shaken up.

I didn't feel too great in my heart and head either, for despite the brisance of friction between us, my wife had not been happy to see me embark on this quest and I felt guilty about being away for those four key dates in our marital year. Also, damn it all, I was missing her, and we'd only been apart for a few hours!

I walked across the tarmac from the 737 to the terminal building along with my plane load of fellow passengers, not sharing in the joy of the babbling Gibraltarians, obviously glad to be back in their beloved enclave after having tasted the sour waters of the outside world. It was raining, but at least it was a relatively warm rain and it was a vast improvement on the vicious unforgiving stuff that had been falling out of the Manchester skies three hours earlier. I cast a glance over my shoulder at the towering floodlit edifice of The Rock – impressive yes, but spoiled and despoiled by the hand of man with his miles of tunnels and obsolete gun emplacements. For years there had been rumours of Britain's nuclear arsenal being stored beneath the mountain, but the rumours had never been proven, and these days nobody cared much anyway. As a place Gibraltar had been kind to me in the past, but it was not my favourite location in the world, and both on a personal level and in a historical sense, it had a lot to answer for.

I cleared customs and walked through into the miniscule arrivals lounge. I'd been told that I would be met, and it wasn't difficult to see who I was being met by. He was tall, well over six feet, with a chiselled Michael Angelo face and thick blond hair bobbing around on his body builder's shoulders. He sported a fabulous suntan with a contradiction of freckles studded across the tops of his check bones. He was dressed in scruffy denim and carried an A3 placard with my name on it.

I went on over and introduced myself.

'Oh right mate, welcome to sunny Gibraltar where it's been pissing down with rain none bloody stop for the past two weeks.' The accent was pure Australian strine that reminded me of Crocodile Dundee and I winced at the verbal onslaught. 'Got transport waiting, but you probably know what the border is like, so we're parked over in La Linea, which means a bit of a walk, but it's better than sitting in queue of traffic for an hour trying to get through Spanish customs. Not a bad idea to stretch the old legs a bit, anyway? I'm Julian, by the way, Julian Boyd. Want me to carry your bag mate, or can you manage?'

I might have been old enough to be his father but I wasn't geriatric just yet. 'I'll manage,' I said, and pushed my little short fat and hairies into double quick march to follow his long strides as he loped out of the airport building in the direction of La Linea and the disputed border between Gibraltar and Spain.

We crossed the frontier – not so bad on foot but a nightmare with a car – and found Julian's wheels parked outside the local McDonalds. It was a Jeep Cherokee that had seen some hammer and obviously not just used for posing or dropping off the kiddies at school. This one had got its wheels into the mud and had done a lot to fulfil its design commitment. I climbed into the right hand seat, and gunning the engine, Julian set off down the sea front towards Campamento and San Roque,

The rain was heavy and persistent, but I really didn't care, for now we were on Spanish soil, and I felt damn good about that. I was back where I belonged.

Years ago, when I'd been living in Jimena and working in Gibraltar as a musician, I had driven this road a thousand times in a battered old series three Land Rover, winter and summer, dry and wet, in baking heat and howling gales. As Julian Freckles Boyd chattered away about the appalling weather, the lack of female talent, the scarcity of spares for old Jeep Cherokees, the poor quality of Spanish beer (my God, did he think that Fosters and 4X were *good*?) I tuned out and counted off the landmarks. The Church at Campamento, Bar Tres Hermanos, the San Roque railway crossing where I'd frequently have to wait for the night train from Algerciras, then would play a reckless game, racing the train along the flat stretch of the campo till we came to the rising land of Castillar. And there was Castillar itself and the turn off for the pueblo of Castillo Viejo, the long straight of pampas grasses followed by the sharp turn and long descending hill towards the San Martin junction. Here I would slip the Land Rover into neutral and coast the hill, gaining a free mile home.

I began to feel a surge of excitement and expectancy as we veered due north and headed down a seven mile avenue of giant eucalyptus trees: soon we passed the old El Vaquero venta at Marchenillas, and shortly after that, like an oblique diamond stretched on the side of a steep mountain, I had my first sight of Jimena de la Frontera, and felt the familiar, almost humbling thrill of the errant son returning to the mother. If Southern Andalucia was my land, then Jimena de la Frontera was my town.

The feeling of familiarity and belonging is hard to explain to anyone who has not felt it themselves. Certainly I was born and bred an Englishman but the very first time my feet set foot on Spanish soil way back in 1972 I knew with that absolute certainty of divine knowledge that I had been born in the wrong place! It was in 1972 that my love affair with Spain began and that affair is still raging torridly to this very day. The love affair peaked when I discovered Jimena in the most adverse of circumstances, back in 1987 – and '87 to '92 were the halcyon days of the relationship... Then in 1992 I returned to England for another love, but Mistress Spain has always smouldered in the background like a jilted lover calling me back to tempt me with her wiles and charms. She'd had me for holidays and vacations, but that had never been enough for either of us.

Julian swung the jeep off the Ronda road and we slogged up into the village, first of all passing the modern blocks of apartments built by the Ayuntamiento to house the Jimenato families who could no longer afford to buy their traditional homes in the village proper because they'd all been bought by rich Brits and wealthy Spaniards from Seville and Madrid. Cuenca's bar was open and as we slowed to deal with the narrowing road that S bended up into the village square I pressed my nose to the Jeep window trying to see if there was anyone in the bar that I recognised. The night was opaque with rain and the window was steamed up, so needless to say, I didn't see much! We cruised past the tree lined village square and then, just past Jacinto's old bar, we took a sharp left onto Calle Jincalata, hooking a dog leg right at the church. Now, for about the first time Julian shut up as he nursed the vehicle up the forty degree climb of Calle Sebastian to hook the sharp forty five degree left turn that brought us into Calle Consuelo. I gave the Aussie his due – he knew how to drive! That corner had been the bete-noir of better drivers than me, and if you could do it without clipping the walls of Eric's old house or denting the wings of Cyndy Riley's ancient Renault 4 that she insisted parking right outside her front door despite the fact that it was a major traffic hazard, then believe me, you were good! He could have taken the softer option of just parking at the bottom of Consuelo, but that would have given me an eighty yard walk up a very steep hill in the pouring rain, so either he was being considerate or he was showing off.

'Okay Mr Christie, get a good night's sleep and unless someone phones you before hand to say otherwise, please be ready to be picked up at ten o'clock tomorrow morning.'

Maybe he was trying to be professional and businesslike, but he just came over as cocky and imperious. I'd already decided that I didn't like this young Australian very much, and although I knew it was frequently a mistake to judge someone by first impressions, I also knew that first impressions lasted the longest and were seldom without some foundation.

'Thanks for the lift.' I said. 'See you in the morning.' Then hauling my bags out of the back of the Cherokee, I walked into Hostal El Anon.

Even standing in the small entrance lobby the familiar and welcome smell hit me immediately. Wood smoke, old leather, oiled wood and rich wine. In a trice the irritating Julian was forgotten and I climbed the well worn tile and timber staircase and travelled back into my history.

The staircase twisted at two right angled turns and led into the bar, which doubled as the hotel reception office. A cheering log fire crackled in one corner. A handful of young male Spaniards sat on high stools along the highly polished wooden counter drinking beer and Bacardi. Low beams arched across the irregular ceiling while all around the walls there were shelves and cabinets displaying model trains and old bits of railway paraphernalia. Garth Odell, the Anon's builder and original owner had had a chequered career as an engineer, initially building railways in East Africa, and then moving over to marine engineering in various ports of call all over the world. He had loved the sea but had never lost his fascination for railways. How he ended up in Jimena running an hotel would be a story in itself, and one which I remember him telling me many times when he was still alive. No one would ever believe the story even if he was still in a position to tell it himself. His love of locomotives followed him through the years into his time as an hotelier, and hence the models, posters and old photographs that festooned the walls. To be sure, there were other pictures – a few pictorial views of the village (one or two photographs that I had taken myself when the El Anon had been my local watering hole) and there were a couple of enigmatic nudes, but generally speaking the theme involved sixteen wheel metal monsters on dusty parallel lines of track.

Suzana, Garth's beautiful widow, was behind the bar, talking to Gabriel, the manager. She gave me a wave of recognition and came round to greet me with the perfunctory Spanish kiss on either cheek. We exchanged the usual long-time-no-see pleasantries then I followed here through the bar annex and out onto the rain sodden sun terrace. The Anon had come together slowly, evolving continuously over a number of years. Garth had bought adjacent properties, linking them together with narrow passages and odd twists of steps. It had become a mysterious place of many levels and moods, and one could easily become disorientated in the labyrinth of architectural design. I have stayed in some of the best hotels in the world, but in terms of oddness, atmosphere and sheer eccentricity, none of them comes even close to El Anon on Calle Consuelo in the Andalucian hill village of Jimena de la Frontera.

Suzana showed me to my room. It was small, but more than adequate for my needs. Warm terracotta walls, low beamed ceiling, thick rugs on a polished wooden floor, and a small window complete with shutters and *rejas* overlooking the inner courtyard. A standard lamp stood in one corner, while next to a large single bed, there was a bedside table with another lamp; both lights had deep pink shades that gave the room a soft glow of welcoming ambience. There was a door leading to the en-suite, and more importantly, a small table next to a built-in wardrobe, which would serve as a work station and an office desk.

'James, I am sorry this is a bit on the small side,' she apologised. 'We're full at the weekend with the start of our Christmas bookings. I could give you a family room for the next three nights, but I'd have to move you back here for Friday...'

'No love, this is fine...'

I dumped my bags on the bed, and agreeing to buy her a drink in the bar later on, I kicked off my damp shoes and started to make myself feel at home. The bedroom *was* quite small but I'd long since got used to living in confined spaces. My life had been full of dressing rooms, holiday camp chalets, ship's cabins, caravans and old cottages. This would be okay. The following day I'd buy some booze and some flowers and maybe light a few sticks of incense.

I changed my clothes, made sure the door locked properly, then headed back for the bar. I bought Suszana and Gabriel a couple of drinks, bumped into a precious old friend in the form of the red haired Cyndy Riley, bought *her* a couple of drinks, ate one of the Anon's superb all-American hamburgers, and then as the little hand moved towards twelve, decided to call it a night.

I thought for a while about taking a walk through the village, but the rain was falling hard and a long day was catching up on me – so as a compromise I stood beneath the archway of the annex, listening to the raindrops splashing against the broad palm leaves, feeling the soft Spanish night carressing my skin, and blowing clouds of pipe smoke out into the damp air.

I leaned my head against the wall and I didn't mind when the raindrops washed my face. Neither Suzana, Gabriel, nor Cyndy knew anything about the occupants of La Casa Blanca down on the river, which in its own way was odd because Jimena was not a big place and the ex-pat community was quite close knit, and yet it seemed that nobody knew anything at all about the mysterious Anthony Zander!

Funny how that name was familiar, even though for the life of me I just couldn't place it.

I grinned into the darkness. Right then, I didn't give a damn. His invitation and his money had brought me back to this place, and for the time being that was good enough for me.

If I tell you that Spain was both my dream and my nightmare I am not sure if I should be placing the emphasis on the past tense, for until this latest summons, I'd thought that my time in Spain was done and the hot summer memories, sometimes interspersed with the deluge of Andalucian rain, were on the distant side of time and destined to come to me only in fleeting fragments of home sickness.

Although I'd spent a lot of time in Barcelona and on the Island of Majorca, for me the *real* Spain was this village of Jimena de la Frontera, inland from the sea, half an hour from Gibraltar, and sprawled like a supine woman across a gentle ridge in the foot hills of the mountains.

Small white houses stood crammed and piled together in an uneven cluster of lichen covered roof tops, red, green and sometimes yellow, angled in supplication beneath the battlements and grey stone keep of the ruined castle, entrenched like an extension of the living rock upon the crag above the town.

Two church spires, one to the north of the pueblo the other to the south, gave a sense of balance to this long thin place: narrow cobbled streets and flagged courtyards gave access to a thousand doors and portals, riotous blooms of bougainvillaea, rhododendron and wild white jasmine provided its colour and heady perfume, with the sharp tang of wood smoke always redolent in the autumn, spring and winter.

When I had lived here it seemed as though an ever present orchestra of sound had welled up from a hundred conversations, the clatter of hooves on hot streets, the tinkling clang of goat bells, the bellow of cattle, the slamming of car doors, the shrieks of playing children, the throbbing strum of flamenco guitars and Sevillanas played on modern stereos... Sometimes, especially in the summer, there had been the haunting call of an evening trumpet, long pure notes that curved their way through the soft night air, and although

25

no one knew the source of this particular sound, it had always been there, sometimes obvious, and sometimes just beneath the threshold of human hearing. I had frequently speculated as to the identity of this spectral musician.

There were seasons in Jimena. Spring was short, lasting only for a few weeks after the mists and drizzle of a dreary March, but it was a period of fecund and burgeoning transformation in which flowers bloomed almost over night after their winter sleep; wild green grasses grew, waving tall and proud in the moist red fields of the campo, and the first rays of the true Spanish sun began to warm my back and tan my face. The skies, hard cobalt blue, would draw my eyes upwards as I looked in wonder for signs of mystic revelation. Perhaps because I never knew *exactly* what I was looking for, I never found it!

By mid-May spring had turned to full summer, destined to spread its glorious wings across Southern Spain until the first violent thunder storms of October. Heat descended upon the land in tangible waves of sunlight that baked white walls, that caused hard parched thirsts, that turned green grass golden brown, drying raging river torrents into muddy arroyos. By July siestas were an absolute necessity rather than a habit or a luxury! One bar owner, a man called Jacinto, would fry eggs on the pavement outside his cafe, eagles and vultures would hover on hot thermals above the castle walls, and those souls who could not sleep or would not sleep found sanctuary in shadowy bodegas and tapas bars. Places like El Vaquero, Bar España and Bar Vargas were never completely empty even in the height of the heat of a scorching August afternoon. Old men played dominos, sipping cubatas or cañas from frosted glasses, aware of their diminishing mortality and choosing not to sleep away their few remaining days of grace.

In September the heat would become oppressive and the vibrant blue of summer skies paled to more pastel hues as the sun became a hazy beacon that hid behind a silky veil of pearl and silver cloud. Always in October there would be the storms – massive cracks of detonating thunder and frenzied forks of jagged lightening that split the sky from horizon to horizon. I would hide, huddled in dimly lit watering holes as the rains came and fell in a torrential deluge that sluiced the cobbled streets free of summer dust, that filled dry rivers with raging heads of flood water that carried all before it – broken branches, dead goats, smooth boulders and even the occasional rusting carcass of some long abandoned car.

November was always a wet month, so too were February and March, but usually in December and January the skies would be a clear cloudless blue and there would be a tingling chill that made eyes water with the sharpness of the thin mountain air. Even in this most Southerly part of Spain you needed to wear jumpers and jackets! Bars did a roaring trade in hot chocolate drinks and the ubiquitous carajillos; every fireplace smouldered with its own burning log with a brazier of charcoal beneath the kitchen table. On many a morning rimes of frost had to be scraped from the windscreens of Jimena's motley collection of motor cars – some of them relatively new, but the vast majority well past their prime. Jimena was not a wealthy village and rare was the car that did not have its fair share of dents and scratches, along with numerous bent panels, rusting fenders and bald tyres.

I'd put up with the winters knowing that they were short, and looked forward to the summers, secure in the knowledge that they would be long. With the Spanish pattern of seasons time distorted into strange dimensions. The days were longer, the years were longer still, and although no man has more than his allotted span of time on this azure planet, that time is stretched into more generous proportions when it is blessed by clean air and blue skies and the gift of golden life giving sunshine.

These thoughts in mind, it seems odd that initially I was carried to Jimena upon the shadows of the moon – but that's another story, old history that has no part in this narrative.

I blew a final billow of pipe smoke out into the damp night, wondering why I was here, and in the same breath not caring. That I *was* here, for whatever reason, was sufficient in itself. Never the less, I sent up two small but ardant prayers of thanks, one to a God whose name I did not know, the other to a man called Anthony Zander.

And come to think of it, I didn't know much about him either

27

Three: *La Casa Blanca, Tuesday 9th December*

Tuesday 9th of December and it was still raining. Not torrential, but that steady drizzle that draped the land in an opaque haze of pearly grey. Neither what I needed nor expected for this time of year. Julian was prompt in picking me up at the bottom of Consuelo and drove us down through the village, hooking a sharp right at Cuenca's bar, and bearing down towards the River Hozgarganta. We turned sharp right again just before the old iron bridge and trundled over the rough cobbles past Casa Amarillo (Vilja and Tony Metcalf's old place) and then went on past Carlos The Third's Napoleonic bomb factory. Once a thriving munitions depot it was now no more than a few rubbled and serrated terraces – a reminder of an older time in another world of conflict. Here the cobbles gave way to thick gooey mud, and Julian dropped the big Jeep into low ratio four wheel drive, constantly glancing left and right; on one side he had the huge boulders at the base of Jimena's forty five degree hill – a small mountain, really – while on the other he had the rushing torrent of the river. There was no room for any kind of mistake, and an ordinary car, or even a 4x4 with a bad driver, would not have negotiated this impossible little camino.

The blond Australian talked incessantly about absolutely nothing. Maybe he was one of those guy's who just loved the sound of his own voice, or maybe I was making him nervous about something. Either way, I just tuned out and looked at the scenery.

The slog along the river bank took longer than I thought it would, and isn't it amazing how the passage of time plays tricks with the memory? I'd had a mental image of La Casa Blanca being just a few yards on from Vilja and Tony's place, but we were a good mile and a half up the track before the narrow road widened into an open arena of trees, large cork oaks to the right hugging the mountainside and tall mature eucalyptus to the left, clinging to and at the same time supporting the river bank. Over to the right was a short driveway that led into the grounds of a substantial white building, part of it bungalow and part of it rising to two stories. It was familiar, and I suddenly realised that the two story section of the building had once been the old mill that had stood here since the year dot and had been a key landmark for the fraternity of walkers that regularly used Jimena every summer as their expedition base. It dawned on me that whoever had built this place (it certainly wasn't here when I had last visited the village a couple of years before) not only had a load of cash in his bank account, but also must have had some influence with the local authorities. This land was on the periphery of the Las Alcondarles national park, and to build here you needed to be in a position to pull a few strings.

It was only when you got really close to the house that you appreciated the fact that it was much bigger than first impressions suggested. There was no access to the two story section from the driveway, but around the bungalow there was a generous verandah terrace made of some expensive looking pale wood. There were a few easy chairs and a couple of tables: a hammock hung in one corner, and there was one of those big portable barbecue grills off to one side. Half way along the frontage there were large double doors. Julian pulled the Jeep to a halt opposite this entrance and I followed the freckle faced Australian into the house.

I found myself in a large reception room, tastefully but sparsely furnished. A couple of Chesterfields in pale leather, a long low coffee table, the embers of a log fire in a large open grate. Walls and ceiling were white with a pale grey tiled floor covered with expensive rugs. In the furthest corner of the room was a large office desk that was glaringly out of harmony with the rest of the décor. There were a couple of telephones and a very expensive looking computer set-up. Behind the desk, now rising to greet me was a pencil thin woman with short dark boyish hair.

'Mr Christie!' She walked across the tiles with a confident outstretched hand. 'Hello. I'm Elizabeth Hammond.'

She wore plain denim jeans and a grey Cashmere sweater. Simple and very effective, screaming "designer label" in exorbitantly expensive whispers. She was a svelte mid-thirty something, with high cheekbones and clear grey eyes. I took the hand – slim and aquiline, and pleasantly cool.

'Morning Miss Hammond, pleased to meet you.'

'Do call me Elizabeth...'

'But don't ever call her Liz or Lizzie,' piped up Julian Freckles, 'or she's likely to throw something at you! When you get to know her really well, if you ever do, you might get to use Beth occasionally. I don't think she minds that too much, do you Beth?'

Interestingly, Elizabeth Hammond completely ignored the rude interruption. 'And what do we call you? James, Jim, Jimmy, or Mr Christie?'

'James will do fine.'

'Do please come and sit down,' she waved to one of the luxurious cream Chesterfields. ' – And Julian, do you think you could find us a pot of tea?'

'Can't Miguel or Maria get it?' he sounded pained.

'It's their morning off, so no I'm afraid not.'

'Ah, okay then Boss Lady.'

…And it was pretty clear that as far as Julian was concerned Elizabeth Hammond was the boss. She was obviously a fair bit older than the brash Australian, but extra age apart, she carried with her an air of quiet authority that was both beguiling and commanding.

I sat on one of the Chesterfields while she sat opposite me on the other. I fidgeted for my pipe but there were no ashtrays, and not just this room but the whole house had a "no smoking" aura stamped into the ether.

'Are you in a position to tell me exactly why I'm here?' I asked, more than anything to break the silence but also to cover the fact that I'd been studying her just as intently as she'd been studying me.

'Yes, you must be very curious…'

I loved her voice, a low sexy contralto, just like my wife's, with no discernable accent other than what you might want to call Posh English.

'But I do think it might be better if you waited for Anthony. He's in the middle of a meditation at the moment,' she glanced at her watch, a Cartier by the look of it, and if not, then certainly a good Cartier copy. 'He shouldn't be more than another five or ten minutes. I know that he's looking forward to meeting you. He was very impressed by both your books and I'm sure that you'll be able to have some interesting and informative conversations. You're our first guest to arrive and Anthony is very excited about having someone new to talk to other than Julian and myself. The rest of the staff don't speak more than a few words of English and Anthony's Spanish doesn't stretch much beyond a few phrases about the weather and the price of wine.'

At that point Julian arrived with the tea tray. He placed it on the table between us, and then slumped down on the Chesterfield, parochially close to our hostess. I wondered if there was something going on between these two, and then decided that there probably wasn't. Even despite the age discrepancy they made an unlikely couple – tousled haired Australian youth somewhat short on manners matched with refined English lady with more than her fair share of poise and sophistication – Nah, it just didn't hang together at all. And yet I still came away with the impression of a familiarity between them, and while familiarity isn't the same thing as intimacy, there was *something* there, even if I couldn't quite put my finger on exactly what it was. Maybe it was just that Julian would have *liked* there to have been something going on. Despite the woman's skinny frame and the age difference, Beth Hammond had a pretty face and there was a sparkle of sensuality quietly crackling away behind her eyes. Rather strange eyes too, I thought. Old eyes set in a young face. A curious juxtaposition.

But then, Julian Boyd, despite his lack of polish, was extraordinarily good looking, and if La Hammond was into brawn more than brain, he'd be ideal for the job.

We talked about the weather, the escalating prices of Spanish property, the subtleties of Andalucian cuisine, and we were at it for a good half hour before the limed oak door behind Elizabeth Hammond's desk opened and a middle aged lady in a nurse's uniform gave Elizabeth the nod before promptly disappearing back behind the door. For one brief moment I wondered if Anthony Zander was into sexual role play games, then dismissed it immediately. The nurse had to have been well into her fifties, built like a brick with milk bottle legs and the beginnings of a matronly moustache.

Elizabeth stood up. 'You can go through now. You might be in there for quite a while but do please check with me when you're finished. I'll either be here or outside on the terrace.'

'Thanks,' I flashed her a half smile, and then I went through to meet the man. Except that he wasn't there, and I found myself waiting in one of the weirdest rooms I'd ever seen in my life.

It was large and square, and apart from two splashes of colour, one from a small red poinsetia plant by a blind covered window, the other from a long shelf of books that ran the entire length of the right hand wall, the room was entirely white. White walls, white ceiling, white window blinds, three white doors, white tiles, a small white table with two facing chairs in bleached white cane. There was the lightest tang of incense and from a small white contraption beneath the white bookshelf there came the faintest of dehumidificational hums. I glanced at my watch. Two minutes, then three. For the sake of something to do, I went over and scanned the books on the shelf. Without exception they were all books on various aspects of the paranormal with a particular weighting towards spiritualism, life after death and different disciplines of clairvoyancy. I would have been blind not to notice my own two books, sitting discreetly between John Edwards' autobiography and half a dozen of the Doris Stokes "Voices" collection. Further along the shelf were books by Colin Wilson, Dione Fortune, Eliphas Levi, Rachel Pollock and Edgar Cayce. Exalted company indeed, and because I'm only human, I felt pleased and flattered.

I was brought back to the reality of the moment by the sound of a flushing toilet. A few seconds later one of the white doors opened and Anthony Zander walked into the room. As soon as I saw him the nagging memory dislocation fell into place and I knew who he was.

There is a fraternity of American actors who never have starring roles in the films they appear in. They are the support team, the character actors whose faces we may well remember but whose names go largely disregarded and unrecalled. This is a great shame because it is this cadre of actors who are the true grit of the film industry.

Let me throw some names at you. Graham Green. James Cromwell. George Kennedy. Mel Ferrer. Steve Buscemi. Sam Elliott. Michael Ironside. J.T. Walsh. Hal Holbrook. Harry Dean Stanton. Colm Feore... and from an earlier generation William Bendix, Jay Silverheels, Chill Wills, Ward Bond, Peter Lorre and Gilbert Roland...

Can you put faces to any of these names? Probably not, but even if you only go to see an occasional film, their faces will be familiar, especially with all the repeats on the various television channels. We all know that Mel Gibson plays Riggs in the successful Lethal Weapon franchise, but how many of us would immediately recall the name of Danny Glover in the Roger Murtaugh role, or the diminutive Joe Pesci as Leo Getz? Most people might recognise Christopher Lambert in the title role of Highlander and they'd certainly place Sean Connery in the flamboyant role of the immortal Spaniard, but how many might recognise the marvellous Clancy Brown in the scene stealing role of The Kurgon?

I'd seen Zander in dozens of films, some of them terrible made for TV on a budget movies, and some absolute big screen blockbusters, even one of the top grossing James Bond epics where he'd played the second villain. For Heaven's sake,. I'd see him on the box only recently in one of my favourite Startrek movies. His name had rung a bell in my head but I'd not been able to place it in the context of a mysterious experiment with clairvoyance. On the other hand if someone had said "Hey do you want to come to Spain and be in a Hollywood movie? Yours sincerely, Anthony Zander" the connection would have been immediate.

He was of medium build and height, short iron grey hair and a neatly clipped beard and moustache. His skin looked pale – almost translucent – and although it may have been autosuggestion with the earlier appearance of the nurse and all hospital white décor, my first thought was that Mr. Anthony Zander was not a well man. He wore white loose fitting trousers and a white shirt, one of those items that is longer at the back than it is at the front; a Billy Connolly special on a flash night out. His eyes were the palest pastel blue, and his voice, when he spoke, was low in timbre with an obvious although not intrusive American accent. Upper class east coast with no trace of a Texan twang or mid-west drawl.

'Good morning Mr. Christie, I'm sorry to have kept you waiting, but Beatrice, my personal nurse, is meticulously fussy, and she wont let me do what I want to do until I've done everything that *she* wants me to do.'

We shook hands, and although his grip was firm enough, the skin felt dry and brittle, and curiously hot. It was not a hand you wanted to hang on to for long.

'I'm delighted to meet you and I'm so very pleased you can be here... Do please sit down, and let me try and tell you what this is all about.'

I pulled out my pocket Dictaphone, and with a nod of permission from my host, turned it on.

He sat in one of the white chairs so I sat in the other. It felt odd and totally unnatural – two facing chairs, four feet apart with nothing in between but white space.

'I have read your books about spiritualism,' he said without further preamble and casting a cursory nod in the direction of the long book shelf. 'You will forgive me, but also I dare say agree with me when I say that they are not literary masterpieces, but that they do have a direct and very honest approach to the highly complex subjects of clairvoyance and life after death. They are refreshingly simple and easy to read and I greatly admire your style of writing.'

'.I'm very flattered,' I said, and despite his left handed compliments it was nothing short of the truth.

'Oh please don't be. I'm simply telling you why I have asked you to be here. You give a lot of yourself away in those books and your connection with Spain, and in particular with Jimena, is extremely convenient and coincidental.

'Basically, Mr Christie, I want you to write a book about me and about the events that will take place in the house over the next few weeks. I did initially speak to Stephen King about the project – I know him slightly – and he would have wanted an awful lot more money than I am going to have to pay you. Furthermore you have some distinct advantages over Mr King that makes you my logical choice of author.'

Hang on! Hang On!

He was speaking here of *the* Stephen King who sold *zillions* of books every year and had seen many of them turned into movies! And Zander was telling me I had an advantage? I needed to know what that was, and I told him so directly.

'First of all, although you will agree, Mr King is a brilliant writer, he tends to write horror novels that border on the genre of science fiction – which is totally inappropriate for the book I envisage having written about myself and La Casa Blanca. Secondly Mr King is not well at this point in time and travelling to Europe would be out of the question, and I do need someone *here* who can write and report on events as they occur. Thirdly he is tied into a very tight contract with his publishers who certainly might not view the book I have in mind as a commercially viable proposition and I simply cannot afford to have my book held hostage to the whim of some pen pushing accountant who doesn't know the difference between a semi-colon and his own rectum. In short, even if Mr King wished to write my book, his publishers would probably not allow it.

'Now, on the other hand, you, Mr Christie, are a free agent! You can write whatever you see fit to write, you are knowledgeable about spiritualism with the required terms of reference, and you have the option of submitting a book to a couple of publishing houses – I actually have three in mind, two in the UK and one in the States, but we'll come to that later – each house will be given a sixty day option, and should they decline, then,' he nodded again towards the book shelf on the wall, 'you are my ace in the hole insofar as you have your own small publishing company up and running so you can publish the work yourself. Either way my book will most definitely see the light of day.'

Frankly my mind was still spinning from the Stephen King connection but I had to interrupt him at that point. He needed to know that it wasn't as easy as he made it all sound. For one thing, major publishing houses did not, as a rule, accept unsolicited work, and even if they did, a sixty day option was not very realistic. The other thing was that Mage publishing, my own small company, was a very modest affair set up originally to publish music and poetry and then suborned into the role of producing and marketing books for one particular clairvoyant client, the vast majority of which were sold across the footlights at that person's demonstrations of clairvoyance. More importantly, if one was to do this as an independent business venture, you wouldn't get all that many books printed for $10,000.

Zander smiled. 'Let me put your mind at rest, Mr Christie. The $10,000 you have already been paid was simply to get you here. You will be paid a further $10,000 upon your return to the UK and a third sum of $10,000 upon completion of the book. Should one of the big publishers offer us a contract, you will at that time be paid a further, and final payment of $20,000 and that will be your flat rate fee for the work we are discussing. All subsequent revenues and royalties shall be paid into a trust fund arranged by myself and although you will retain the copyright of your work, you will be asked to sign a contract committing all proceeds from book sales to the trust fund that I have just mentioned. Should the option *not* be taken up, then that last $20,000 should go towards Mage's publishing and production costs, all subsequent proceeds shall go to Mage, but with a 10% royalty committed annually to my trust fund.

'I know this must sound very confusing, but Beth has all the details down in contract form for you, and you are at liberty to study my proposition in your own time.'

Zander was one of the stillest men I'd ever met. Throughout our conversation he had sat upright in his chair, hands resting lightly on his knees, feet placed neatly together on the white tiled floor. He spoke with a normal degree of animation, but without the movement of body language, it was really rather unnerving.

Mentally I was digesting all that I had been told and I was trying to keep a cap on my excitement. Zander was handing me a win win opportunity and as I counted the permutations of the dollar signs, I began to see just how beneficially life changing this proposition might be. My wife, for example, was itching to move to a bigger house, and while the £6,000 Zander had already paid me would help a bit, a further £24,000 would help an awful lot more.

I am not a great writer, and Zander was quite right in his assessment of my abilities – literary masterpieces are beyond my talent and technique. I think that some of my poetry is pretty good, but who is interested in poetry these days? However, as a jobbing journalist I can usually deliver the goods and if Anthony Zander wanted me to write "Mary had a little lamb" a few thousand times, for the money he was offering I'd be more than happy to oblige him with a smile on my face.

'So,' I said, trying to marshal my thoughts. 'I've got the next few weeks for research, then I go back home and write the book, then, assuming you will want to see the rough draft first and advise me on any corrections and omissions, I'll get on with the submission copy, and providing all goes well, we should be in a position to approach your three publishers in the Spring or early summer – and one way or the other we should have the book out by Christmas of next year, or at the latest, depending upon their schedule, the Spring of 2005. Autumn or Christmas of 2004 if it turns out to be a Mage publication.

'Obviously,' I paused, 'I'll need to have quite a number of conversations with you. I've got to know what kind of a book you want writing, what's going in and what is to be left out. You know, the high points and some of the low points in your life and...'

He raised a hand, just a few centimetres from where it rested on top of his left knee. 'Just a moment Mr Christie... If I may interrupt. I think you are forgetting something of great importance. You were, if you remember, invited here to report on and record an experiment with clairvoyance.'

Lord, in my enthusiasm for those flashing dollar signs I'd completely forgotten all about his bloody experiment.

'I am really not at all interested in having a biography written about me. It would be a tedious and repetitive undertaking and of very little interest to anyone. No, Mr Christie, I am sorry to say that you are not here to write about my life. You are here to write about my death.'

'Your death?' I echoed, looking at him with blank incomprehension.

'Yes sir, my death.'

I waited, and for the first time his confidence in his own words faltered just slightly. 'Mr Christie, I am a very sick man. I have multiple cancers in my body, mostly in my stomach and my gut, but in the last three months it has spread just about everywhere. Quite amazing to think that two years ago I was as fit as the proverbial fiddle, and although these last two years have not been easy, I suppose that I should be thankful that it has happened as quickly as it has. I have known people who have suffered much more for much longer. By nature I am a fighter and although I have fought this disease tooth and nail, I have known for the last eight months that it is a battle that I cannot possibly win. Eight *weeks* ago I was advised that I only had a very short amount of time left. I might see the spring but I most certainly shall not see the summer.

'Now given the fact that my life is almost done and the physical pain that I suffer is *just* tolerable but only with vast amounts of drugs, which take the edge off my mind in the same way that they take the edge off my physical discomfort – which is why I only take the minimal dosage when I can stand the pain no longer, for above all I need to have my mind clear at this time – I thought that I might as well put my passing to some good use. So I shall die at five minutes past twelve on the afternoon of December 17th...'

'How on earth can you possibly know that?' I exclaimed, still not getting it, and in any case, not really knowing what to say anyway, now that our conversation had gone down this incredibly macabre pathway.

'I know that because I was born at five minutes past twelve on the 17th of December 1941 and on *this* December 17th 2003 at the appointed time, I shall swallow a large blue pill with a glass of water, and effectively terminate my own life.'

Another blow to my emotional senses, but there was more to come. 'And then,' there was the faintest trace of a mischievous smile, 'and then I shall do my level best to come back and tell you what it is like over on the other side of the grave.'

I stood up. God I needed to smoke and I needed a drink. Above all else, I needed to move. Anthony Zander watched my discomfort with sympathy.

'At least,' he said quietly, 'you now know what it's all about. We'll terminate our conversation here – quite enough for our first meeting, I think – and obviously you need to look at Beth's documents. Then I dare say you'll have some questions for me, so let us meet again tomorrow...'

He got up from his chair, slowly, and extended his hand. Automatically I shook it, now even more acutely aware of the dry heat of the parchment skin. The hand of a dead man standing.

'This isn't what you thought it was going to be, is it?' he asked.

'No,' I answered shortly. 'It's not.'

'It will still be an incredible experiment,' he said. And then, 'We'll talk about the details later. After you've spoken to Beth."

I found her sitting outside on the terrace – and glory of glories she was smoking a cigarette. On the table in front of her was an open packet of Marlboro lights. As she heard my footsteps she turned in her seat and started to get up.

'Don't bother,' I said, and sitting down in the rattan chair next to her, helped myself to one of her cigarettes...

'Do you mind?'

'No of course not.'

... lit up and blew a long stream of grey smoke up towards the beams of the terrace roof. Amazing, I'd only been in with Zander for less than half an hour, but it seemed a whole lot longer and I felt absolutely drained and exhausted.

'How did it go?' she asked, somewhat nervously, and then 'Oh I'm so sorry! Can I get you a drink or something? Some more tea?'

'Frankly Miss Hammond I could do with a bloody stiff brandy!'

She uncoiled herself from her seat and disappeared into the house to reappear less than thirty seconds later with a bottle of Torres ten year old and cut crystal brandy balloon. She poured generously and I drank gratefully.

'Well?' she said.

'Well what?' I countered, still trying to get my thoughts in order.

'What do you think?'

'I'm still in a mild state of shock, but off the top of my head he's either an extraordinarily brave man or he's completely off his trolley.'

'I'd like to think the former,' she offered, and glancing at her out of the corner of my eye I could see that she was studying me intently. In a moment of totally inappropriate male ego, I was flattered to think that my opinion might be of importance to her.

'Let me see if I've got the basic facts right,' I began, more for my own benefit than hers. 'Anthony Zander is dying of cancer. The guy's in a lot of pain. He's going to terminate that pain, and his life, prematurely, and then he's going to come back and make contact through one of three mediums, or for all I know, all three of them at the same time, and tell us what it's really like on the other side of the grave. For this purpose he's hired the services of three "top" clairvoyants, whom as yet, I know bugger all about, and he's hired me. All I've got to do is observe what happens, write it all up, get it published, collect $50,000 and pass go."

'Crudely put, but in a nutshell, yes.'

I helped myself to another of her cigarettes. 'There's a lot here that I don't know.' I said. 'A lot of blanks that need filling in.'

'Yes. I have a file of information that you might want to read this afternoon, then I can fill in any details over dinner this evening.'

'Dinner?' I queried.

'We've got to eat,' she said.

Elizabeth Hammond drove me back to El Anon. She was a much more nervous driver than Julian, and thinking about Goldilocks, prompted me ask where he was.

She shot me a smile. 'Why? Is my driving that bad?'

'No not at all,' I laughed, caught out by her perception. 'I just wondered where he was, that's all.'

'Probably looking after Anthony,' she said. And then, with a quick sideways glance – 'Appearances can be deceptive, Mr Christie. He might look like a chunk of Antipodean Beefcake, but actually Julian is a very highly trained nurse.'

I raised an eyebrow in genuine surprise. Julian a nurse? If I'd had to guess his profession nursing wouldn't even have been on my list of possible occupations. Life guard, surf bunny, sportsman, model, actor, drug smuggler – yes, any of those jobs would have been more imaginable than nursing.

'And you?' I asked. 'Where do you fit in the scheme of things?'

'Oh,' she swerved to miss a rock. 'I'm just on the admin side of thing really...'

And a bit more than that, I thought – but didn't pursue it. Not then anyway.

She dropped me off in the village square. I had a drink and a few tapas in Bar La Tasca, then wandered up to the Anon, ostensibly for a siesta, but I thought I'd better have a look at the dossier I'd been given, and once I started on it, I got locked in to the subject.

In black and white text it was all quite clinical and straight forward. The legal stuff appertaining to my fees and responsibilities were clearly stated and I signed on the dotted lines of agreement and confidentiality. And I'd been right in my hunch about Elizabeth Hammond. She wasn't just on "the admin" side of things, she was his flaming lawyer!

There was a professional biography of Zander's working life – eighty seven feature films, over two hundred television roles, loads of TV commercials, and thirty seven plays, five on Broadway, the rest "out of town" whatever that meant. There was little or nothing of a truly personal nature, other than listed membership of several organisations and charities including The White Eagle Lodge and The Spiritual Venturers Association, and for a while he had been on the periphery of the Dianetics movement. I smiled at that. Tom Cruise and Nicole Kidman had a lot to answer for!

The smile was a shallow thing and did not last for long. In complicated medical terms there was a resume of his illness and the formal prognosis of his deteriorating condition, which brought me back to the hard fact that this man was not only going to die, he was going to die a premeditated death. This touched something deep inside me that I did not enjoy having touched. Of course, all of us must die – we are born with that inevitability hanging over our shoulders like a Damoclean sword, but it was the element of premeditation that made me shudder. No man should know the time of his own death for that knowledge cripples and corrupts whatever there might be of his life remaining, be it an hour, a day or a decade. It is this which causes me to be totally appalled by the thought of capital punishment, and I'm sure that in a previous life I have been led to the gallows or the guillotine experiencing the horror and the disbelief of what was to befall me. In times of great stress my dreams take me up long flights of stairs from the cold despair of dark dungeons to the waiting terror of the hangman's noose. Despite his motives, Zander's so called experiment was taking me along these dark and turbulent pathways of psychic memory, and on that wet Tuesday afternoon I began to feel very lonely and vulnerable. The idea of a siesta had long since gone out of the window so I put on my coat and went out for a walk.

I slogged up Granadillos, turned left up the serrated 40 degree hill to the end of Calle Alta, where, believe it or not, I'd once owned a small house. I resisted the temptation to and see what state it was in, knowing that whatever the result, it would only depress me. I battled my way up Calle Misericordia, puffing and panting and cursing cigarettes and heart by-passes and encroaching old age, then steeled myself for the final half mile pathway that dog legged it up to the castle that sat perched, part of the living rock, on top of the small mountain crag that overlooked the village.

For me the castle was a point of pilgrimage, and from the base of the old tower of the Christian keep, you could pivot around three hundred and sixty degrees and Spain fell at your feet like a soft multi-coloured tapestry of magic carpet. Immediately beneath you to the east and to the south, the village of Jimena offered a quaint picture of white houses, lichen covered roof tops, narrow cobbled streets; two church spires, the campanile in the village square with masses of verdant greenery – orange trees, palms, bougainvillea and wild jasmine. Further to the east were the rising mountains of the Sierra Morenos, while swinging around to the south one found oneself looking down a long fertile valley; thirty miles in the distance there was the unmistakable profile of the Rock of Gibraltar, about as big as your thumb nail but clearly recognisable for what it was. To the west your eyes lifted upwards across and beyond the Hozgarganta gorge and river to the towering shadows of blue mountains that marched across the landscape towards an unseen Algerciras and the Atlantic coast. As you swung your attention towards the north, the mountains became steeper and more mysteriously enigmatic and the Hozgarganta gorge narrowed into a dark zig zagging ravine that cut its way into the hinterland of the campo. To say that it was impressive was like saying that Mya Fayad was quite pretty. It was totally stunning and overwhelmingly beautiful.

Once I had brought a poet friend called Adrian Spendlow to this place – we'd come to Spain together for a writing sabbatical and I had delighted in showing him "my place" in the sun. He'd loved the ambience of the bars, had adored the Spanish food, had celebrated every different bottle of booze, and he'd admired the scenery (except on those occasions when the mountains got in the way!) When I'd brought him to this hill top and he had surveyed the scene, just as I was doing now, he had fallen strangely silent. I'd thought it might have been because of the subject we'd just been discussing for I'd been saying that when I passed from this mortal coil into the kingdom of whatever came next, I wanted my ashes scattered on this very spot, and he, one of my best mates, was charged with making damn sure that it happened. He'd agreed that he would, and agreed also that he'd conduct my funeral celebrations. Then he'd gone quiet on me.

'Hey, lighten up,' I'd laughed. 'I'm hoping that what we've been talking about isn't going to happen for a little while yet.'

'Oh I wasn't thinking about that... I was just thinking how totally fucking gorgeous this place is.'

The F word is not one that usually finds its way into Spendlow's vocabulary, so when he'd used it in this context I knew that it wasn't gratuitous. Then, he'd turned to look at me and his cheeks were slicked with a sheen of tears. 'James, this is the most beautiful beautiful place I've ever seen in all my life!'

Then he'd wrapped his arms around me and had given me a big brotherly hug and I had been gratified by his reaction, for then I knew that even if nobody else did, he understood why this place was so important to me.

Now, some time later, standing in the very same spot, the irony was not lost on me. I could not dictate where I might die, but I could (and had) dictated where my mortal remains would rest – flying to the four winds from this Andalucian eagles eyrie and seeding the soil of the Jimenato valley. Anthony Zander had also decided he was going to die in this place, so that was something we had in common. Reverence and recognition for this precious, ancient land.

I hunkered down in a crevice on the west side of the keep, pulled my jacket collar up and the brim of my hat down. Getting a pipe going in the breeze was a challenge but I'm an old pro when it comes to lighting pipes in adverse conditions and before long the beautiful blue smoke was doing its marvellous thing to my mind and its dreadful thing to my lungs.

Smoking – yeah well, one day it would kill me, but there were worse ways to go, and one thing was for sure in my own mind, and that was that I wouldn't go out like Zander. I sucked the Amphora down into my system, felt it begin to unravel the knots of tension, sighed with an exhalation of pipey aroma, feeling really good about the protest of independence I was making against the cadres of people who were stuffed so full of their holier than thou authority who demanded that I should conform to their standards. *You can't be who you want to be,* they screeched. And they were right, because I couldn't! *You can't do what you want to do,* they howled, and again they were right. *You can't be rich and famous and powerful,* they chortled, and they were definitely right about that. *You're an artist, but we deny you the right to live your life as an artist* they crowed, and they damn well did deny me that right. *You can't live where you want to live*, they commanded, *and you can't live how you want to live*, they instructed restrictively, and I was powerless to fight against their dictat. *And by the way, just to rub salt in your wound, we forbid you to smoke! It's dirty and it's antisocial, and we don't like it, so you've got to stop!*

Well screw you, said the rebel within. We've got to start fighting back somewhere along the line. We've got to do something to make sure that you don't get it all your own way! I'll smoke my pipe until it kills me and then when I'm dead, maybe you'll all be sorry – and then again, maybe you won't, but by then it won't matter because I'll have gone to that smoking room up in the sky knowing that it wasn't tobacco that did the damage, but the driving cold acid rain, the grey polluted skies of England, the belching soot that soured and scoured the land from ugly power stations and tall factory chimneys, the fumes that choked the air from gridlocked motorways: get rid of that shit first, and then maybe there might just be an argument for throwing my pipes into turgid waters of the poisoned river.

What caused more damage... A pipe of tobacco smoked on a crystal clear mountain in southern Spain, or a discharge of thirty litres of odious black diesel smoke belched out from the exhaust pipe of a so called public service vehicle as it slogged across the crowded streets of some Godforsaken northern town.... All aboard the number 47 for your local shopping centre and permissible poisoning by politically correct pollution.

I sighed and knew I would have to take another Prozac capsule before the end of the day. Given time Jimena would perform its usual calming miracle, but this was only my first day and even miracles need some time to get their energies together.

So focus, James, focus.

Fine, but focus on what?

Focus, perhaps, on synchronicity and the phenomena of coincidence? Focus on the Stephen King thing...?

I'd grown up with Stephen King being my favourite author of all time. I'd loved most of his books, I delighted in his genre, and although he was writing popular fiction rather than serious literature, his command of the English language was superb. Furthermore, and maybe above all else, his gift as a story teller was matchless, and within a few short sentences, a couple of paragraphs at the most, he could draw you into a world of his own making and imagining: his ability to see the world through the eyes of children and adolescents was quite remarkable, his characterisations were always faultless, and his plot lines, especially in aspects of motive and cause and effect, were always credible.

I loved Stephen King's books so much that I'd even tried to write one, set here in this village of Jimena, wherein something ancient and evil dwelt beneath this very mountain upon which I was presently sitting. Three hundred and thirty thousand words about demons and monsters and the thinning veil of reality between conflicting dimensions... My literary agent at the time had balked and had gone a gentle shade of pale and my magnum opus had never even found its way beyond her desk.

My work with clairvoyance had inadvertently brought me into contact with Anthony Zander, which in turn had brought me back to this place where there was already a loose connection with Stephen King in an ephemeral sense, and now another strand of connection was being woven into the matrix by Zander's own connection with the great American writer. There was a pattern here, but trying to see it clearly was like trying to plait fog.

I've got what I euphemistically call 'The Jigsaw Theory' which revolves around the concept of each and everyone of us being born with a mere handful of pieces of the great life puzzle. On their own they are disjointed and meaningless, but as you move along the journey through life you meet other people who've got their own pieces of the puzzle; you put your pieces with their pieces, and over a span of years, sometimes even decades, the pieces start to connect and fit together and you start getting an idea of what the picture might be all about. I doubt that you might complete the jigsaw in one lifetime – perhaps it takes half a dozen lifetimes – but sometimes with some impinging degree of psychic awareness there are occasions when I sense the jigsaw pieces knitting together. I sensed that something like this was happening now... My pieces and Zander's pieces and even Stephen King's pieces were all being shuffled together: the gulf between me and Mr King was enormous insofar as he earned millions while I earned hundreds... He had written books that were read by tens of millions, while I had written a couple of small offerings that had been read by a few tens of thousands, and yet through our mutual if disparate connection with Anthony Zander, our jigsaw pieces were being placed on the same board, and although we had vastly different roles, we were playing in the same game.

It was a sobering thought but I'd be a liar if I didn't admit that it was also an extremely exciting one.

A gust of very cold wind and an increasingly numb bottom told me that it was time to make a move, so I hoisted myself up out of the crevice and started strolling back towards the village (down hill all the way this time, thank God.) To my surprise I found that I was quite hungry, and glancing at my watch realised that I'd better put a bit of a spurt on otherwise I was going to be late for my evening dinner date with Elizabeth Hammond.

Elizabeth arrived at seven thirty with Julian in tow, and I was surprised that they'd both seen fit to change for dinner. Nothing formal – Julian was in grey flannels with a button down blue shirt and a light suede jacket while Elizabeth was wearing in a dark green dress, exquisitely tailored and with dark gold braiding around a Grecian collar. Even so, this was still only Jimena, not even Sotogrande, and I was still in my Millets chinos and brown woollen roll neck.

We had a couple of quiet drinks in the bar then went down to the small but beautifully elegant dining room and were shown to a table in a recessed alcove half way between a gently glowing wood burning stove and the patio doors that led out onto the inner court yard. In the summer the courtyard would be filled with dining tables and chairs strategically scattered beneath the grapevines and mature palm fronds; tiny strands of fairy lights would be strung through the branches of the aromatic beys and oleanders while scented citronella candles would flicker among the small shrubs and potted exotic plants. It was only a small space but quite incredible in its special sense of mystery and atmosphere of intimacy. In the depths of the Spanish winter the indoor restaurant became the epicentre of energy: warm terracotta walls, rich Moroccan rugs and throws, the highly decorative Moorish tiles so ubiquitous in Southern Spain. Discreetly erotic pictures tantalised in crevice corners while strategically hung mirrors reflected flickering highlights from a dozen tallow candles set in wall sconces and supported in free standing wrought iron candelabra.. In its own way it was just as intimate and atmospheric as the courtyard, and I thought a sour thought with regard to Julian's presence at the table. This was not a place for gooseberry threesomes but of sensual couples planning a long night of gentle or ferocious lovemaking.

This inadvertently brought my attention to Elizabeth Hammond. She looked lovely in the soft light and if I'd been fifteen years younger, two stones lighter and had I been free and single, I dare say I might have been interested. But I wasn't fifteen years younger, I wasn't single and I wasn't interested – at least, not in any kind of sexual sense – and I was never going to lose that extra thirty pounds of weight! But I'd be a liar if I said I wasn't interested in her role in these odd proceedings and I had to admit that she did carry a powerful and magnetically attractive energy with her. Without there being anything sexual about it, I did find myself liking this lady – which is more than I could say for Julian Freckles!

It probably wasn't his fault, but just the sound of his striney Australian voice was enough to raise my hackles, and maybe the fact that he was so disgustingly young and good looking did him no favours in my aging and envious eyes. That he was on such obviously good terms with Elizabeth bemused me and tweaked my curiosity and not for the first time that day I found myself wondering about their relationship.

We ordered our food and sat back sipping good Rioja (Julian mixing his with alternate mouthfuls of lager) and as is frequently the case in such circumstances, we struggled to make pleasant conversation. It was all a bit stilted and restrained, and so as an ice breaking tactic I found myself telling them about El Anon, how it came into existence back in the late 1960's and of the seminal role it had played in my life in the 80's and 90's. Inevitably I found myself talking about its original owner, the late Garth Odell, who in a gentle overseeing way maintained a haunting presence in this very special place that had been his life's work to create. Even with the arrival of the food the conversation still lingered on Garth's continued presence at El Anon. Half way through a mouthful of *rabo de toro* Julian waved a questioning fork at me.

'When you say that Garth Odell still haunts this place, what do you mean exactly? Have people seen his physical form or are we talking about poltergeist activity, or are you just being totally subjective within the framework of your own sensitivity?'

It was a surprisingly intelligent question and my respect for Julian Boyd went up a couple of notches – which wasn't saying much because hitherto it had been somewhere between zilch and zero.

'Entirely subjective,' I admitted, 'although having said that, I have talked to a few people whose impressions coincide with my own and apparently there have been some instances of electrical anomalies and some stories of teleportation... You know, lights blowing despite the fact that the fuses are all okay, and things going missing only to reappear in places that have be scoured and searched half a dozen times. For my own part, on more than one occasion I've had a brief glimpse of the man out of the corner of my eye, but I'm quite prepared to accept that as auto suggestive imagination, but only because I can't prove otherwise. But I do feel his presence in the building incredibly strongly. Every corner, every nook and cranny has its own memory. He was a good friend who proved that friendship time and again, not just by what he said, but also by what he actually did. He was incredibly generous but never overtly so… Look, someone in the village could be in trouble and in the middle of the night an envelope would find its way under their door with a few thousand pesetas or a few hundred quid. Someone's car might get stolen or blow a gasket or something, and out of the blue a loan car would turn up to see the person through a transport-less week. You could be really down on your heels and Garth would let you run up the most ridiculous bar tab without every pressurising you for payment and never the thought of charging any interest. He was a lovely man, very clever, very dry, extremely funny, and when he was in the hotel, even though he might have been in the office or the kitchen, you knew he was in the building somewhere. And when he wasn't, you knew that he wasn't. Forgive me, I know I'm not being particularly articulate, but either you know what I mean or you don't. When he died, I think the whole bloody village went into mourning, and although I wasn't here to see it, I'm told that more than half the village including the mayor and the local politburo turned out for his funeral…'

I sat for a moment in quiet reflection. 'I don't suppose I was his best friend,' I mused, 'but he was certainly one of mine. And there's an odd aspect of synchronicity here, for here we are, at this table, brought together by Mr Zander, who knows he's going to die, and just like Mr Zander, Garth knew that his days were numbered. He didn't tell anyone, not directly, but he started talking a lot about the value of time – okay so he smoked two packs of Celtas every day and polished off a bottle of vodka before tea time, so you could say that his common sense must have told him that he was killing himself – but we, his friends and mates, never saw it like that. We thought the old bugger was eternal and indestructible. We were all wrong and it *was* just a matter of time before Garth started sliding down the slippery slope, and when that happened,' I paused with a sudden lump in my throat. 'Well, let's put it this way, it was the complete opposite of what our Mr Zander is planning for himself. I admire Zander's motives, but you could say he's taking the easy way out. Garth fought and struggled for every last breath, and if you were to ask me who is the braver man, Anthony Zander or Garth Odell, I'm not sure I could give you a straight answer.'

It had been quite a speech and I realised that I'd been talking far too much. So, in an attempt to swing the conversation round into another direction, I asked: 'Anyway, how did you two get to be involved with Anthony Zander and this crazy experiment with death?'

'As I told you,' Elizabeth said, looking at me rather coolly. 'Julian is a trained nurse and...'

'I'm his son,' Julian cut in bluntly. 'And Elizabeth here is his daughter. We're half brother and sister.'

I'm not saying that Elizabeth left in a huff, but after I'd opened my big mouth and put my size nine foot in it, she did make an early departure pleading a headache and the need for an early night. This left me alone with Julian who showed no sign of wanting an early night or anything like it. Thinking that I'd committed a major faux pas with my comments about Anthony Zander I felt I had some ground to make up. We'd been in El Anon long enough so after Elizabeth had made her exit we walked through the rain slicked lamplight labyrinth of Jimena's narrow streets to Bar Marilyn, where Angel and Juani were busy behind the bar serving a motley crew of *trabajaderos* and *gitanos* – about a dozen masculine souls scuffing their boots and shoes over the old tiled floor, for the better part littered with empty fag packets and cigarette butts. Mischi the cat prowled around the frayed weave-wear chairs and in the back room a dark eyed gypsy called Raoul strummed sad palos on an old but much loved guitar.

I looked at Julian sideways. 'This is going to be a session, isn't it?'

He grinned. 'Could be, Mr. Christie. Could be.'

'What do we want? Brandy?'

'Sounds good to me.'

I'd known Angel since he was about sixteen years old. Familiarity had not bred contempt in this friendship, but it did give me the leeway to be cheeky within the framework of drinking hole tradition. I leaned around the bar, and catching Angel's eye, helped myself to an almost full bottle of Centenario. Angel responded by raising an eyebrow as he slapped two empty copitas down on the bar next to me. I nodded, telling him in the nod, that I wanted, and was paying for the whole bottle. Julian picked up the glasses and we went and sat in a corner beneath a detuned and flickering TV set; a football match, in shady colour, minus the sound.

A small window looked out onto the hilly street of Calle Romo, the glass cracked and grimy with plaster peeling from the flaking wall that might once have been white but was now a deep tobacco stained yellow.

I loved it! Screw the Costa del Sol! This was the real Spain. The Spain that sparkled in my spirit and dwelt with love within the confines of my heart.

'I get the impression you're well known here,' Julian said, glancing at the brandy bottle. 'Nice touch with the booze.'

I smiled and let him pour the brandies. He wasn't backwards in pouring forwards and splashed a liberal triple measure in each glass. We quaffed from the balloon shaped copitas and looked at each candidly across the scarred and cluttered table. I've never been much good at apologising but in the circumstances I felt that one was in order.

'I'm sorry if I spouted off back there. I had no idea that you were all family.'

'Don't worry mate. No way you could have known. And as for the family aspect I don't know how much weight that carries anyway. Before last year I'd never met my father and I never even knew that I had a half sister.'

'Are you going to tell me the story?' I asked.

'There's not a lot to tell,' he said. But as the amber liquid of the Centenario bottle progressively dropped to well below the label, he told me anyway.

In 1977 Zander had been filming in Sydney, Australia and had had an affair with his principle make-up artiste – a leggy blond called Maggie Boyd. Although Zander had been serious enough about the affair, Maggie Boyd was a lot more serious and started putting Zander under some pressure for a marriage commitment. Zander had patiently pointed out that he simply was not in the marriage market, and although a very long time separated he still had a legal wife back in the United States. This put the relationship with Maggie under an ever increasing strain and he was about to break the whole thing off, but then in a last desperate attempt to catch (or trap) her man, Maggie deliberately allowed herself to fall pregnant.

This stratagem misfired badly because Zander was under contract to finish a film and that very week the crew was moving to a new location in Hawaii, and he had little choice other than to move on with them... And of course there was the small matter of a legal wife back in The States. So Zander left and Maggie Boyd never forgave him for leaving.

Julian: 'I grew up as a single parent kid. My mother never talked about my father other than to say he'd left us before I was born. Any curiosity I had was stamped down hard on from up high. It was a taboo subject. She was obviously as bitter as hell about the whole thing, and yet I guess she must have loved him a lot because to the best of my knowledge she never went with anyone else. There was never the trail of mysterious "uncles" that a lot of other kids in my position had to deal with.'

'So how did you find out?' I asked.

'Easy mate. My old lady died twenty months ago and everything came to me.'

'I'm sorry.'

'Don't be. It was a pretty awful relationship and we were always fighting with each other. During the last few years of her life I hardly ever saw her or spoke to her, other than the odd birthday call and Christmas visit. She was living in Sydney and I'd moved over to Perth. I'd finished all my training and I'd done pretty good with my exams, and I landed a really good deal with the local A&E unit, and believe me mate I had no desire to go back to Sidders... As it was I didn't even know she'd been ill until one of her neighbours phoned me to tell me she'd died of heart failure following a bad dose of pneumonia... And then, of course, I had to go back to sort out the mess. And that's when I discovered that my old man was this American actor guy called Anthony Zander.

'It was all there in triplicate. She'd kept a diary with all the details, and then there was a file full of letters from him, and then there were the bloody bank statements. Do you know, he sent her a thousand US dollars every month from the day I was born right up to my eighteenth birthday. There was never any kind of legal injunction against him and he just did it because he figured it was the right thing to do. There were letters going back twenty five years, asking about me and requesting news and photographs...

Hey look, I dunno if she ever responded, but by the sound of it she never did because after four or five years he stopped writing, even though the money kept on coming through on a regular as clockwork basis.'

After Maggie Boyd's estate had been sorted out there was a substantial chunk of money deposited into Julian's account and another chunk followed after the sale of the family property in the upper end of the Sydney suburbs. This brought Julian to one of those major crossroads that we all come to at some time in our lives. What the hell do we do next?

Julian: 'I could have just put the cash in my pocket and buggered off back to Perth and carried on with my life... But for Chrissakes, I'd been wrong footed and taken by surprise, and I was as curious as hell. It's one thing growing up without a father, but another thing ignoring him when you know he's out there and once upon a time he was interested in you enough to write letters begging for photographs and putting a grand in the fucking bank every month.'

'So what did you do?'

'It was a sheer impulse thing. There'd been a contact phone number on some of the legal stuff from the bank, so I just phoned the number.'

'And?'

'And I found myself talking to this Sheila with a posh English voice who told me I couldn't possibly talk to Mr Z because at that point in time he was (a) indisposed and (b) he was in a meeting. I figured that he couldn't be both, so I told her to piss off and put The Man on the line, and to tell him this was Maggie Boyd's son who was calling.'

I made an intuitive leap. 'You were talking to Elizabeth?'

'Yeah, only, of course, I didn't know that at the time... Anyway, I'm put on hold and I'm waiting about thirty seconds and I'm thinking I really don't give a fuck and I'll wait thirty frigging hours if I have to, and then my old man comes on the line.'

Julian went quiet.

'What happened then?' I prompted.

'For fucks sake, we both started crying... and then we started talking... he wanted to know everything and I wanted to know everything, and in the end he begged me, please would I go and visit him in the States? He'd come to me only he wasn't too well at the moment, and so he'd send me the air fare, and I told him to stuff it,

52

I didn't need a flight stake, and I told him I'd be there within forty eight hours. And I was. And that's when I learned that I had a sister and that my old man was dying with cancer...'

Julian took a very large mouthful of brandy and looked at me with laconical bemusement. 'As we say in the Antipodes, Mr Christie, what a fucking bummer! You spend your whole damn life thinking and wondering about your father without anything, anything at all forthcoming from your old lady, and then your old lady kicks it, and you realise that not only do you have a fucking father but this guy supported you for the best part of eighteen years, and then you talk to him and you realise that he wants to see you as much as you want to see him... no change that from want to *need*... and then you get on a bloody aeroplane and fly half way round the bloody world to meet this guy only to find that he aint got a lot of time left because the big C has got him in a major way... Jesus Christ, what a fucking fucking bummer!

'Anyway,' he looked at me with bleary brandy sodden eyes and I realised he was as drunk as I was only I was holding it a damn sight better than he was, which is something which only comes with age and experience of drinking into the late hours of the night in Spanish bars where the hours are short and the drinks are cheap and long...

'Anyway... I went to LA and met him, and apart from a few hours here and there I've never left his side since. Weird, that of all the jobs and professions I could have gone into I chose nursing... Now if you ask me *that* needs some paranormal explanation if ever anything did, don't you think? What other job could I have done that would serve Anthony any better? And then, of course, there's the double *double* bummer!'

'What's the double *double* bummer?' I asked.

'Aren't you supposed to be psychic?' he asked, half drunkenly, half mockingly.

'Want me to guess?'

'Well, let's put it this way. What do you think of my half sister...' he emphasised the word *sister* 'Elizabeth?'

'I think she's extremely beautiful and very elegant,' I said, immediately knowing where this conversation was going but not wanting to take it there myself.

'Damn right Christie, she's all of that, and she's fourteen fucking years older than me, so what do you think I should do about it?

53

And don't give me a glib answer. Give me an honest answer from the bottom of this flaming bottle.'

I drank from my own goblet. And I thought.

'Julian, old love, I don't think there is very much you *can* do about it.'

'Yeah, well, I've thought about it too.' His eyes crossed in a poor attempt to focus. 'And you know what? I have come to exactly the same conclusion! But do you think that makes me happy? No Mr. Christie, it most certainly does not!'

'So what will you do?' I asked, hiding behind my own intake of high octane spirit.

'Do?' he echoed forlornly and with a note of animal desperation, 'Well there isn't much I can do is there? Other than to pretend that the situation doesn't exist and... Oh shit I'm as drunk as a fucking kangaroo and I've spilled the beans to someone who I know doesn't like me all that much, so the question is, changing the subject, but not, if you know what I mean, can you keep your bloody mouth shut?'

'As tight shut as you ever need it to be, Señor Boyd.'

'Seriously Mr. C.?'

'Seriously Mr. B.'

'And you won't put this in your book?'

'Not unless you tell me that I can.'

He looked at me strangely across the out of focus table. 'You're not such a stiff old fart after all, are you?' he asked.

'You decide later,' I said – and in my pocket, I turned off the mini tape recorder that had captured every word of our drunken conversation.

Five: *La Casa Blanca, Thursday 11th December*

By Wednesday morning the weather pattern had begun to change. The rain had stopped and although there were still massive cloud banks climbing thousands of feet into the sky, there were also patches of pale and hopeful blue, the pale blue counterpointing the darker bruised blue of the departing thunderheads. And on the subject of thunderheads my own head felt like thunder with a blatting ache throbbing at my temples and pin cushions of distortion twisting away in the corners of my eyes. It had been three a.m. before Julian and I had parted company on the corner of Calle Sevilla, him staggering back towards the Hozgarganta with me shuffling carefully back towards The Anon. In the old days I could have polished off half a bottle of brandy in one session without a problem, but I had yet to get my system back into the Spanish drinking routine, and on top of the wine we'd drunk earlier in the restaurant, the Centenario had exacted its toll.

It was too cold to sit out on the terrace so nursing the hangover I had coffee and toast in the bar, sitting next to the newly lit log fire and feeling decidedly the worse for wear. I wondered if Julian was feeling any better, and seriously doubted it. If anything he'd put back even more than I had – and I now had to revise my first opinion of this man. It had been too easy to pigeon hole him into the category of being your usual loud mouthed Aussie, but the previous evening he had shown that he was much more than that; his abrasive manner hid a sensitive and insecure young man who'd had a pretty messed up life by all accounts and who was now wrestling with an emotional problem that could have no successful resolution. I wondered if Elizabeth knew – and decided that she probably did. She was too astute not to be aware of that degree of repressed obsession.

I wondered why Julian had given the game away to me. If you'd told me on the Tuesday morning that we'd be having our "true confessions" conversation by Tuesday night, I'd have probably laughed in your face. And yet maybe I was the catalyst that he'd needed. He couldn't very well talk things over with Elizabeth or Zander and it was fairly obvious that despite his good looks he was a singularly solitary person. I was the convenient stranger – supposedly older and wiser – and maybe I'd just been in the right place at the right time to be selected as the soul to share the burden.

Although I'd only been in La Casa Blanca once the degree of tension in that place had been sufficiently powerful to make me feel that I really didn't want to go there again. Experiment or no experiment, we were waiting for a man to die. I'd been there for barely two hours and the pall of impending doom had got through to me very quickly. I couldn't begin to imagine how Elizabeth and Julian had coped with it, week after week, month after month. I shivered – and not with cold – for once again I had that feeling of Poe-like Gothic horror born of the inevitability of death. I searched for my own faith and spirituality and I couldn't damn well find it. Not that particular morning anyway.

No formal time for my second interview with Zander had been set and no arrangements had been made for me to be picked up. I considered taking the long walk down to La Casa Blanca, but that would be an hour's hard slog for my short little legs, and the way I was feeling right then, I didn't fancy it at all. I considered phoning Miguel down at Gabilan's garage and seeing if I could hire or borrow a car for a few days. The hills in Jimena could be quite wicked on the calf muscles and I suddenly liked the idea of being independent where transport was concerned. I borrowed the Anon's phone book and checking the number, was about to put a call through to Gabilan when my mobile shrilled with an incoming text message. I hoped it was from my wife back in England, but it was from Elizabeth Hammond down on the river. In clear it said Zander was indisposed and would I mind putting my interview back 24 hours and could I look after myself until then?

Curious question, and the damn thing with texts is that you can seldom measure a person's mood in the abbreviated gobbledegook English that appears on those ridiculous little screens. On the one hand, I was damn glad to be let off the hook, but on the other hand, especially in light of my previous night's conversation with Julian, I wanted to know more of what was going on. So I phoned her.

I was assured that everything was all right apart from the fact that Zander was having a bad day and really did not feel he could cope with a long conversation. I asked about Julian – trying to keep my tone of voice light and innocent – and was told that Julian was taking a morning off duty. There was nothing in Elizabeth's voice that gave anything away, so then I asked her if she was all right, and she said she was perfectly fine and that either she or Julian would pick me up at ten thirty the following morning. Okay, fair enough. I had a day off. The clouds were still messing up the sky, I still felt dreadful, and so I did what any sensible man would do in the circumstances. I went back to bed.

Thursday and thank God the sun was shining. Bright, fierce and beautiful, not a cloud in the azure blue sky. The hunchbacked grey English spirit began to unwind inside me as I breakfasted out on the terrace and by the time I was on my third cup of Columbian, the terrace thermometer was reading a very acceptable sixty five degrees Fahrenheit and the old Quasimodo shroud had lifted in favour of the ebullient Sancho Panza. Around nine thirty Sancho Panza's look-alike in the form of Miguel Gabilan met me outside the hotel and handed over the keys to a well past its prime Seat Ibiza and I handed over a couple of signatures and a couple of hundred euros. Then I phoned Elizabeth's number and told her not to bother coming to collect me because I was making my own way down.

I stopped off at Cuanca's bar on the way and had another quick coffee (and okay a small anis) with Jan Miles, my estate agent friend, then carried on to Camino Hozgarganta and the white house that nestled among the grove of mature Eucalyptus trees. On second viewing La Casa Blanca was much bigger than I'd first thought: a direct front view vision gave an impression of a modest building, but looking at it obliquely, you realised that there were double wings off the back, and a large walled garden with a three port garage nestling among smaller Eucalyptus trees and a profusion of wild Rhododendrons. What with the rocketing prices on the Andalucian property market the place had to be worth at least a million euros and probably all the rest. It was a choice location, private, secluded, but with reasonable access and it was amazing to think that the westernmost houses of Jimena were barely a half a mile away on the other side of the mountain, even though it was the better part of a mile and a half to the village road and the iron bridge striking south along the river bank.

I parked next to Julian's Jeep. Sideways across the front of the house there was a late model mint green Mercedes with German plates and even as I was getting out of the Seat, a tall thin stick of a man made his exit from the building and climbed into the Merc. At first glance he looked a bit like the American actor John Malcovitch, only not quite so good looking. There was a weasely, almost furtive air about this guy and with the thin rimless glasses that he wore high on the bridge of his nose, he reminded me of someone you might have found running a Nazi concentration camp back in the second world war – *and in light of what was to come later, what a very odd thought that was!* – He must have seen me but he totally ignored my presence. Gunning the Merc. into life he drove down the short driveway, and then, curiously, turned right, rather than heading left which would have taken him back to Jimena. What was further down the river to the right? It had been a long time since I'd been here, and I racked my brains to remember. As far as memory served, there wasn't anything much. The river road petered out another half mile up the valley, there were a couple of small fincas, and then nothing more than a few goat paths that wove their way back up over the mountain to Jimena's northern quarter.

Of course, there was that big lump of granite embedded in the river that the locals called *Torre de Muere* – literally, "death rock" where three young boys had drowned a score of years ago; they'd found a hollow beneath the rock and had surfaced to find it full of methane gas and Jimena had taken a long time to get over that particularly sad incident. The boys had been good boys, young and well liked. A shadow stole its way across my heart and I couldn't suppress a small shudder. If an untimely death is dreadful then the death of innocence is significantly worse.

As I walked towards the verandah Julian came out to greet me. He was already eight inches taller than I was but with the added height of the porch step he towered above me like a blond giant. He had a very wary and uncertain look in his eyes.

'Are we all right?' he asked, and in view of the departing Mercedes I was reminded of Laurence Oliver asking Dustin Hoffman if it was safe.

'Yes Julian,' I answered directly, meeting his eye and holding his intent gaze. 'We are all right.'

Knowing that his confidence would not be breached, his face split into a welcoming grin. 'Come on in then, and I'll fix you some coffee. You want it with milk or…' his smile grew broader 'would you like it with a brandy?'

'Give it to me black with plenty of sugar. How're you feeling, by the way?'

'Today, okay, but yesterday…' he rolled his eyes. 'Well, let's just forget about how I was feeling yesterday!'

58

I smiled and followed him into the house. 'Who was the guy in the Mercedes?' I asked casually.

Julian laughed out loud. 'Well mate, I call him Doctor Death, but if you really want to know, he's Doctor Luther Martinez. Genuinely a doctor, and supposedly an old friend of Anthony's.'

'Supposedly?'

'That's what I've been told Mr. C. and so that's what I'm telling you.'

Which suggested to me that either Julian was not being told everything or that there were things that I was not supposed to know about, at least not yet anyway. I didn't pursue it and followed him through the reception room and then off through a door on our right which led to a large modern kitchen that my wife would have killed for. You could have put our whole cottage in that one room and there would still have been some space spare for a kitchen table and a few extra chairs. He flicked the switch on an electric kettle and shovelled spoonfuls of Nescafe granules into two large mugs.

'The bad news is that we've only got instant coffee, but the good news is that it isn't decaffeinated. One sugar or two?'

I wanted three but told him two.

'Look, Mr C...' he spooned the sugar into the mugs, looking out of the kitchen window onto a view of an attractive side garden with a small rockery and what appeared to be a natural spring bubbling through the stones. 'About the other night... I just want to say that if you and me got off to a bad start and if it was my fault, then...'

'Please don't worry about it. We all drop bollocks sometimes and I dare say I'm just as much to blame as you. First impressions aren't always the right ones.'

He turned from the sink, my mug of coffee in his left hand, right hand extended. 'Ah well, that's okay then mate, isn't it?'

We shook hands, and as we were doing so Elizabeth walked into the kitchen from the door at the far end. She raised an eyebrow. 'A little male bonding?' she asked quizzically. There was no sarcasm, just curiosity, and I toasted her with the hot coffee.

'Shall we say a male understanding?' I suggested.

'You want some coffee Beth?' Julian cut in before the conversation could progress any further than that.

'No, I'll have some tea later...' and then to me, 'James, Anthony is out on the back porch if you'd like to take your coffee and join him.'

'Sure, which way do I go?'

She directed me through the door behind her. 'Just watch the time will you. He thinks he's feeling a lot better today, but he only has so much energy, so don't push him too hard.'

'I won't push him at all,' I said. 'That's not the way I work. All I'm going to do is listen and take notes.'

I found him sitting on a nicely padded bench in a small alcove outside a pair of French windows that obviously led into his bedroom. He was wearing a white roll neck sweater and pale trousers, partially covered by a draped rug in a mock Scots tartan. Beside him was a steel trolley, the sort you find in hospitals, with a jug of water and a glass and a tablet tray.

There was a profusion of plants and flowers and in this natural sun trap there was a glorious sense of warmth. In the background there was the gentle tinkling of running water and although it was the wrong time of the year to hear the persistent call of the cicadas, the garden was full of morning birdsong. Zander did not look strong, but he did look well – at least, a damn sight better than when I'd seen him two days before. He waved me to a chair close to him.

'Mr Christie, my apologies for yesterday, but as you may have been told, I have my good days and my bad days. Yesterday was a bad one and today is a good one! Ah good, I see you have a cup of something that smells like coffee, and between you and me I'd kill for a cup but Julian would scream at me if I did and my doctor would give me one of his hardest frowns... Now, do tell me what you've been up to...'

We chatted for a while, and although as before, he remained relatively still upon his seat, today there was more colour and animation and more passion to his speech. He was easy to be with. Easy to talk to, and easy to listen to. We talked about Elizabeth and Julian, not in any great depth, but it was interesting to note that he had been briefed and now knew that I knew of the family connection and whether wittingly or unwittingly he filled in a few of the genealogical gaps.

While Julian had been born out of wedlock to Maggie Boyd, Elizabeth was the progeny of a happy but tragically short marriage in the mid 1960's and indeed it had been the pain of bereavement that had set Zander on his quest.

'Elizabeth's mother was the love of my life,' he said matter of factly. 'We were both very young, still only in our mid twenties, but it was the 1960's and we'd both been round the block a few times. We both knew within a few hours of meeting each other that we were destined to spend the rest of our lives together. As it was, we had four great years, we produced a beautiful baby daughter, and then one day Susan was crossing a road with an arm full of shopping, on a zebra with a green light telling her it was okay to go, when this crazy drunk driver hit her at sixty miles an hour and that was the end of Susan and the end of my marriage, and for a long time it was nearly the very end of me. The only thing that kept me going was Elizabeth, but even then there were some very long days and some very long nights...'

He talked at length about the slow healing process, of how, as much for Elizabeth's sake as his own he tried a second marriage a few years later down the road...

'Elizabeth needed a mother and I needed a body in my bed. It was a recipe for disaster, and I should have known better. It was a terrible mistake and I hold myself entirely responsible...'

And eventually, he brought the conversation around to his interest in clairvoyancy and the concept of life after death.

'I suppose I had been interested in the idea for most of my adult life,' he admitted. 'Certainly subconsciously if not consciously since my late teens when both my parents died within a year of each other. Susan's death, on the other hand, provoked me into some very serious research and study, and I became increasingly intrigued by the concept of the spiritual continuation of the human soul and the human identity – and that word *identity* is a very very important word, for without identity there can be no memory and without memory of who we are, where we have been, what we have done etc., the entire concept is flawed! This has neither been a morbid fascination for me born out of bereavement or a new age peccadillo, but a serious research subject and I'd like to think I've done my homework to the best of my intellect and ability.'

He shuffled uncomfortably on the bench. 'Do excuse me, Mr Christie, but if I don't get up and walk or do something, my butt is going to find itself glued to this seat.'

He rang the bell on the trolley, and within seconds, the middle aged nurse called Beatrice came through the French windows. 'Ah Señora' Zander turned on the charm. 'I should like to go for a walk. Could you be an angel and bring me my stick? I think I have left it just inside the bedroom by the side of the bed.'

'Walk no is possible,' Beatrice scowled at me suspiciously.

'Ah, but a walk *is* possible,' Zander insisted, not losing his smile.

'But Doctor Luther and Mr Julian say no is possible.'

'But Mr Zander say is *very* possible.'

'No. I get Mr Julian!'

Beatrice buggered off and Zander sighed in exasperation. Within seconds she returned with Julian in tow, looking very smug, while Julian looked, well, professional. He wore a short white tunic, complete with thermometer in his top pocket and a stethoscope around his neck, and his big hair was now wetted and slicked back into a tight pony tail.

'Is there a problem?' he asked, and I noted that his tone of voice towards Zander was totally different from the tone he would use with either me or Elizabeth.

'Yes there is. I want to take a very gentle stroll around the garden with Mr. Christie and Beatrice tells me I can't!'

'Do you really feel up to it Anthony? You've been out here for almost an hour as it is...'

An hour? Hell that had gone quickly!

'Yes, of course I feel up to it.'

'Well okay, but I think maybe I should walk with you in case...'

'Oh do please stop fussing, I'll be fine, and if I'm not then I'll shout, and if for any reason I can't shout I'm sure Mr. Christie has got a loud enough voice to shout for me.'

To Beatrice's dismay and Anthony Zander's delight, Julian capitulated and went and brought back the walking stick. He gave me a warning nod that said that if there *was* a problem he was going to hold me personally responsible.

'Now Mr. Christie,' Zander said gleefully, almost like a small boy who'd won a weekend in a chocolate factory. 'Let us, you and I, take a very slow stroll around this lovely garden of mine, and I'm sure you won't mind if we do go *very* slowly.'

I gave him my arm, and with the stick firmly in place, we started out at a very gentle pace. The whole garden acted as a suntrap, and with high dry stone walls and the profusions of plant and flowers and shrubs and bushes acted effectively as a wind break. This mid-winter Spanish morning was like a lazy English afternoon in the height of a good summer. The air was clear and clean, warming against the skin and redolent with the scents and sensations wafting up from the flowers and drifting down the valley from the river and the forest.

Zander told me about La Casa Blanca. 'When I knew, eighteen months ago, that my time was, well shall we say limited? I knew immediately that I wanted to come here. I've known about Jimena ever since I was on location with Chuck Heston filming El Cid. I've owned this plot of land since 1992 and I always intended to retire here, maybe write a book or something, but you know how it is, you never get round to these things. But as soon as I got the red light alert, I got a couple of architects together and kept the plan simple because I needed them to be quick. From the first drawings on the back of an old serviette to the last brick being painted took less than four months! Wouldn't find that in the States, I'll tell you!'

Nor the UK, I thought. I was about to say something to this effect, when we turned a corner at the back end of the house, and in front of my eyes a slope of land curved upwards amid a handful of ageing cork oaks towards the boulders at the base of a huge slab of rock face sixty or eighty yards distant. Zander stopped, looking at the two nearest cork oaks with a distant glint in his eye. He waved his stick in the direction of the trees.

'I've done a little deal with the Junta de Andalucia' he said conversationally. 'And that's where, over there, between those two lovely old trees, I'm going to be buried. It might just be a little bit illegal, but money in this world can buy anything.' He smiled wanly and turned his head from side to side taking in, or so it seemed, every detail of these most lovely surroundings, 'In some ways, it is going to be very difficult to leave all this behind.' I suppose I gulped, not prepared to deal with this aspect of our conversation. '...But in others,' he continued, 'it will be such a blessed relief to be gone.'

'Is the pain bad,' I asked tentatively, not knowing what to say at all, but knowing I had to say something.

'James,' he looked at me sideways, 'it is totally dreadful! Today I have taken some of the good Doctor Luther's drugs and I am one degree removed from it. It's still there, of course, but I can deal with it after a fashion.' He cast another glance at the waiting cork oaks. 'I suppose,' he mused, 'that it might be like a man who is terrified of dentists, but then he comes down with the most God-awful tooth ache. He might hang on for a while, but sooner or later the pain in his tooth is going to get the better of his fear of dentistry!'

I didn't know how he could be so calm about it. 'How on earth did this all start?' I asked.

He shrugged – and winced – and I gently steered him back towards the porch. 'I was filming in Egypt a couple of years ago and came down with a case of food poisoning, which wasn't anything too serious in itself but it brought on a nasty attack of IBS, which is something I've always had a chronic problem with. Wasn't too worried, took the usual medication, did the usual stuff, and the whole thing calmed down for a while. Then about five weeks later, by which time I was back in L.A. it came back and hit with a vengeance. The pain was really bad and I was excreting blood, so I got hauled down to the hospital, they ran a few tests, then ran a few more tests, and ran a few more tests after that, and they told me I had prostate cancer. They were pretty confident they could do something about it, and they tried, and for a while they thought they were winning, then the damn thing started spreading like wildfire, stomach, lymph glands, even my lungs.

'Did I drink a bottle of Bourbon every day? No sir I did not. A glass or two of good wine with a nice dinner was about the only homage I ever paid to booze! Did I smoke a packet of cigarettes a day? Again sir, no I did not. Never smoked. Not even the occasional cigar.' There was no great bitterness here, only a sense of profound irony. 'As I told you, until about eight months ago I still thought I might have a chance of licking it, but I'd got a good medical team, and they gave it to me straight. I could fight like Genghis Khan or Attila the Hun, but it was not going to make any great difference. They gave me about year, fifteen or sixteen months at the most. But hell James, by then they didn't have to rub it in, because by that time I knew. My body told me and my spirit told me so as well.'

He managed another tired wan smile. 'Crazy, isn't it, I'm one of those guys who's never had a day's serious illness in his life, and then whammy, it all comes at once. God, not that I believe in God, can play some very malicious tricks.'

'You don't believe in God?'

'I did once. I suppose you've got to when you're brought up in the Catholic church, not that there was any great religious conviction within my family. Hey, I guess my mother believed strongly enough, but my father just paid lip service, partly to keep the peace at home and partly to fit in with the rest of the community. As for me, well I just went along with it, at least until I was old enough to start thinking a few things out for myself. I suppose the catalyst came when my father died. He dropped dead in the street with a heart attack and he wasn't even fifty year old. There was no warning, nothing. One minute he's walking down Sunset Strip and the next minute he *is* the Goddamn sunset!

'I was eighteen years old and my father dying like that had a pretty profound effect on me, believe you me it surely did! My mother was in tears for weeks, no not weeks, but months! She kept saying that Daddy was with Jesus and Mary and The Saints, and that it had been God's will to take him before his time, but I wasn't buying it, not for one little minute. I thought that any God who was going to take my Daddy without any good reason was one heartless son of a bitch... But it did ignite a curiosity in me and it was only then that I really started thinking about God and the whole religion thing. I started reading a lot and I started talking to a few different people who believed in lots of different things.

'My mother died a year after my father. The romantic in me wants to think that she died of a broken heart, but the fact of the matter is that she died of breast cancer – and in those days that was a sure fire lady killer. Now, well with all the new drugs and medical knowledge we've got, its different ball game. Maybe...' he looked reflective '...this cancer thing is genetic. You know, it kind of runs in the family?'

'We've all got to die of something,' I said and immediately realised that I had said the wrong thing.

'Yes Mr. Christie, that we do, but not before our time, and if you ask me who dictates that time, then I don't have an answer for you, but in my heart I do not believe it should be some angry God who permits wars, famine and a million other shades of human suffering.'

'The general belief is that those things are caused by men, not God...'

Zander stopped and turned to look me directly in the eyes. His own eyes, glinting in the low sunshine, were full of challenge, 'Do you really believe that? Really, in your deepest heart of hearts?'

'I... er... don't know,' I answered feebly. 'I'm not sure.'

He nodded in this small pyrrhic victory. 'Just remember "And God created Man in His own image",' he quoted, 'so if someone picks up a gun and blows away a couple of innocent kids in a school playground, sure you can blame the hand of man, but you've got to ask yourself this... Who directs the hand of man? If you say it is man's own troubled mind, then I happen to think that's a cop out, but if you *do* say that, then again I ask – who is responsible for man's troubled mind? If the answer is man himself then that suggests to me that there is no God, not one with any real power or influence and therefore one not worthy of praise or consideration, but if you say that God *is* ultimately responsible for man's troubled mind, then in my opinion, the son of a bitch has got a lot to answer for! And I'm talking here about God, not Man!'

We'd got back to the bench on the porch, and before sitting down – he was now looking very tired – he reached up and gently plucked a Eucalyptus leaf from a nearby treeling.

'This is exquisite,' he said in awe and admiration. 'A beautiful little leaf, fresh and perfect in every way.' He stroked the leaf between his finger tips, and then brought his fingers to his nose inhaling the scent like an aficionado celebrating the opening of a bottle of very fine wine. 'If Channel could capture this in a bottle they'd double their profits overnight! But James, is this leaf the work of God or is it the work of Nature? I know people who would say that it is one and the same, but I personally find that very hard to believe. This little guy...' he looked at the Eucalyptus leaf with great tenderness, '...is absolutely perfect and I do not think that there is a much of connection between this little leaf and dead children in school playgrounds. It's got nothing to do with wars, rape, murder, death, and every other kind of disaster you might care to mention, but it has got *everything* to do with flowers, trees, sunshine, moonshine, rains, rivers, life force and the power of nature in its purest form.'

I opened my mouth to say something – maybe something like *Whoah, Zander, hang on, you're forgetting the other side of nature's coin* – but he got there before me.

'Sure, nature has got its downside – tempests, typhoons, earthquakes, volcanic eruptions, but to me, these dreadful things are acceptable if they are seen as acts of nature, but they are totally unacceptable if they are seen as acts of God.'

For the first and only time in the whole of our association I saw a flash of anger cross Zander's face. He wasn't angry at me, or even at himself – just at the God that he didn't believe in. 'So, no sir, I do not believe in God, but here's a thing... I do believe in spirit and I do believe in post mortem survival of that spirit. I've never had hard proof of this, but I've certainly had my share of evidence and not just circumstantial evidence either, but the kind of thing that really opens your mind and makes you think... But even without that evidence common sense dictates that there has got to be something after death otherwise the whole life process becomes a travesty of purpose and a meaningless mockery of cause and effect. The human condition demands that we believe in God and an afterlife, for without such a belief life becomes unbearable – but as you know, I have a problem with God and I see little in this world which is Godly, and so I am plagued by the question, can there be an afterlife, which I do believe in, and can there be any continuation of spirit, which is something that I also believe in, without this God business getting in the way?

'Now I have always been interested in finding the answers to these questions, and I have longed to find some hard tangible proof rather than just persuasive evidence. If I had been one of Christ's disciples I'd have been Doubting Thomas and since I've had this...' he paused a second, groping for the right words, ' – this *illness*, it has become imperative that I find the answers and the proof, not so much for my own sake, but for my children and for anyone else out there who looks death in the face and does not like what they see. This experiment cannot take away my own fear of death, but if the result can do anything to alleviate other peoples' fears, then my life, and my death, will not have been in vane or without purpose.

'I've attended countless séances and I have read, quite literally, hundreds of books. I was damaged when my parents died, but the real quest kicked in when I lost my first wife, Beth's mother. Since then I've talked to scores of mediums, clairvoyants, psychics, all kinds of gurus, churchmen, seekers and seers, and everyone seems to hold a little piece of the puzzle, but no one has ever fitted all those pieces together to give us the complete picture. I've met more than my fair share of frauds and charlatans, but I've met some seriously sincere people as well, and the overall consensus is that I should seek and find my own truth. The problem that I have with that is the fact that it could only be a subjective truth, and I am looking for the absolute.'

'Are there ever any absolutes?' I asked.

Zander offered me the young Eucalyptus leaf and I reached out and took it from his pale hand.

'James, tell me, is that a leaf you're holding or is it a 1969 Corvette Stingray with a 5.7 litre engine and a rag top roof?'

'Okay Anthony, it's a leaf.'

'Yes it is,' he smiled. 'I agree with you. Absolutely.'

Then something he'd said a few moments earlier suddenly hit me like a ton of bricks. 'Anthony, can I just back track to when you were talking about the point and possible value of your experiment...?' He nodded. 'Are you telling me that despite all these preparations you've made, you're still frightened of dying?'

'Frightened?' he echoed with a slightly raised eyebrow and a note of resignation in his voice. 'No Mr. Christie, I'm not *frightened*. I am absolutely terrified by the prospect!'

And although we talked of other things for another hour, that was the most sobering thing I'd heard all morning.

They were angry with me. All three of them – Beatrice, the moustachioed nurse, Julian in his white smock, and Elizabeth, chain smoking her Marlboro cigarettes. Julian and Beatrice steered Zander back into his bedroom, while Elizabeth passed over one of her smokes with a cup of not too hot coffee that had been seriously over percolated.

'You kept him far too long James!'

I sat in the rattan chair on the front veranda. I had a headache and I wasn't really in the mood for chastisement. 'Sorry,' I retorted without really apologising. 'He talked and I listened. That's what I'm here for, isn't it?'

'Yes, but you were nearly three hours!'

'Then someone should have interrupted us. Anthony had a lot to say this morning and I wasn't prepared to shut him up. He, and you for that matter, are very familiar with this situation and I'm new to it.'

'Don't you have a watch or something?'

'Yes of course I do, but so what? How much time is too much time? In future,' I stubbed out the cigarette, 'just come and tell me if you think it's time to end the interview. I promise you, I won't be offended, and if Anthony has a problem with that, well it will be your problem not mine.'

I drove grumpily back to El Anon and had a light lunch with two bottles of San Miquel. The headache persisted so I had a couple of coffees and brandies, which didn't make my head feel any better, but it did begin to relax my body. Coming away from a three hour session with Zander had left me tensed like a wound spring, and I realised that this whole business was having a negative effect on my psyche. I felt oddly ill at ease, out of sorts, out of place, with an all pervasive sense of isolation... I tried phoning my wife but all I got was her answer machine message, so then I tried getting hold of Harry Andrews and got his answer machine message. I needed someone to talk to, but apart from Gabriel behind the bar, who, beautiful man that he may be was not the world's best conversationalist with ex-pats, there was no one to talk to. A good afternoon TV movie would have been a welcome distraction but there was not a television in the hotel. I'd have welcomed the chance of getting into a good book, but I had nothing to read. Someone was pointing the finger, so I pulled out my notebook and started to write.

Six: *Jimena, 11th – 13th December*

The following two days were weirdly surreal. There was a text from Elizabeth to say that I wouldn't be needed for a while, and that unless I had something better to do, would I be able to start getting on with the book because Anthony hoped to read a few pages before his departure. (By "departure" I presumed she meant his premeditated death.) Our next meeting was set for three days hence at which time we would, she informed me, be talking in detail about the experiment and the various conditions and controls. I told her this was all fine, and then started "getting on" with it, which, of course, was easier said than done.

Never less than fully aware of the gravity of the job I was supposed to be doing, I was still looking for a literary angle and a style of presentation, and I was in Southern Spain and the skies were blue and the sun was shining, so I did my thinking while I was drinking, talking to myself or into the Dictaphone while I did some walking: in the mornings I sat writing on the Anon terrace with Garth's ghost and the whispering palms, and in the evenings I sat writing in the corner of Bar Marilyn, drinking too much wine and eating too few tapas. On both nights rather than falling asleep it's fairer to say that I passed out, which I wasn't unhappy about. Sleep can be both a challenge and a battleground when you've got too much on the mind.

And by then I'd got far too much on my mind. Anthony Zander had got into my brain and under my skin and his presence in my head provoked some very deep and soul searching thoughts and questions... Two kinds of questions, ones that I didn't have the answers to and one that I'd thought I had the answer to, but was now having to revue. One thing was very clear to me, and that was that I was no longer an objective observer and reporter of this business with the impending death of my new found friend. I was involved – and although I would be hard pressed to define it at this early stage, I had a vested interest in the outcome of this so called experiment with clairvoyance. Which was a misnomer if ever there was one. Far better to call a spade a spade and think of it as being an experiment with death.

On a purely personal psycho-emotional level there was some tension and confusion: I loved being in Jimena, but I knew that my wife hated me being in Jimena. We'd managed a couple of mobile phone conversations and we'd sent each other a couple of texts, and it was fairly clear that my absence was causing her some grief and a few problems that she hadn't anticipated having to deal with. I was feeling guilty about it all, and then angry and defensive because I didn't feel that I should be feeling guilty. On the second night after I'd written about two thousand words in painful longhand scrawl, I walked just about every quadrant of the village, trying to put this ramshackle collection of white houses into some kind of historical context with my own past.

Why should this place be so important to me? Certainly it had played an important role in my earlier life, but I could think of a dozen other places that had had their important roles to play and they did not resonate and reverberate in my spirit the way in which Jimena de la Frontera did! Was it that I had experienced one of my greatest defeats and one of my greatest victories in this village, or was that some romantic notion and might it not be just a factor of familiarity from a past life? That was an attractive idea but untenable because it was unprovable. So was there something magnetic beneath Jimena's streets that reached up through the soles of my feet to make contact with the magnetic impulse of my brain? A lay energy within the very land itself, connecting with the lay energy of my own spiritual existence?

Back in 1987, a couple of months before I had arrived in the village, a friend of mine had dowsed Jimena looking for lay lines, and instead of encountering one, she had encountered no fewer than four, running in diagonal parallels, almost in the shape of a computer hash mark # . The northern lines crossed at the castle and then lower down in the village where Calle Loba intersected with the top of Calle Sevilla at Bar Vargas. The southern lines crossed in the Anon and then down in the eastern barrio at the end of Calle Llanette. In all truth, there wasn't much obvious energy in Calle Llanette, but there was a tremendous energy both at El Anon and up at the castle. As for the intersection outside Bar Vargas at the bottom of Calle Loba, there was definitely an energy there to be felt, although it was subdued, and quite frankly, not always very nice.

Never the less Jimena's magnetic vibration was extremely powerful and some very strange people had found their way to this village over the years When I had first arrived people had thought that I was a bit strange, the long haired poet Englishman with a weird glint of masdness in his eyes... but not quite so strange as some of the other folk that had climbed the hill to find sanctuary within Jimena's walls.

There'd been a beautiful girl called Juliette from Bilbao who'd been on the run from the police for planting ETA bombs on the beach at Marbella and, as an untimely challenge late one night in Bar El Paseo, I had read the palm of a man called Nicky Figgis who had murdered both his wife and his wife's lover – and who had got away with it.

Then there were tales of the rather peculiar Dutchman who called himself Colm Magus and who had acquired the reputation of being something of a magician, and not the sort that did party tricks for the kiddies at their birthday celebrations. With a penchant for wide brimmed black hats and flowing cloaks, on more than one occasion he had been observed striding through the village in the hours of la madrugada muttering incantations to himself and with streaks of blue fire arcing to the ground from his long boney fingers. Yeah, I know that sounds crazy, but that's what more than one person said they saw. Imagination and a little bit of hysteria? Probably, but this Dutchman had some remarkable gifts of healing and more than one Jimenato came to benefit from the Dutchman's talent. With a laying of hands Pepe Ortega's ulcer vanished over night and Angel Guadiaro's herpes dissipated over a weekend. Anna Sanchez, daughter of the local doctor, had her failing eyesight restored much to the amazement of both her father and medical science. Nobody knew where this man came from, and nobody knew where he went after he left town in the middle of one stormy night in October...

Things *happened* in Jimena that had no right to happen. Hailstones the size of marbels in the middle of June, falling out of a cloudless blue sky, lacerating flesh and breaking car windows. Spectral lights appearing on the walls of the castle battlements in the middle of the night – St Elmo's fire sparkling up and down the turret of the old Christian keep! It had gone on for days until Father Sebastian had gone and blessed the castle walls in the name of the Virgin Mary and that had been the end of the light show – which relieved some of the villagers while annoying others who felt that Sebastian should have kept his Christian censorship to himself.

A personal experience is well worth recounting... I'd sort of made friends with a very old Spanish shepherd called Miguel. I'd got to know him gradually over half a year, had won his confidence to the extent that he had allowed me to photograph him up on his mountain above the village while he tended his flock. He must have been well into his seventies, old craggy and gnarled, toothless and almost hairless. He could neither read nor write and spoke in an Andaluz accent that rasped across his throat like rusty chains being dragged across crumpled tin.

On a particular day in the middle of July I'd spent the morning with him, burning off a couple of rolls of HP5. I'd brought him a bottle of half decent wine from the supermercado and he'd shared his meagre lunch with me, patatas bravas cooked over an open fire. I'd then been happy enough to stretch out in the long grass and allow myself to be touched by the scent of full summer. Butterflies buttered, bees buzzed, cijadas chattered; the gentlest of warm breezes wafted across my face giving some relief from the 90 degree sun and carrying with it the perfume of wild flowers. Idyllic!

I suppose I must have dozed off and when I woke up half an hour later Miguel was no longer sitting on his rock surveying his flock, he was among the sheep, rounding them up in some hurried degree of agitation, and trying to herd them into their pens beneath the crag of the mountain. I sauntered over and asked him what was going on.

'Hey amigo, there is a big storm coming. A big big storm. She will be here soon and I must safety the sheep.'

I'd looked up into that cloudless blue sky with a grin of scepticism. 'Miquel, this is Spain in the middle of July. There are no storms coming.'

'She will be here in three hours, maybe four, but no more than four.'

Thinking that he was cracking up with geriatric hallucinations, I'd left him to it and had wandered back down the mountain to the village – and damn me, three and a half hours later the skies clouded over faster than you could say Mary had a little lamb and within a further few minutes the rain was lashing down in torrents and the wind was howling around the white houses like a demented banshee. All across the village people scurried for cover and I ended up sodden and saturated in Angel's bar with another half dozen ex-pats, wondering at the tremendous detonations of thunder that exploded throughout the length of the valley and wincing at the jagged forks of lightening that stabbed out of the heavens like Satanic stilettos hellbent on murdering the ground. I thought of

Miguel up on the hill and felt a trickle of moisture run down the middle of my back that felt like blood – it could have been sweat – but it certainly wasn't rain.

I remembered the day that I had arrived in Jimena for the very first time. I had parked my hire car in the Plaza Victoria up in the northern barrio. Even as my feet had made contact with the damp tarmac all that time ago in November of 1987, I'd felt that thrall of now familiar energy buzz up through my feet that said this place was special and this was the place in which I was meant to be. Therefore, this seemed to me to be the most feasible explanation as to why Jimena was so important to me, but even this could not be proven or explained sufficiently to make any kind of objective sense – and this line of thought brought me four square back to Anthony Zander.

He was trying to prove something which had hitherto been unprovable, and God knows I admired him for that no end, but there was a fly in the ointment of his thinking. Assuming that his experiment was a resounding success (baring in mind that at that time I still did not have the details of how the experiment was to be conducted or what it entailed) it could only constitute proof to those people who had been directly involved.

To us, in Jimena, it might be seen as fact but to Tom Bloggs living in Scunthorpe, hearing about it second hand some time after the event, it could only be hearsay.

I became increasingly depressed by this thought – and if I am to tell you the truth, despite those blue skies and that gloriously golden Spanish sun, I became a little bit depressed, full stop.

So I turned my mind away from this way of thinking, picked up my pace and allowed my thoughts to become memories, and there was certainly no shortage of those in these narrow picturesque streets.

After trekking the length of Calle Sevilla twice (once up and once down) I ended up back at The Anon. There were a few late drinkers – and among them was Julian. He needed to talk about Beth and he needed someone to listen, and we ended up sitting on the terrace until three o'clock in the morning, freezing on the outside, warm on the inside from the contents of a bottle of Magno provided by Gabriel from behind the bar at an inflated price that I could only afford, thanks to Zander and his ten thousand dollar cheque. What Julian and I discussed that night will not be repeated. There was no tape recording. After he had gone, feeling better for having unburdened himself, I sat there for another half hour mulling things over in my head and heartily thankful that my name was James Christie and not Julian Boyd. I didn't envy him his position. The pure Joy of Beth's presence in his life mitigated by the ongoing distress that same presence caused in his heart. Unrequited love is bad enough but a love that is impossible to consummate is probably a dozen times worse.

In the dim glow from the hanging lantern I reached for my pad and my pen, not sure whether I was writing for Julian or Beth, but feeling the need to ejaculate some of the pent up emotion within my own dark soul.

You sleep in a warm bed
while he stands alone.
If you saw him
you would not know him
for though not a dream
he is scars and shadows.
You sleep because he lets you sleep
and you sleep despite him,
but because he shivers
with warm intent
at least you sleep in safety.

My third meeting with Zander convened in his bedroom on the morning of December 14th. He was propped up in bed with a saline drip hooked up to his arm on one side and a trolley tray with a cocktail of tablets on the other. He looked rested and well, even with a spark of colour in his otherwise pallid cheeks, and I told him as much.

'He is looking better because he's had two days of bed rest.' Julian said. Both Julian and Elizabeth were present in the room, sitting on chairs on either side of the bed, whilst I was on a third chair towards the bed end. At first I thought they were both there to make sure I didn't "tire" the dying man, but it soon became apparent that there was another agenda.

'I was perfectly well enough to get up yesterday,' Zander protested.

'Doctor Luther didn't think so,' Julian spoke firmly, 'and neither did I.'

'How's the book coming James?' Zander asked, knowing that he wasn't going to win in his argument with Julian, and seeking to change the subject.

'I've started making a few notes,' I said cautiously, 'but it's an unusual process. When a writer starts on a book he usually knows more or less how it's going to finish, and he has that thought in mind from page one. That rule doesn't apply to this project, so I've been groping a bit to find a starting point and a style. I've got about a dozen pages done, and some time this afternoon or this evening I'll find someone who can lend me a typewriter and get it down on paper for you to look at tomorrow.'

'Oh can't I read some of it now?' he sounded disappointed.

'You'd never read my handwriting,' I excused myself. 'There are times when I can't even read my scrawl.'

'I have a perfectly good PC in my study,' Elizabeth said quietly, 'you're more than welcome to use that if you want to.'

'Yes thank you very much!' I accepted the offer gladly, wondering if I was hearing a note of apology in her voice for the other day's aggressive attitude.

'Good, good, then let's get on with things, shall we?' Anthony exclaimed impatiently. I may have been wrong, but I could see him glancing out of the window into the sunlit garden where we had been three days earlier, and given half the chance, I thought that was where he would have preferred to have been right now.

'I think we must all agree that the success of our experiment will depend upon the controls we put in place,' Zander began. 'Our three clairvoyants could deliver some persuasive evidence, but we are looking for hard proof and not just persuasive evidence. Any one of our sitters could tell us that they'd "got a lovely guy here who passed over recently after a long illness, and oh I'm getting the initials A and Z, and I'm getting lots of bright lights so I'm wondering if this gentleman was an actor or something" – and that might well satisfy a theatre audience, but we're not in a theatre and we need to have something a lot harder, a lot more tangible than this. Let's not forget that these three mediums are the crème de la crème of their professions. They're supposed to get it right, for Pete's sake! They could pick that stuff up out of the ether or they could easily and inadvertently be tapping into any one of you three – telepathy, mind reading, or whatever – let's face it, none of it is too far removed from genuine clairvoyance, and we simply cannot allow that degree of speculation to raise its ugly head.'

I coughed politely, not wanting to interrupt, but feeling that I had no choice. 'Anthony I've worked with different mediums over a lot of years and I've got to say that if any one of them was able to come up with a couple of initials, make the theatre connection and mention a long illness, they'd be doing pretty damn well.'

'Perhaps, James, but I want and expect a lot more than that. So all three clairvoyants must give you my full name. If they give you Tony rather than Anthony then that's simply not good enough. I've never been called Tony, not by parents, lovers and friends. It's always been Anthony. All three of them must identify cancer as the cause of death, and I expect all three of them to get the time and the date right. As far as I'm concerned, I'm going to be standing there right behind them or inside them or whatever, telling them what to say to prove that I'm still alive, so they've got no excuse to get it wrong!

'On Sunday morning I will do three things. They are the last things I shall physically do before I go to sleep...'

What a wonderful euphemism, I thought, for committing suicide!

'First, I shall plant a small tree in the garden next to where they are going to bury me...'

Bad move Tony... The roots will play hell with your coffin!

77

'… And then I shall write a poem. I shall expect our mediums to pass on both of those critical pieces of information, and I regard that as being the first part of our control procedure.'

The first part? – And hang on, didn't he say three things? Tree planting and poems were only two…

'Now for the second sequence of the experiment, there are three mediums, and there are, of course, three of you. Each of you must put something personal inside my coffin before the lid is closed and sealed…'

I shuddered. This was becoming more than macabre.

'None of you will know what the other has placed in the casket, at least until the experiment is concluded, and that way if any of our mediums can tell you what it was that you put in the box, you will at least be sure that it is coming from the horse's mouth, and I expect our mediums to be able to tell each of you what it was you gave me for my going away present.

'Each of you will sit in an independent reading with each clairvoyant and the three of you will compare notes and assess the evidence afterwards. Let me, again for the record, stress that none of our clairvoyants have been told the true nature of their role in this experiment, and although I do happen to know one of these people personally, she has no knowledge of this set up, and she actually thinks that I'm in Aspen, Colorado, in bed with a dislocated hip as a result of a skiing accident.

'Phase three of the experiment will be an open séance with all parties present. At that point our three mediums may be told that there is a specific energy trying to get through, and let's see how they handle that! Our three visitors will all be staying in the guest accommodation, and, of course, there will be nothing anywhere within this building that will have any association with me. From that point of view it will be a neutral and sterile environment and the three of you will have to watch your words when you are in the company of our guests.

'There is one other aspect that might be useful. Just before I take my sleeping tablet, each of you will be given a sealed envelope with an "open on" date. In each envelope there will be a simple piece of code uniquely significant to the individual. If all other parts of the experiment fail, I shall do my best to contact you separately, using the codes or code words that you will have been given, and again in that way there can be no doubt in any of your minds as to who is trying to make contact with you... But you can't open the envelopes until the specified date.

'And I think that's about it! Any questions, anybody?'

Oh yes, I certainly had a few questions! But which ones to ask? And how to ask them? Elizabeth and Julian looked at their hands saying nothing, so why did I sense that for them the "any questions" question had been somewhat rhetorical? So, if they weren't going to say anything, it was obviously down to me.

'What happens,' I asked tentatively, 'if you fall asleep, as you put it, and then wake up on the other side on a fabulous film set where you're the star of the movie and your supporting actors are Bogart, Cooper and Gable and your leading lady is Monroe, every friend and loved one you've ever met in your life is there slapping you on the back and telling you what a great guy you are, you're warm and well, and out of pain, and you're having a wonderful time – and you only remember you've got this experiment running after a couple of days of wild partying, but while that couple of days is only a couple of days for you up there but it turns out to be a couple of years, or even a couple of decades, for us down here?'

'I don't think it will happen like that.'

I looked at him directly, not willing to let this one go. I was neither being awkward nor belligerent, but I wanted to smoke and couldn't smoke, had forgotten to take my Prozac that morning, and what I was talking about was a very serious issue. He was postulating theory, and at the end of the day, theory could be horribly wrong.

'You've never died before,' I said bluntly, and felt Elizabeth wince at my choice of words. 'So how do you know?'

'All right James, I don't know, but I've been focusing all my mental energy on this project for many months, and if I don't come through to you with proof it won't be because I have forgotten you or have become distracted, it will be because I can't, and from that you may draw your own conclusions about the whole experiment!'

He shuffled in the bed with discomfort and although Julian altered the position of his pillow, I suspected that his discomfort was more mental than physical.

'Look James, as far as I know nobody has ever tried to do this before, not in the way we're trying to do it anyway. Not science, not the church, none of the spiritual or philosophical groups... None of them...' he patted the bed sheet for emphasis '...has ever attempted and experiment of this nature, and although I'm not certain – for God's sake how can I be certain of anything? – I am confident that something positive will come out of this. We've got some very big guns trained on this, after all!'

Okay, I thought. Let's talk a bit about those big guns and let's see how you react when I point out the big black hole in your thinking!

'Anthony, I don't know who your big guns are, and I appreciate the reasons why I shouldn't know until they get here, but I've come into contact with some very big guns myself over the years and I have to tell you that even if any of them had been invited to this party they would have declined, purely because in my experience we don't always get the messages we want from the people we expect to get them from, and to make specific contact with a pre-identified spirit, other than in romantic literature, has never been done!'

'That's why we're trying to do it,' Zander replied, not in the least bit phased by my negativity.

'Anyway Mr C. you're wrong!' this was from Julian, with a faint gleam in his eye.

'Really?' I answered mildly, waiting for him to go on.

'Doris Stokes! One of the best mediums ever to come out of your country!' he exclaimed triumphantly. 'She made direct contact with the spirit of George Orwell for the BBC back in 1984, and she did it in front of TV cameras to prove it!'

'Oh I'm sorry.' I couldn't help but smile. 'I'd forgotten that particular event, but Julian, as far as experiments go, that one was flawed right from the very beginning. It wasn't objective and it wasn't open to any kind of investigation or criticism. Doris knew well in advance that the TV people wanted to communicate with Orwell and therefore she had plenty of time to research her subject. She even had a list of questions that the TV people wanted answering. The only account we have of this incident is in Doris's own words in one of her own books. The TV footage was never broadcast, and no one seems to know what happened to it. After all, 1984 was a very long time ago.'

'How do you know all this?' Elizabeth asked in her little Miss Cool voice.

'It's my business to know,' I said flatly. 'Which is one of the reasons why Anthony brought me on board.'

The lady met my eyes and for a heart beat there was a brisance of tension. We could well have got into an argument, but Zander prevented it most astutely.

'James I take your point entirely, I really do, but let me put this to you. I believe that all true post mortem communication is carried out on the vibration of pure love, and the two people that I love most dearly in all of this world are Beth and Julian, and it is the energy of that love that will make the communication possible, if it happens at all. Can you go with that?'

I took the olive branch and capitulated. "Yes Anthony, I can go with that.'

Which was what I said, but was not exactly what thought.

'I think,' said Julian, coming to an executive decision, 'that this session has gone on long enough for the time being, and I want to call a halt now. Anthony, it's time for some tablets...'

'I don't want to take any tablets and I assure you I'm feeling fine, and besides, there are some more things I want to talk about with James!'

'It's time for some tablets,' Julian insisted firmly. 'Then you can have a short sleep before lunch, and then you can talk to James again this afternoon.'

'Oh all right,' Anthony sounded like any typical grumpy old man being told to do something he didn't want to do. Then he caught my eye. 'Will you be around for this afternoon?' he asked.

'Yes of course. I'll borrow Elizabeth's PC and type out what I've put together so far, and you can give it a first pass.'

'Excellent!'

Elizabeth took me into the rwo storey section of the house. Not her bedroom, but something that came half way between a small sitting room and a private study. Thank God the antiseptic white was missing, and instead the walls were painted a pale terracotta. There were book shelves with a catholic and eclectic collection of literature and instead of the ubiquitous Andalucian tiles there were thick rich coloured rugs over a wooden floor. Beneath a window there was a computer work station complete with a Swivel King leather chair and in the corner furthest from the door, there was an open fireplace. In the middle of the room there were a couple of very old over stuffed sofas and a generous coffee table made of some smoothly polished dark wood. This was a different ambience entirely to the rest of La Casa Blanca – it was warm and cosy, and whilst not sexy – that would be the wrong word entirely – it never the less carried an energy of personal intimacy.

While Elizabeth went to find me a coffee and a sandwich I browsed her book shelves. Here were the poems of Ted Hughes and Sylvia Plath. Omar Khayyam stood next to The Kama Sutra, and beneath them on the next shelf there were half a dozen Beatrix Potters sitting next to Tolkien and Harry Potter. Karl Marx's Das Kapital shared shelf space with The Good News Bible while Delia Smith flirted with Alan Titchmarsh and Ken Follett. You can tell a lot about a person from looking at their books and you can tell even more by tasting the atmosphere of their living space – and it seemed to me that a revue of Ms Elizabeth Hammond-Zander was well over due.

She brought the coffee and some ordinary cheese sandwiches, fired up the PC for me, and then disappeared while I hammered the first few words of this book onto the printed page. I was being thrown in at the deep end, and therefore had little choice other than to forget about style and angle and I simply started telling this story as it had been presented to me thus far. I worked for a couple of hours, frequently referring to my notebook and my Dictaphone, and without realising that it was happening, began to get lost in the work. The sandwiches were forgotten about. The coffee went cold and the first inclination that I had to suggest a passing of time had taken place was the awareness of someone watching over me. I jolted and turned in my chair to find Elizabeth, less than three feet away, reading what I was writing over my shoulder.

'Good God girl, you scared the living daylights out of me!'

'I'm sorry. I didn't want to interrupt while you in full flow.'

'Full flow be damned, I'm struggling for every word.'

'I think Anthony will like what you've written so far.'

I sighed and hit the print key. The machine coughed and whirred and spilled out a dozen sheets of A4. I handed them to her, then walking over to the window, thrust it open. I stuck my head out onto the verandah and lit my pipe while she curled up on one of the settees and read the very rough and ready draft of chapter one.

'Yes,' she said thoughtfully after ten minutes or so. 'I think Anthony will be very pleased with this.'

'That's not the point,' I retorted drily. 'The question is, will a publisher be pleased, and will a reader be pleased?'

'Does it really matter as long as the story gets told?'

I laughed, but it wasn't altogether a pretty laugh. 'It might not matter to you or your father but it sure as hell matters to me! In any case, the publisher has got to be pleased otherwise the project will never see the light of day.'

She went quiet for a moment. 'Do you want some more coffee?' she asked.

'Yes please, but not that instant rubbish that Julian concocts in his kitchen.'

She smiled. 'Yes it is pretty horrible, isn't it! Don't worry, I'll make some fresh. Do you want it in here, out on the terrace, or will you just take it straight in and sit with my father for a while.'

'Is he awake?'

'Yes.'

'Let's have it outside on the terrace. I could do with some fresh air, and I'd appreciate a few moments with my pipe.'

She laughed at that, and in truth it was a merry laugh. 'Isn't that a contradiction in terms? Pipe smoke and fresh air?'

'Nah,' I grinned. 'Pipe smoke is fresh air, especially if you've been without it for a while.'

We had ten minutes on the verandah then I went in to see Zander for the second session of the day.

He read my first dozen pages while I sat next to him on one of those unforgiving hard backed chairs. On the one hand, I hated anybody reading something that, in my opinion, was a long way short of being ready to be read, but on the other hand, I found that I was willing him to like it, and looking for his approval of my preliminary efforts.

'This is fine.' he said. 'In fact it's better than fine. I am confident that you're going to write something good here.'

I wished that I shared his confidence.

'You do realise, though, don't you, that you are going to have to change some names and identities?'

I looked at him blankly, thick dick head Yorkshireman coming to the fore. 'Why?' I protested. 'Changing names and stuff like that will only diminish the book's authenticity!'

'James, think this through for a minute. My death certificate will state that I died of heart failure, and initially nobody will argue with that. However, once this book is published, the cat will be out of the bag, and there could be a few most unwelcome repercussions. Beth and Julian could be accused of being accessories to an illegal act and my good friend the Doctor could find himself in a very untenable position. Euthanasia is still frowned upon by society and is still illegal in most western nations. Talk to Julian and Beth about this, and see what they think with regard to their own position, but you must totally disguise Doctor Luther and my dear friend Beatrice, and as for me, depending upon what my children say, use your own judgement.'

'Couldn't I just say that you died from natural causes?' I asked, grasping for a leaf of literary integrity.

'You could, but it wouldn't be the truth, would it? Apart from that, I want to prove the church wrong in its view of suicide. You of all people should understand that.'

What was he saying? Had he read my books, put two and two together and got four, or did he know something that I didn't think anybody in these chapters of my life knew about? I felt chilled and very uneasy, and decided to change the subject as quickly as I could.

'What about the date and time of your death? Can they stay as they are, true to the facts?'

'James, yes of course they must! The first reason is that it will act as control data for our mediums and post mortem communication, and secondly, if you recall one of our earlier conversations and if you have read the dossier that Beth has given you, you will be mindful that I was born on that date and at that time sixty two years ago. Call it an irony of humour if you like. As far as we know a man is not in a position to choose the time and circumstance of his own birth, and therefore the least he should be allowed to do is choose the time and circumstance of his own passing.'

The conversation carried on for another hour or so covering a range of subjects, then Julian arrived with the humourless Doctor Luther in tow and it was time for me to make my exit. So an exit I made, but I was not, it has to be said, in what you might call a light hearted mood. In fact I felt totally bloody awful. I went and found Beth in the kitchen, we shared a coffee and a couple of cigarettes, then with her permission, I went back to her study, fired up the PC and worked for an hour. It wasn't easy. Nothing flowed. How was I supposed to write this bloody story? Was I writing fact, fiction or faction? Couldn't very well do it like a company report, couldn't do it as a novel and couldn't do it like a blow by blow factual diary account, so therefore I would have to edit, but what to edit? In the end, I swore and deleted the half dozen pages I'd produced.

'Waste of bloody time' I snarled and went out into the sunshine.

And there was something else as well. I was supposed to be writing a book about Zander and his experiment and I realised that I couldn't do that without writing a book about Jimena de la Frontera and James Christie – and I wasn't at all sure that I should do that. I wasn't even sure that I *could* do that. But the subjects were inexorably interlinked. I could not just report on what Zander said or what he did; for the work to make sense I had to write about his motivations and how he felt. Feelings could not be written about without putting cause and effect into context and it was obvious that Jimena had woven its spell over Zander just as it had woven its spell over me. You could say the cause of Zander's action was his illness, and that might be true but it is equally true that he could have chosen any place in the world to die. His "any" place was this place and that connected with my inner spirit on an incredibly deep and personal level, for his place was also my place even though his time might be before my own.

Even in my own mind the book defied categorization – and that was a publisher's nightmare. Was it to be presented as a biography or a novel? A dry factual account, or a diary of a man's last days on earth and his subsequent attempt to communicate through the barrier of death? Either way I was writing fact and not fiction, but the facts were so emotive and so personal that one could not write honestly or convincingly without subjective impressions and emotions. Thus, if impressions and emotions were to be part of this, and they would have to be for Beth and Julian were just as involved as I was, then I would have to write about Jimena and I would have to write about James Christie, and I would have to do so with complete honesty and without embellishment or self consciousness – and if that gave my game away, demeaned me in any way in the eyes of my wife, my family and friends, then that would be the price I would have to pay.

Writing Zander's book was no longer a matter of charging a penny a line and collecting a fee at the end of it all, because by now I was immersed and involved and had developed my own agenda and ambition. Maybe his experiments would fail miserably and the book would become irrelevant, in which case my bank manager would still be pleased with the result, but I would be gutted beyond belief. But if Zander's experiments were successful, then both he and I demanded that the world should know about it, and the only way the world might get to know was if I was honest and wrote the truth. Zander's story would need to be accepted and believed before it could have any impact and for Zander the man to be believed, then Christie the writer must be believed – and if that meant candid disclosure and the messy business of writing about feelings then that was what I would have to do.

Zander had said that he had been "told" that one way or another the book that I was to write would be published and I was pondering on that point when an image of my grandmother flickered across the screen of my psychic mind. As always, when she came to me in this way, she was sitting on a small wooden bench backed against a sun kissed dry stone wall and surrounded by deep red wallflowers. In the "vision" I could smell their scent and saw this most precious lady as she had been when I was a very young boy – 60 years old, slim and sprightly, slightly stooped with silver hair and a long dark coat and bonnet style hat. A far cry from the shrivelled bed ridden husk that she had become thirty five years later, battling with bed sores and waiting to die. I have never seen my grandmother as my "spirit guide" in the same way that some mediums claim to have Indian braves or Chinese Mandarins as their guides, but Elsie Maud Elsiegood is always a presence within me and around me, especially in times of trouble and stress and on this afternoon she looked up at me with caring grey eyes, just as though I was standing there in front of her, all of four feet tall and three years old. "Of course you'll write your friend's book, luvvie, of course you will!"

And I felt better after that.

Eight: *Bar Cuenca , Friday 15th December*

After a very restless night I telephoned Beth first thing Friday morning. 'What's happening today?' I asked.

'Nothing urgent is scheduled,' she said, 'although I think Anthony was hoping to read a bit more of the first draft of your book.'

'Yes, well I'd like to talk to you about that. Can you meet me for lunch somewhere?'

There was a moment's hesitation. 'Well yes I suppose so.'

'Good. In that case meet me at Cuenca's Bar for twelve noon. You know where that is?'

'Yes, that's the place opposite the little supermarket, isn't it?'

'You've got it. See you at twelve.'

I hung up before she could change her mind. Made a few notes over breakfast, then walked down to the Friday market. Once upon a time the market had been held in the El Paseo square, but the market had swollen and the square had become smaller with the maturing of the orange trees that had been planted a dozen years before, so the market had been moved down the hill to a scrub of wasteland. Once upon a time the market had been an exciting place to shop around, you went to see and be seen, and you could browse through tables full of junk, olive stalls, leather goods displays, and everything that gave a market its name. These days it was a poor imitation. Mostly cheap clothes and poor fruit and veg. I exhausted the experience in the space of fifteen minutes flat and went and sat in Cuenca's a good hour and a half early for my meeting with Elizabeth...

...Which was no great sacrifice. It was a lovely morning, bright sunshine without a cloud in the sky, and sitting on one of the outside tables with a splendid view of the castle on the mountain I was content to drink strong coffee, probably the best coffee in the village, and watch the world go by. Cuenca's was traditional old Spanish and although some of the long standing ex-pats used it, it was more a place for the locals. It was always busy on market days, but I'd got there early and claimed the best table out on the sidewalk. I pulled out the scruffy notebook and tried to get a few thoughts down on paper, but I really wasn't in the mood and there were too many distractions.

I marvelled at how quickly a place could change. Fifteen years before I had frequently sat at this same table watching a slow parade of tatty Renault 4's and battered Citroen CV6's as they battled for road space with mules heavily laden with sacks and panniers; the village bus had been an antique from the 1950's with flaking cream paintwork and frequent streaks of rust and it was not unusual to see old men and young boys pushing or pulling hand carts piled high with local produce from the fields. Oranges from the groves, barrels of olives and acetunas, shards of cork bark.

Those days were gone! The Renaults and Citroens had been replaced by Mercedes and BMW's, the village bus was now a sleek modern giant from the Costa del Sol and of the mules and hand carts there was no sign. Rural Andalucia had moved into the 21st Century with ease and aplomb and the last vestiges of third world poverty had been replaced by a degree of wealth and new found financial confidence. The peseta had been deleted and the euro had arrived and while I didn't doubt that times had improved for the local Spaniard, in the transition from the old world to the new, something simple and quite beautiful had been lost.

First one old friend would come up to say hello and offer a drink – and then another – and another after that. I ended up having conversations with half a dozen people I hadn't seen in a dozen years or more. I spent a good half hour chatting to Jimena's oldest ex-part... An incredible character called Barney who had a penchant for large Panama hats and rather naughty little poems.

> " 'Twas in the month of November
> As far as I can remember
> I was walking down the street in drunken pride,
> When my legs fell in a flutter
> And I fell down in the gutter
> And a pig came by and lay down by my side.
> As I lay there in the gutter
> Thinking thoughts I could not utter
> A lady passing by was heard to say
> - You can tell a man who boozes
> By the company he chooses –
> And the pig got up and slowly walked away. "

My schoolboy humour thought this was very funny, or maybe it was the early day drinking. Either way I had a lot of time for Barney. He'd been a brilliant jazz piano player in the forties fifties and sixties and he was a walking library of musical anecdotes – an encyclopaedia of 20ᵗʰ century musical lore. Then in his seventies (he must have been pushing ninety by now) arthritis had started playing hell with his hands and his days of professional playing came to a gentle end after a long and illustrious career. He'd known Errol Garner and Duke Ellington on a first name basis and had had a nodding acquaintance with Count Basie; apparently he'd had an on/off romance with Peggy Lee and had once got disgracefully drunk with Ella Fitzgerald. These were some of the stories he told. I don't know whether they were true, but I believed them because I wanted them to be true.

By the time Elizabeth arrived I'd had a brandy and two beers, and whilst I was still stone cold sober I was feeling a damn sight more relaxed by lunchtime than I'd been feeling at breakfast. Spain does that to you, soothes the sinews, massages the muscles both of the body and the mind, and obviously while the warmth of the life giving sunshine has got a lot to do with the process, there is more to it than just the sunshine! I think it revolves around the life style and ambience that the sun provides, and to be sure you don't just find it in Spain; Southern Italy, Greece, any place where the pace of life is slow will produce the same effect. In Britain and Northern Europe we mock the *mañana* mentality of the Mediterranean nations, but in reality, the *mañana* attitude actually works wonders. There is less stress. Men live longer. People laugh a lot more and our Mediterranean cousins look at our Northern life styles with equal measures of scorn, disbelief and profound sympathy!

Elizabeth arrived looking fresh and sophisticated in a plane yellow dress made of some body hugging woollen material. She was far too skinny for my taste, but the dress emphasised what curves she did have, and she certainly turned a few heads when we walked into the bar and found a table at the back by the patio doors. We could have stayed outside, but there would have been interruptions. The bar was busy with the market trade so a discreet corner of the restaurant seemed more appropriate. Juan brought over a menu and we ordered drinks – Fino for Elizabeth and, playing it safe this early in the day, another beer for me. I don't think that either of us was in the mood for a heavy meal, so we elected to share a plate of *gambas al ajillo* – prawns stuffed with garlic and served in a garlic sauce.

'It's a good job,' I reflected dryly, 'that neither of has got a heavy date this afternoon. When it comes to overdosing on garlic these prawns can be killers.'

'A heavy date in Jimena?' she raised a bemused eyebrow. 'The chance would be a fine thing!'

And that, I thought, was interesting. Of course, it could just have been repartee, but while not clairvoyant I do have some psychic instincts and I reckoned that I was being told here that if there was a candidate and there was a chance, Beth Hammond might well be in a mood to take that chance. I thought back to my conversation with Julian, and wondered if it might be a good time to throw my brick into the pond and see where the ripples went... No, probably not yet. In any case, she swiftly led me away from the subject.

'Anyway, you wanted to discuss something about the book?'

'Yes. I don't know how to write it! It's not a biography, it isn't a novel, and it isn't something that could be written as an elongated magazine article. I can't get a handle on it.'

'Anthony was very pleased with what he read yesterday.'

'That was just me quoting and paraphrasing some of the things he'd said, and you can't construct a whole book on that basis.'

She pondered for a moment then pulled out her packet of Marlboro Lights. 'What's wrong,' she asked, offering me a cigarette, 'with writing it in the same style as the two books you've already written? I don't know about Julian, but I read them and enjoyed them very much and I know that Anthony was also suitably impressed.'

I lit the cigarettes and shuffled uncomfortably. 'Beth, they were different books. I knew where I was coming from and I knew who I was writing for. More importantly I knew that I didn't have to get those books past a publisher because they were coming out of my own company's press. I also knew that most of those books would be sold directly to audiences on the evenings of clairvoyant demonstrations. Now, with Anthony's book there can be no direct sales, so as I see it, a publishing deal with a major house has got to be preferable, especially when you take into consideration all the problems with nationwide and possibly international, distribution.

90

That kicks up a personal dilemma for me because I can't just write for myself and Anthony. I've got to come up with something that will impress and inspire confidence in a commissioning editor and...'

'If I were you,' she cut in, 'I'd throw that mind set out of the window straight away! That's not why we invited you here. You are not writing to impress anyone, least of all some anonymous commissioning editor. All you have to do is write the story of what is happening, as it happens, using your own words and in whatever style comes most naturally to you. Anthony has absolute faith in your abilities, and if it means anything to you, so do I and so does Julian.'

'Julian?' I echoed in surprise.

'Julian,' she confirmed with a mischievous twinkle in her eyes. 'For what it's worth, you've made quite conquest there. When you first arrived he thought you were a "boring old fart" but now he regards you as "a good straight bloke".'

She mimicked Julian's Aussie accent to perfection, and I had to laugh, at which point Juan arrived with an enormous platter piled high with lightly battered prawns smothered in half a litre of aioli. I squeezed some fresh lemon juice over the feast and watched in anticipation as Elizabeth picked up a prawn, dipped it in the garlic dressing, then popped it into her mouth. Her eyes opened wide at the unexpected gastronomic experience.

'My God,' she murmured, 'that is orgasmic!'

I duly noted her choice of word, then watched as she systematically began to demolish the plate of food, albeit with no small degree of help from myself. Ten minutes later she sat back with a satiated look, dipped her long fingers into the lemon scented finger bowl, and delicately dabbed around her mouth with a serviette.

'That,' she said emphatically, 'was better than sex!'

I duly noted those words as well, and wondered briefly if she was flirting with me? I weighed up the factors, and decided probably not – but she was opening up to me a little bit on a personal level and dropping her guard, which might make subsequent conversations easier and more informative. Time now to throw a brick? No definitely not – but maybe a small pebble?

'I don't know if Julian would share your opinion,' I remarked lightly.

'He doesn't like prawns much,' she said.

'Wouldn't have thought he'd have too many problems with sex, though,' I suggested.

She shot me an odd look, slightly on guard now, but trying not to show it. 'I wouldn't know,' she said shortly. 'That part of his life is none of my business.'

But it's in the back of your mind love, whether you're prepared to acknowledge it or not!

'Anyway James, we're not here to talk about Julian. We're here to talk about your book, and all I can say is that you should write it in your own way. Become your own commissioning editor and have a bit more faith in your own abilities.'

Nice words.

Juan came over to clear the plates and I ordered more drinks.

She looked at me solemnly, and basically did not understand the problem.

'Let me,' I began slowly 'tell you the story about a book I wrote a few years ago. It was a modern morality tail wrapped up in the form of a humorous gothic horror novel. It was a good book and I wrote it to the best of my literary ability, and most important of all, I told the story I wanted to tell. My literary agent sent it off to four different publishers and all four publishers sent it back, praising the author's literary skill and saying how much they had enjoyed reading the manuscript. Having said that, all four publishers turned the book down. Two of them because they said the work was far too bloody and gory, and the other two because they thought the book was far too light weight and didn't have enough bloody bits to fit into their schedule. In other words, I'd written an admittedly good, but unpublishable book, because it didn't fall within the publisher's idea of what was commercially viable. And all I'm saying, Beth, is that we could have exactly the same problem with Anthony's book.'

'We could have but we won't.' she replied promptly.

I raised a questioning eyebrow. 'Do you know something that I don't?' I asked.

'No not really, but I do know this. Anthony is a very spiritual person and he's very psychic in his own right. He has dreams and visions – they're not the right words, but they'll have to do – and if he says that James Christie from York is going to write a successful book about his experiment with clairvoyance, then you can take it as gospel that James Christie *is* going to write a successful book about Anthony Zander's experiment with clairvoyance!

'Now, if you don't mind, I think I'd like another drink.'

'Oh no, you can't just leave it like that!' I protested.

She laughed. 'No, I don't suppose I can, can I?' But then her brow furrowed. 'But I'm not sure what else I can tell you other than to say that right from the very beginning Anthony wanted you. I mean, he does know Stephen King slightly and we *did* have some jokey conversations about him writing the book, but it was never a serious option.'

'But where the hell did he hear of me?' I asked, and then, as an afterthought, 'and when, just as a matter of interest, was the beginning of this? You know, from your point of view?'

'Anthony and I started discussing this project more than a year and a half ago. At that time it was simply a "what if" scenario. We started planning seriously about eight months ago when Anthony was told the cancer was terminal. I suppose it would have been then that your name came up for the first time. Anthony was in LA and I was in London. He phoned me to say he'd just read a book by an English author called James Christie called "The Light In The Darkness" – that there was a new book out called "Out Of This World" which he wanted me to get hold of and send out to him, and while I was about it, I was to find out all I could about you and Mage Publishing.

'So I did the research, and James, I'm truly sorry, but when I spoke to Anthony, I had to tell him that hardly anybody had heard of either you or Mage Publishing, but Daddy was adamant that he wanted you, and he said that if I had any doubts I was to read the two books. So I read the books, and I saw where he was coming from, but I still couldn't understand why he was so determined that it had to be you.'

'When I spoke to him he did give me some reasons,' I mused thoughtfully, remembering our very first conversation, 'but it still seems improbable.'

'The only thing to do is ask him directly,' she said. 'But I know Anthony of old. On something like this he might give you a straight answer and then again, he may not. Now, if you don't mind, I really would like another drink.'

So I got us a pair of brandy and cokes and at my suggestion, now that the business bit had been concluded, we went and sat out on the pavement. The market crowds had thinned and we sat in the warm afternoon sunshine chatting away amiably like a pair of old friends. I wasn't looking for book material, but I did ask how come the English rather than an American accent and learned that Susan, her mother, had actually been British, and that Beth had spent a lot of her childhood and teens in the UK with her mother's family while Zander had been globe trotting. She had attended school in Bournemouth and had got her law degree at Oxford. She enjoyed dual nationality and with a second law degree from UCLA she was able to practice both in Britain and in America. In my part of Yorkshire we'd call that a nice little earner!

I learned that she'd been married to a fellow lawyer called Stewart, but that it hadn't lasted more than a year before they'd both realised that they'd made a mistake. They'd divorced (amicably) and had remained good, if not close, friends. There had been no children.

She'd always had Zander in her life as the doting, if at sometimes distant father figure, and when his illness had been diagnosed she had given up her law practice to concentrate on looking after his needs, both legal and practical.

'That must have been a difficult decision for you,' I suggested.

She shook her head. 'No, not really. Anthony has always been the most important person in my life, and to tell you the truth I'd stopped enjoying law. It wasn't too hard to see what I had to do.'

So what would she do with her life after he'd gone?

My eyes squinted against the sun as I gazed thoughtfully in the direction of the river and not for the first time was I struck by the surrealism of the situation. Here we were at a Cuenca's bar pavement table, surrounded by the hustle and bustle of life: the skies were blue the scenery superb, we were drinking and talking like two ordinary people who might have just met on holiday or something and yet less than two miles away there was a man we both knew, and a man that one of us loved dearly, who was waiting to die – a man who would be dead by his own hand in slightly less than forty eight hours. I suppressed an inner shiver and for a brief second the sun moved behind a dark cloud of the soul.

'Now where have you gone to, I wonder?' she asked lightly.

'I was just thinking that this last couple of years can't have been too easy for you. I mean, for heaven's sake, I've only been part of this for a few days, and the tension and the suspense has got to me. You and Julian have been exposed to it for months.'

'No,' she admitted. 'It has not been easy, but we've all helped each other, and I suppose that the thought of Anthony's experiment has kept us all going... But...' she looked at me and I could see the pain and desperation in her eyes. 'I have to tell you the truth and say that I need this to be over now. I've buried my father a thousand times in my mind, and now I need to do it for real and then do my best to get on with my life and begin the healing process. Oh shit!'

A tear had formed in the corner of her eye and had begun its descent along the curve of her cheek. She grabbed for a tissue and dabbed it away.

I reached across the table and gave her hand a little squeeze. 'I was talking with Julian the other night and he feels pretty well the same as you do about it all. I'm sure you don't need me to tell you that he's there for you if you need him...'

She opened her mouth to say something, then thought better of it and remained silent. She went through the palava of lighting a cigarette – probably not really wanting one, but needing to do something to cover her thoughts with small routine actions. I'd got as close as I was going to get with the Julian business, so now it was time to back off and change the subject... Except that I didn't.

Spain is not England. Being in Spain is not like being in England. There are different rules, different energies and different states of awareness. Two fellow countrymen in a foreign place forge psychological links that would be impossible in any other set of circumstances. The common bond of ex-patriotism draws disparate people together in strange strands of unity and apart from anything else, where Elizabeth Hammond and I were concerned there was that other conspiratorial link created by our mutual involvement with Anthony Zander.

'You do know,' I said gently 'that you've got a bit of a problem with Julian, don't you?'

She gave me a swift non-committal glance, then looked away, eyes focused on the middle distance of nowhere. She was silent for two or three seconds, then stubbed out her cigarette. Not meeting my eyes, she sighed. 'Yes James. I know.'

And her words told me everything.

'Any idea what you're going to do about it?' I asked

'Like what?' she replied in neutral tone.

'I don't know,' I admitted. 'But if I think of something I'll let you know.'

I shut up and averted my gaze, aware of the fact that I'd probably said far too much and uncomfortable now in the brooding silence which followed.

'It would be odd, wouldn't it...' her words sounded reflective, as though she wasn't talking to me at all. 'Yes, it would be odd if you *were* able to come up with a good idea. If nothing else, that might me one of the reasons Anthony asked you to to come and be part of all this.'

Yes, what was an interesting thought and my mind went wandering off into the nether worlds of fate and jigsaw puzzles. I had absolutely no idea of how I might help Elizabeth Hammond in her emotional distress, but in that moment, I did know that I was going to try.

'You want to talk about this some more?' I asked tentatively.

'No James, I don't.'

'Answer me one question?'

'What's that?'

'Do you want Julian as much as he wants you?'

She didn't answer.

She really didn't have to. The expression on her face said it all.

That Saturday, the last full day of Anthony Zander's life, was not a good day. When I saw him late in the morning, it was obvious that I was talking to a dying man, a man who even if he chose to stay the action of his own hand, was not destined to enjoy many more days of grace abroad on this planet. His pallor was awful – almost parchment white – and rather than sitting propped up in bed, he was flat on his back with a drip in each arm. With the nurse, Beatrice, sitting in one corner, this was no longer a bedroom, but a terminal station in a hospice or a private ward in some expensive clinic. An antiseptic smell mingled with the mild pungency of sandalwood incense, but beneath that, there was something darker and dirtier that I did not even want to contemplate. Music was coming from a small CD player beneath the curtained window; Samuel Barber's agonisingly poignant Adagio For Strings quietly filled the room, and that in itself brought a natural but most unwelcome lump to my throat.

There was only one chair drawn up to the bedside, so I sat on it. Despite his frailty, Zander managed a small welcoming smile and thankfully it was he who broke the silence: his voice was much weaker than it had been the previous day, and rather than being a few hours away from his sixty second birthday he looked, and sounded, more like someone in their nineties.

'Well Mr Christie, we're almost at the last chapter.'

'Or the first,' I said, as kindly as I could, trying to match his tone.

He acquiesced with a gentle inclination of his head. 'How's my book coming along?'

This was no time to tell him the truth. 'We've made a good start,' I said mustering some enthusiasm.

'I wish you luck and I know you'll do a good job for me... And on the subject of writing, I find myself needing to ask you a favour?'

'Absolutely anything at all. Whatever you need.'

'I have been trying to write my poem, but I find that I can't do it. If I was able to sit at a table and hold a pen, I might get something out, but the truth is I've never written a poem in my life and I'm not sure where to start, especially when I'm trying to do it in my head. As you might gather,' he said ruefully 'I'm pumped up with rather more of Luther's drugs than I would like to be, and although it's keeping the worst of the pain at bay...'

I told him not to worry. I took out my notepad and pen, and suggested that he just keep it short and string a few words together than expressed some element of his inner feelings. He said he'd already tried that but had got nowhere, so I asked him if he had a favourite poem written by somebody else.

'Nope. Can't remember any of my Shakespeare, but I never liked him much anyway, and although it's a sad admission, I never had time to explore poetry. Always too damn busy earning a living and learning asinine lines from bad scripts. I suppose we could always put "you'll never get away with it and we'll head 'em off at the pass" but that not at all what I'm feeling right now and it certainly isn't poetry...'

We both laughed, and his laugh became a short cough and Beatrice was there with a glass of water...

And there then followed one of those rare and almost impossible examples of synchronicity that told me that my presence at Anthony Zander's bedside was no accident.

'There's one poem that I heard a couple of years ago that I thought was quite lovely. It was just before I got that bout of food poisoning when we were filming in Egypt. We had a day off and we all trouped along to see the sound and light show at the temple of Karnak...'

Something five times stronger than déjà vu pushed deeply into my solar plexus and all the hairs on the back of my neck stood up and bristled with static electricity. I knew *exactly* what was coming next.

'...It's a pretty spectacular event. Quite incredible. Very powerful. Very moving. Anyway, at one point in the presentation, the narrator tells the story of a four thousand year old papyrus unearthed from beneath the ruins and on it, apparently, is a poem that some young wife wrote for her husband just before he went off to the wars. I wish I could remember it all, but I know that it started something like "I hold your love in my heart"...'

'"Your love is held in my heart," I corrected, '"Like a reed is held in the arms of the wind."'

Zander stared at me blankly. 'My God, that's right. That's exactly right! But how did you...?'

'My wife and I were in Karnak a couple of years ago too. We saw the same show. We heard the same poem. It had the same effect on us.'

We stared at each other, aware of the coincidence, neither of us believing in the coincidence.

'James I think we must use that as my poem.'

'Yes I think so too.'

'Lend me your pad and pen... Beatrice, *por favor!*'

With the nurse's help, Zander pushed himself up into a semi sitting position, laboriously wrote out the few lines, tore the page from the book and handed it to me. 'Just read it to me James, and make sure I've got it right.'

'"Your love is held in my heart like a reed is held in the arms of the wind."'

'Yes James, thank you so very much, that will do just *fine.* '

He was tired and it was time to go, but still I hesitated, and he looked up from the bed quizzically.

'Anthony, I was talking to Beth yesterday, and basically I need to know why you chose me for this job.'

'I told you why.'

But there was a glint of mischief in his pale blue eyes.

'Okay, well tell me again, but not the version you gave me before.'

'I dreamed it,' he said shortly. 'I'd read your two books, and then I dreamed that you would write this book for me. And that sir, is it! Is all you're getting.' And then he added something that sounded odd at the time and even odder when I thought about it afterwards. 'If you want anything else, go and find it in your own dreams.'

Karnak is more than a place. It's a taste, it's a sense, a flavour of a folk memory that reminds us that our civilisation is *old.* The temple, breathtaking in its grandeur and magnificent in its majesty, was built more than four thousand years ago in a land that was old even then... A testament to Man's faith in an afterlife and Man's incredible ingenuity, for no modern builder armed with the most advanced tools and aided by the artefacts of science could build anything like it in our present age. To walk through the colonnades of heiroglyphed pillars that reach achingly into the sky supporting the massive cross members of stone is to reach back into history, to forget one's parochial nationality and to be reminded that one is a member of the human race. The inner humanity that envelopes our soul is touched by the thrill of awe at our achievement and yet at the same time is calmed and humbled by it. With the hot wind sighing from the burnished desert carrying the pungent perfume of scorched sand and exotic spices and with the very earth exuding a vibration of exaltation, one cannot fail to be touched and moved by this unique and splendid place.

I remember walking around the ruins and through the colonnades, hand in hand with my wife, our necks aching as we gazed upwards and away with disbelief and amazement; Karnak effected us both equally; we lost time, we lost all consciousness of the present, and we were catapulted into another time and another world. We thought we might have been there for a couple of hours, and yet coming back into the 21st century and riding in the taxi that took us back to our Luxor hotel, we realised we had been there fore the better part of six!

Later in the day, washed and showered and courting like a pair of young lovers, we had returned for the evening tour of the floodlit temple and within the folds of darkness the power and the mystery of the magic was enhanced. With our emotions and senses on overload we allowed Karnak to wash over us and as we became one with it, it became one with us, touching us deeply in places hitherto undiscovered and unexplored.

The culmination of this life changing experience came with the son et lumiere presentation at the end of the tour. Here modern Man's ingenuity and artistic flair came together in a spine tingling presentation of Karnak's history, enhanced by sympathetic music and one of the cleverest voice over commentaries I think I've ever heard. It was during this part of the evening that the narator told the story – the same story that Zander had heard – of the papyrus discovered that contained the fragment of the love letter from a wife to her husband upon the eve of his departure. Joanna and I had sat, hands clenched, tears streaming down our cheeks, deeply deeply moved by what we were seeing and hearing.

'You remember the first bit,' I'd said. 'That first line – your love is held in my heart…'

'And you remember the second part,' she'd replied. ' – Like a reed is held in the arms of the wind.'

'It will be our poem,' I'd said.

'A code poem... If one of us dies and the other is trying to get through, we use the lines of the poem to prove it's us!'

'Are we going to die?' I'd asked with mock seriousness.

'Absolutely not.' She'd given big a big hug and a big sloppy kiss. 'We're going to live for ever and grow as old as Karnak!'

There was not an argument as such but strong and heavy words were exchanged that left all three of us feeling just a little bit differently about each other.

After the very emotional, and dare I say quite spooky session with Zander I had gone out into the garden for a smoke. I strolled around to the back of the house and was brought up short by the sight of two young gravediggers excavating a large hole between Anthony's chosen oaks. Propped against the back wall of the house was a beautiful olive wood casket draped in black muslin and some tatty blue tarpaulin to protect it from the elements. My heart skipped a beat and there was the sudden taste of bile in my mouth.

Feeling nauseous, I did an abrupt about turn, hurrying away like a thief in the night caught by the reality of his untenable position. Passing the kitchen window I heard raised voices. Julian and Elizabeth – not in quarrel but certainly in argument.

'He *has* to be there,' Julian was insisting. 'There's no point in him being *here* if he isn't going to be *there!*'

'He might not want to be there,' Elizabeth countered.

'Tough shit! Anthony will expect him to be there, and God knows, he's being paid a fare fee so he should be prepared to take the rough with the smooth.'

'But I think it should be private. Just you and me.'

'Can't be that private, not with Luther and Beatrice in attendance, and they've *got* to be there, haven't they?'

'Well, I suppose...'

'There you are then!'

'I think in this case we should let James decide for himself.'

'No way!' Julian sounded adamant. 'If he's gonna do his job properly, he's *got to be there!*'

'Where is it that I've got to be and what it is I should decide for myself?' I asked, entering the kitchen.

They both looked guilty. They'd been talking about me not knowing I was within earshot.

'James,' this was Elizabeth, 'putting it bluntly, do you want to be there tomorrow morning – when Anthony takes his tablet?'

Ah so that was it. Another knot of tension coiled in my gut. I thought of the gravediggers and their growing pile of rich red earth and I wanted to fly and I wanted to run – out of this kitchen, away from this house and away from this situation. I wanted to be where there were bright lights, where there was loud music, cheerful laughter and wine on tap. I wanted humour, sexual promise and a dozen kinds of hedonism. Above all, I wanted to be gone from this pressing thrall of impending death.

'Elizabeth…' I looked at her then turned to meet the eyes of her half brother, 'Julian! No, I do not want to be there, but if either of you needs me to be, then so I shall be and if Anthony wants me to be present, then I *must* be present.'

…And it was left at that, but twenty minutes later I drove away from La Casa Blanca with a heavy heart and a growing feeling of dread. And yet what choice did I have? Zander and his two unlikely children had become my friends, and for friendship's sake I owed them my support.

I mooched through the village. Mooched. Mooching. Funny word. Walking without aim or destination. Obeying the body's demand for movement and exercise – to oxygenate the blood, to clear the head and create space for thought.

By that Saturday afternoon the weather had become moody and changeable: there were still vast swathes of blue sky but now there were massive ramparts of crenulated cloud and an unpredictable wind ruffled my hair and the feathers of my mind. As I walked Jimena's familiar streets – Calle Sevilla and Calle Loba crossing down to Calle Santa Anna and Calle Llannette – I was either two degrees too warm or two degrees too cold. I'd work up a sweat then the perspiration would start to chill against my flesh. I stopped in Bar Perez and had a couple of brandies and coffees and that just made things worse. The ever present redolence of wood smoke got in my eyes and made them sting and there was that empty sicky feeling cloying and coating the lining of my stomach. Part of me wanted to run as fast as my little legs would carry me, just to burn away the negative energy that contaminated my system, while another part of me just wanted a warm bed in a dark room and the luxury of oblivion. There were too many thoughts. Too many emotions.

I tried to analyse my feelings and realised that I wanted someone to talk to; not one of my new found acquaintances, but someone who knew me. Someone I loved and trusted. Mrs Christie wasn't answering either the office phone or her mobile, Harry Andrews wasn't answering his and I knew that my ace in the hole free counselling service, aka friend and guru poet Adrian Spendlow never answered his phone in daylight hours anyway! There were other friends I could have called, but none that could have salved this particular wounded feeling...

And I suppose that was how I felt. Wounded. The Anthony Zander scenario had got under my skin and had invaded my conscious streams of thought like some nasty virus contaminating the system with insidious degrees of corruption. Being so close to Zander's impending demise made me acutely aware of my own mortality, and he was quite right, death is a haunting spectre, tantalisingly tapping us on the shoulder, and the older we get the harder and more insistent that tapping becomes.

Those people who had the gift of great faith were to be envied and Zander's determination to conduct his experiment in the face of his own lack of faith made his gesture all the more poignant and provocative. It also made me, much against my will, examine the depth of my own faith and I clearly realised the vulnerability of my position. In my own mind and belief structures I was uncannily close to Zander's philosophies and opinions and my conversations with him had done enough to force my head above the parapet of preconception. And *that* made me feel afraid.

If Zander came through with hard proof of post mortem survival, then, depending upon the depth and detail of that hard proof, my fear could be assuaged for ever. But if he did not, then that same fear would be multiplied in its intensity. Sure, either way I'd be a bit richer in hard cash terms, but financial bribes carry no weight with The Grim Reaper. All the money in the world cannot keep you out of the mortuary. Some 1960's pundit once said that "you can't take your money with you when you die but you can send it on in advance" and that unbeckoned thought gave me some insight into the extent of Zander's financial commitment to his experiment with death, and his altruism humbled me.

I turned a corner and found myself staring at my own distorted reflection in a mirror – one of those round things that they put at awkward road junctions so that you can see what traffic is heading your way from the other side of a blind bend.

I stopped dead in my tracks, half humoured, half horrified by this hall of mirrors image. I looked like a squat toad, a modern gargoyle – brown hat pulled low over my eyes, old blue anorak, collar turned up against the cool of the day. Thick glasses, heavier lenses every year now, perched sweatily on the end of my nose. Grey beard, loose straggling ends tugged maliciously by the mountain breeze. I smiled at myself and the reflection of the shadows between my teeth made those same teeth look like fangs. Not too many teeth these days to call my own.

The humour was draining away like grains of sand falling through a man's clenched fist while the horror gained in strength with mounting waves of desperation.

My God, I had never been beautiful, but once I had been young. I'd had some youthful vitality, a ready laugh, and my eyes had tended to sparkle a lot back in those years when my hair had been black and my stomach had been (relatively) flat. Now this toad-like gargoyle laughed at me with evil delight, showing me the true image of the man I had become. Rumpled, crumpled and dishevelled, both inside and out. Mean, greedy and cynical with an inability to recognise the reality of my true self.

That wicked image counted every one of my fifty six years, reminding me of the heart surgery I'd undergone thirty months before and counting on skeletal fingers the thousands of cigarettes I'd smoked before and the unremembered bottles of wine and brandy that I had drunk to smooth a troubled soul.

Fifty sodding six years old. I would blink once and be sixty, fart twice and be seventy! Sometimes in my spirit I felt like Methuselah, and yet perversely there was still a vibrant corner of my mind that was only twenty one. I remembered what it was like to be eighteen and twenty eight and I mourned with bitterness and regret the passing of that youth. On a few rare occasions the twenty one year old forced his way through the barriers of time and took a hand in the running of my life and for a fleeting moment I would feel that I was capturing the essence of my younger years, but there would always be someone close at hand telling me to calm down, to be quiet and to act my age... Well, if I was to act my age, I might as well put one foot in the grave that Anthony Zander had dug for himself; he and I, despite our different backgrounds, were kindred spirits and journeymen. He was sixty two years old and he was going to die the following day. Only half a dozen years older than me, he was my writing on the wall.

In that despairing moment on the corner of Calle Sevilla and Rincon de Romo, my own death beckoned, tantalisingly close, but as always wreathed in the shadows of the ever uncertain when. I thought of my beautiful wife, waiting for me in the gothic horror conurbation of Northern England and no doubt wondering what the hell I was up to in these Andalucian hills. She professed to love me, and I knew that she did love me, but looking at this dreadful reflection, I was hard pressed to figure out why. This unholy reflection suggested that there wasn't much here to be loved.

Biting my lip and becoming more aware of the sudden sting of tears behind my eyes, neither caused by the wind nor the woodsmoke, I cut down the steep incline onto Calle Romo thinking of just how much I needed this experiment with Anthony Zander to work. Not for his own sake, but for mine.

Unexpectedly from somewhere very close I heard the sounds of a flamenco guitar and the stamping clack of heels against a wooden floor. I looked up from my reverie and realised that I was passing La Pena de Flamenca – Jimena's flamenco club. The door to the street was open, and I paused by the entrance letting the rhythmic palos find their own resonance inside my head. The music touched me, connecting with something primeval, and without thinking I quietly crept across the threshold and stood at the back of the room.

Chairs were stacked on tables and the place was obviously closed. But upon the stage at the far end of the club and beneath a couple of unshaded low watt bulbs, there was a single dancer working out a routine to taped music that came from a small cassette player on the corner of apron. She was very young – at a guess no more than sixteen or seventeen – with the haughty face that frequently confused Spanish aristocracy with the gypsy bloodlines of the south; long tresses of raven wing hair cascaded down her back, as black as the flamenco shoes that cracked like gunshots against the cheap plank wood of the stage. She wore unglamorous work pants in grey wool and a plane blue tea shirt. Her clothes were stained by dark patches of perspiration and yet as she posed and postured, moving lithely and rhythmically to the tumbling cadenzas of chords, she oozed with sensuality and overt sexuality. It was a totally innocent thing. First of all, it is the nature of the dance and secondly she was so wrapped up in the magic and passion of her work, she was oblivious to my quiet presence. Her eyes were tightly shut, the muscles in her neck strained with the tension held in her body and her brow was a furrow of concentration. She was lost in her own worlds of love, legend and tradition. The worlds of art and flamenco.

I stood transfixed, my eyes locked onto this sinewy young dancer, my senses touched by a moment of pure *duende*. As the moments passed away, so did much of my caged negativity – lifted and released by the power of this music and the visual intoxication of the dance. In the end I had to sit down. I was feeling weak and emotional, captivated by this harsh ballet and beginning to feel healed by this fiery music that cauterised many old wounds. I had a lump in my throat, and there was the ever present sting of dangerous moisture behind my eyes.

I must have watched her for at least fifteen minutes, and then without warning the music ended and she dropped to her knees on the stage panting with exertion and exhaustion. Before she had chance to look up and find me sitting there watching and intruding on what, after all, had been a private practice session, I silently made my exit and went and sat on a rock twenty yards up the road towards Calle Quiros.

Here the dam broke and I felt the tears streaming down my cheeks and a series of sobs caused me to close my eyes tightly shut and to hold my aching head in my hands.

That part of me which I loathe and detest took three steps to one side of my fractured mind. "Good God, why all the tears?" it asked with cruel indifference.

I could have told it that I was crying for Anthony Zander, and that would have been true, but only part of the truth. I could have said I was crying for the beautiful young dancer and for all the pain she might yet have to suffer in her life, and that also would have been part of the truth. More honestly I could admit to weeping for my own lost youth, all the lost opportunities I had frittered away. Crying, not so much for the emotional pain that I had suffered in my life, but crying now with so much remorse and regret for the pain I had caused and had inflicted on others.

Shedding tears of loneliness, for although I loved this village in the Spanish mountains, on this particular afternoon I felt bereft and alienated, the proverbial stranger in Heinlein's strange land. I wanted to feel my wife's arms around my neck and to sense the silken purr of much loved pussy cats on my lap. I wanted to tell La Flamenca that I thought she was a great dancer and that I wished her all the luck in the world for her uncharted future... But I knew that I never would. I wanted to tell Anthony Zander that I'd write his book with as much honesty and integrity as I could muster...

...And in that quest I knew that I could only do my best.

Tiredly I made my way back to the Anon, damning all emotions to hell and beyond. Question: Christie's home cure recipe for unwanted tears? Answer – drink brandy. Haldf a bottle usually does it, then you pass out and the pain goes away for a while.

Eleven: *La Casa Blanca, Sunday 17th December*

I didn't get drunk on the Saturday night, but I did have too much to drink... It was one of those nights when I could have tippled from every bottle on every shelf and remained stone cold sober. In search of oblivion I trawled the bars in the northern barrio, Bar Vargas, Bar Mena, Bar Perez, Bar Espana: I wanted to be able to go to sleep and wake up somewhere else – wake up and be some*one* else! And the bitter irony? When it came to going to bed, I still could not sleep. God knows my body was tired enough but my mind would simply not close down.

Over and over again I replayed my conversations with Anthony Zander: I wondered if he was sleeping away his last night on earth, and if he was, what was he dreaming? And if he was not, what was he thinking? Was he thinking anything at all, or was his pain so great that Doctor Luther Martinez and his moustachioed nurse had him on so much medication that he was simply drifting over the hours in a miasmic haze of confusion?

Somehow I didn't think that would be the case. Zander had said that he wanted a clear head for his last hours in this world – and I tossed and turned in the narrow sweaty bed trying to imagine what it would be like to be in Zander's position – and this line of thought opened dark chasms in my own head and fragile state of mind...

Two o'clock in the morning. I got out of bed and smoked a stolen cigarette. Poured a brandy from the bedside table – was I becoming a bloody alcoholic? I didn't know but the brandy helped. Tried to doze. Dozed. Woke at three. Made some coffee and filled a pipe. Tried to write something in my notebook – and ten minutes later was still staring at a virgin page of paper! Did some swearing and pacing round the room. Opened the bedroom door and took in the still air from the velvet black terrace. Went back to the table, studied the blank sheet of paper. A writer so screwed up by what he was supposed to be writing about that he couldn't write a single bloody word. Great. Just great! Did some more swearing, drank some more brandy and went back to bed and did battle with demons that you don't even want to know about! And *still* sleep did not come.

At five o'clock I gave up and got up. Took a long shower, pulled on some clean clothes, and walked out into the dark morning. The stars were down and the moon was down and it was cold. I pulled up the collar of my coat and started walking. No dog barked. No cock crowed.

I had a car. I could have taken the car. But instead, like some pathetic pilgrim battling along the Santiago de Compostela de Camino, I walked through the village and then out along the Camino de Hozgarganta to the white house that once upon a time had been a mill in the service of a forgotten king who had decided to make bombs to try and win a forgotten war.

I arrived at La Casa Blanca with the first grey light of dawn. Lights burned in three of the rooms but it was too early to go banging on doors so I settled in one of the rattan chairs on the verandah and wrapped my old blue anorak around me as tight as it would go. I'd worked up a sweat marching through the deserted streets of the sleeping village and now the perspiration was turning to ice against my clammy skin. I filled and lit my pipe, closed my eyes and listened to the almost imperceptible rustle of the first trace of the morning breeze weaving its way through the groves of eucalyptus trees, this faint whispering counterpointed by the ever present rush of water from the winter river.

Strangely, now that I was here and sleep had been forgotten, some of the tension began to ease out of me, and as I began to relax, my eyes, full of gritty sleeplessness, closed of their own accord and I dozed off into an uneasy slumber.

I awoke to the sound of clinking crockery and the rich aroma of freshly ground coffee. I opened one eye, and then the other. The first eye caught the shape of the cafetiere while the second focused on Beth Hammond as she slid into the chair next to me.

'How long have you been sitting here?' she asked in a bemused tone.

My mouth felt like dry leather. 'What time is it?' I muttered.

'Nine o'clock.'

'Oh hell.' I struggled into full wakefulness and looked at my watch to confirm the impossible. And then, rather sheepishly: 'About three hours.'

'Couldn't sleep?'

'No, not until I got here.'

'It's been the same for us.'

'What about Anthony?'

'Julian helped him plant his tree at first light. He virtually planted it for him. All Daddy did was give a few directions but even that tired him out. He's resting now, bless him.'

'How did he get through the night?'

She bit her lip. 'It wasn't easy for him. He's pretending to be very calm, but the truth of the matter is that he's very frightened.'

'Well I suppose...?'

'No James, don't say it. Don't even *think* it! He's focused and he's committed and he isn't going to change his mind. Not now, anyway. I was hoping against hope that he might have done a few weeks ago, but he's become ever more determined to see it through to the bitter end. In fact Doctor Luther thinks that without the idea of this experiment to keep him going he could easily have slipped away already.'

Well that was good news, wasn't it? Made us all feel a whole lot better! Beth Hammond looked calm and composed, but it was pretty obvious that if I had had a bad night, hers had been one hundred times worse.

I stood by the door at the back of the room. Nowhere to sit. Nowhere to run. Nowhere to hide. Anthony sat propped up in his bed. No drips in his arms and no signs of the medical support he had depended upon these last few days. Both sets of curtains were drawn back and light flooded into the pale and austere room, accompanied by the sound of birdsong and the distant rushing of the river. Julian sat on Zander's left, Elizabeth on his right; their backs were turned to me. Beatrice and the doctor stood off to one side – holding hands for heaven's sake? – the former looking quite terrified, the latter looking his usual impassive self. Zander saw me and half raised his hand in greeting.

'Morning James...' his voice was soft and low and raspy and contained a tremulous note of something uncertain. Perhaps it was fear. Perhaps it was pain. 'Glad you could make it!'

And what did I say to that? *Thanks Tony, wouldn't have missed it for the world!* I simply nodded and which point Beth got up from the bedside and came over to where I was standing. She reached out and handed me a small manila envelope upon which was inscribed my name and the short instruction "not to be opened until December 24th." Beth didn't say anything but her eyes spoke volumes. She squeezed my hand which I took to mean "thank you for being here". Then she resumed her position back at her father's bedside.

The silence in the room rang in my ears like Quasimodo's bells. The air of tension and the atmosphere of suspense became greater with every thudding heartbeat. In the end it was the doctor who broke the silence. It was the first and only time I ever heard this man speak.

He looked at his watch. 'If you are going to do this thing the way you have said you want it done, then Anthony, the time is now.'

Zander nodded imperceptibly. 'Oh well,' he whispered, and these were his last words. 'Here goes.'

At 12.05 he put a large two-tone blue capsule in his mouth, swallowing it down with a sip of water from a plastic glass on the bedside table.

At 12.05 he closed his eyes, taking Beth's hand in his right hand and Julian's hand in his left.

At 12.06 he fell asleep.

By 12.15 he had died.

I stared at him in those last minutes, focusing every measure of attention on his face and form. I cannot tell you the precise moment his spirit left his body: there was no shift in the atmosphere, no flutter of eyelids, no last lingering sigh, no paranormal change in temperature. His heart beat stilled to silence but none of us knew whether he had passed, or whether comatose, he still clung to the last straw of life. It was only when Doctor Martinez put a stethoscope to his heart and nodded somberly towards Beth and Julian that we knew for certain that he had gone. Beatrice went down on her knees and started praying in Spanish. Beth laid her head on her father's pillow and wept silently. Julian uttered a single animal cry of anguish, and wrapping his arms around his body, rocked backwards and forwards with grief. The doctor watched on silently. And as for me, well I started weeping too, and then, moving closer to the end of the bed I noticed something I shall never forget. Anthony Zander's closed eyes and cheeks were awash with his own tears

Later on… I passed through the silent house and exiting through the front door, wandered down to the river. Here the sharp white water rushed in a relentless cascade across the rocks, rustling the long wispy reeds which grew in profusion along the banks; the low winter sun danced its rays upon the droplets of spray causing auras of rainbows to glance across the gorge and striating the leaves and branches of the eucalyptus trees with shards of light which caused a leopard-like dappling upon the lichen moss and long green grass of the earth.

I sat on a rock using the trunk of a tree as a backrest. Here there was a gap in the canopy of branches that allowed the sun to fall on my face. That was the only thing that felt good on this bad, sad day. My mouth tasted like the bottom of a parrot's cage, but never the less, more out of comfort than need I filled and lit my pipe, then just closed my eyes allowing the scents and sounds of the river to massage my senses.

Where was Zander now? I wondered. Oh to be sure, his body was still back at La Casa Blanca, but where was his spirit? Where had it gone? What was it doing? What was it thinking? Indeed, was it thinking or doing anything? Did it even have an awareness of anything? Was there any spark of sentience that could identify it, even to itself?

The breeze rippled the surface of the river and pushed the reeds towards my feet, rustling through the leaves above my head. The mature wood of slim and silver trees groaned softly as they leaned against the gentle wind. Was this Zander's spirit slipping in to make some subtle contact? I grinned mirthlessly at my imagination. No, I hardly expected him to come walking across the waters of The Hozgarganta wearing a long white robe with a halo round his head, but I needed a bit more than a coincidental wafting of wind and leaves to prove the post mortem survival of his soul.

My mind was crowded with images and memories. Zander. A couple of weeks ago I had never met this man, but there had been some kind of connection between us and either he or his circumstances had touched something deep within the essential core of my being. Now he was gone, and on a purely personal level I experienced a truly profound sense of emotional loss... And if that was how I was feeling, then again I had to put myself in Beth and Julian's shoes. Even though they had been part of Zander's plan from the beginning, and therefore had had more time to come to intellectual terms with the situation, if my own reactions were anything to go by, they must both have been in a pretty dreadful state and that awful cry of anguish that Julian had uttered at his father's death bed still rang in my ears.

I thought of the talks I'd had with Zander and re-ran the conversations in my memory – but the conversations became jumbled with disparate images, leaving my mind in a state of kaleidoscopic confusion.

I banged out the pipe and then refilled it, studying the eddies of the river as they rippled indiscriminately through the reeds that stood like mourning sentinels along the bank. Somewhere, from the mountain behind me, there was the distant sound of tinkling goat bells. The sun warmed my face and for a while I tried to take my head off the block.

Except that it wasn't easy, and that other part of me, the nasty "Mr. Hyde" who was guaranteed to fuck up a good thought ever given half a chance, kicked in to make an offering of cynical mischief.

So Anthony Zander was dead. So what? Millions of people died every day all over the world; they died in combat, in cataclysmic disasters. They died of illness and disease, of hunger and starvation and far far too many died in poverty and despair. For every gentle geriatric passing there were thousands who were prematurely plucked from the tree of life in tragedy and in agony. Against this, what was one man's life? And a damn good life at that!

Zander had been successful and wealthy. He had tasted the grape on the vine, had known love and fulfillment and had received a degree of recognition for his efforts. He had enjoyed many of the materialistic pleasures and securities that are available to what, in real terms, is but a very tiny percentage of men, and while one had to acknowledge that death at sixty two years old could be regarded as being a bit premature, how many men passed into the shadows long before this moratorium of years? And Zander, by anyone's assessment had lived a good life... so was it better to die at sixty two having had a generous slice of the cake, or was it better to stretch things out to ninety two, surviving on crumbs? And what, I asked myself angrily, of the poor bastards who died at forty two, thirty two, twelve and twenty months who'd never even got *close* to the crumbs of the cake!

And so Anthony Zander was dead, and unlike so many millions of people who might have died mangled and bleeding on a battleground, or starving and drowning in an Indian flood, or falling

113

from a skyscraper in a fireball like that that poor bastard on 9/11, he had died gently and serenely in the arms of his loving children, and so again... So fucking what?

And so *something*...

Otherwise why was I feeling like this? Why was I so gutted and why was I grieving at the passing of someone I'd only just met?

The "good" me, the nice Doctor Jekyll, the part of me that I actually quite like, ricocheted back into my consciousness and demanded an answer, so I sat up a little straighter on my rock and went in search of one. And in searching, I found not one, but three, which once I'd flicked the mental switch fell into place like smooth and well oiled cogs finding their predetermined place within the mechanical workings of my brain.

One: I'd only known Zander for a short time but in that time we had talked about things that few men ever candidly discuss other than in the darkest and most forlorn hours upon some hopeless battlefield. He had shared his innermost thoughts and secrets with me and had drawn me into his world igniting a spark of familial recognition and familiarity that transcended his work in the film industry and hinted loudly at the possibility of an earlier contact in a previous life. Either way, that bond had been there, had been very easily forged, and I was ever mindful of the déjà vu like sensation of meeting a total stranger and just knowing that you knew them from *somewhere*.

Two: while I'd only known Zander in the flesh for a number of days I had known *of* him and had admired and appreciated his professional work for more than twenty years. I'd seen him in scores of movies, and for a film buff with an appreciation of character actors and supporting casts, I was gratified to meet him face to face. Not easily impressed by celebrity, I am impressed by talent, and as an actor Zander had had no shortage of that particular gift.

Three: there was the question of predetermination. Man, I am told, is the only species born with the foreknowledge of his own mortality. And while none of us knows the day or the hour of our own death, we can, albeit with some difficulty, deal with the concept, even if it is by hiding behind the "it can't happen to me" philosophy. Once given notice, however, the rules radically change, and we are placed dipso facto with the man on death row awaiting his execution in abject terror as the hour glass runs inexorably out

114

of sand. And that was something that Zander had dealt with bravely and with dignity, especially in the face of his self admitted fear. Going deeper into my own psyche I was ever more convinced that in one of my past lives I have gone to my own premeditated execution, which if nothing else would explain my abhorrence of the concept in this life, and Zander, through setting up this experiment had strummed heavily on these discordant notes within my subconscious.

Maybe these ruminations were incorrect, but they did provide me with acceptable answers that I could deal with and rationalize, and I felt better in my head for having gone through the process.

There was a footfall from behind me and the sound of pressing grass. I didn't need to turn my head. I knew who it was.

Beth handed me a mug of coffee. A bright yellow mug with a smiley face on the side. By contrast her own face was drawn and solemn; even in the golden glow of the afternoon sun, she looked translucently pale. I shifted up and made room for her on my rock.

'I saw you sitting here from the house.' She said. 'You've been here for ages. Are you okay James?'

It was not a time to try being clever with words. 'Thanks for the coffee – yes, I'm surviving, but I just feel dreadfully and terribly sad. More to the point love, are *you* all right?'

'Yes, I think so. I feel numb, but at the same time,' a huge sigh wracked through her body, 'I'm glad that it's all over now. Julian is taking it very badly though...' I would have been surprised by that information a week ago, but not now. Not any more. ' – But, of course, he's still so young.'

'It's not over yet Beth.' I tried to make my voice sound positive but I don't know to what extent I succeeded. 'In fact you could say that it's just the beginning, if your father has his way.'

She turned towards me. 'James, do you think that Daddy's experiment is really going to work? Is there any chance at all? I mean, we've been talking about it and planning it for weeks and weeks, but now that he's gone and we've got to this point, everything seems so final and I just don't see how it can happen.'

There was such a look of pleading desperation in her eyes that I simply didn't have the heart to say anything that wouldn't bring her some modicum of reassurance. She was fighting back the tears, so I wrapped my arm around her and gave her one of my none too brilliantly clean tissues. 'Yes Beth, I do think it could work, but there are so many variables and so many things that we just don't understand, so whether or not it works the way that you guys have planned it, well I guess that remains to be seen. I do think that if there is *any* way that Anthony can get back to us to let us know that he's okay, then he will do it or cause a revolution in heaven in the attempt.' The breeze caressed the riverbank again causing the long reeds to shiver with excitement. I was immediately reminded of Karnak and the amazing synchronicity of that short but exquisite little poem. 'Beth love, it's in Anthony's hands now, or in God's hands.'

And then remembering Zander's thoughts about God, I added... 'Or maybe it's all in the arms of the wind.'

Part Two
In The Arms Of The Wind

Twelve: *Jimena 18th – 20th December*

If the days immediately prior to Zander's passing had been surreal,
then in some ways those first few days after his death were even
more peculiar. An event had taken place which, because of our
proximity to it, had been an *enormous* event that had touched and
changed our lives, and yet apart from one small incident involving
Julian, we carried on almost as though nothing had happened. And
this, I might tell you, in the face of a constant emotional
bombardment of unfolding situations.

First there was the business of getting Anthony into his coffin,
which was easier said than done because someone had cocked up
with the measurements and the casket was three centimeters too
short. Three centimeters isn't much, but the man from the *funeraria*
had to cut a slit in the lining and remove Anthony's shoes before the
body would go in straight. I didn't see this, thank God, but Beth
told me about it, and if it hadn't been so pathetically sad it might
have been funny.

On the morning of Monday the 18th Beth completed the
paperwork up at the town hall and late in the afternoon we buried
him between the trees. Prior to the lid being closed for the last
time, the three of us each placed something in the coffin to send
Anthony on his way. Neither of us knew what the other put in
place, and for my part, I tucked a small book of my Spanish poems
down by the side of the head lining... which brought me up very
close to the actor's dead face.

Not nice. For while I had come to like and admire this man in
life, and while I profess to have a degree of spirituality about my
character, I have an aversion – a phobia if you like – to dead things.
When the cats bring in a bird, or kill a mouse, then Mrs. Christie has
to sort it out. I can't go near. In return for this understanding, I
remove and deal with spiders. I turn my eyes away from road kill
and was physically sick a few years ago when they were burning
cattle in the fields during the BSE epidemic. I don't like corpses and

most of all I don't like human corpses. Maybe it has something to do with past life bloodlines – half of my father's parental family was wiped out in Belsen – and maybe it has something to do with having seen a few human corpses up close and personal in my earlier life. Either way I did not linger over Zander's coffin for long and was glad when this part of the ritual was over and done with.

Witnessed by the man from the *ayuntamiento* (the same gentleman who had accepted Zander's burial fee and who had written out the *permiso* for Beth) we secured the lid and lowered Anthony's casket into the ground. Half way through the process of filling in the pile of waiting earth the village priest arrived and wanted to know why we were burying a body in unconsecrated ground. The man from the town hall explained that there had been special permission granted, and because I had crossed swords once before with this nasty little clergyman, I put my oar in and pointed out that Señor Zander had neither been a Catholic nor a Christian and therefore it was none of Father Sebastian Moreno's business as to what we did with the body. Muttering something under his breath about the blasphemy of those who were not of the Catholic faith, the skinny little priest buggered off and I watched him go with a deep sense of personal satisfaction and spiritual one-upmanship.

By this time in the afternoon, I'd had enough. I was on emotional overload and was in desperate need for my own space. Also, I suspected, Beth and Julian would now need some space in which to do their own grieving. I retreated back to my room at the Anon and slept solidly for the better part of three hours before the shrilling of the mobile phone dragged me back into consciousness.

It was Beth Hammond wanting to know if Julian was with me. I told her no, and she asked me if I could go and find him because there had been an argument between them, and in a very upset and distressed state he'd done a disappearing act.

'Have you got any idea where he might be?' I asked.

'No, but I suspect he's gone looking for you.'

'Me?'

'Yes. Where are you?'

'At the Anon.'

'Well the first place to look will be the hotel bar.'

'What was the argument about?'

'That doesn't really matter, does it?'

'No I don't suppose so. Anyway look, I'll have a scout around and I'll get back to you later.'

'Thanks James. I appreciate it.'

When it came to tracking down Julian Boyd I didn't have to work very hard. Literally ten minutes after the phone conversation with Beth I found him standing on the terrace of the hotel bar, sipping from a bottle of San Miguel and gazing moodily over the vista of late evening rooftops and out along the Jimenato valley. The sky, not yet full black, was a deep deep blue and filled with a firmament of stars and twinkling lights from streetlamps that cast their warm welcoming glow across the irregular and uneven cobbles of the narrow streets: the familiar perfume of wood smoke mingled with the scent of wild jasmine and the tang of wet earth... It had been raining and the taste of the raindrops still lingered in the air with droplets of moisture still audibly dripping from the grapevine and the evergreen palm fronds that arched their protective layers above our heads

In the soft glow of light that spilled out from the bar I could see that he looked tired and drawn, and yet at the same time some weight and tension had gone from him. On a purely psychic level I sensed that all the sullen negativity that had been such a part of his earlier persona had now been exorcised and in its place there was an aura of emptiness – a space waiting to be filled with new feelings and emotions, the nature of which he had no precognition.

'I'm sorry about your father.' I spoke quietly from a position someway behind him and off to one side. He inclined his head in acknowledgement of my condolence and recognition of my presence, but he didn't say anything in response, simply, or so it seemed, tucking himself even more deeply into his introverted reverie. I leaned against a damp wall and went through the ritual of filling and lighting my pipe. Even as I blew rich clouds of aromatic tobacco smoke upwards and through the vine, I wondered what other words I could offer. What do you say to a lonely man whose father has been dead for little more than a day?

In the end it was Julian who broke the uncomfortable silence. 'It's strange, isn't it,' he mused, neither turning his head nor his body but maintaining his gaze to the south. 'Yes it's definitely strange. I spent the first twelve years of my life not knowing that I had a father, then I spent the second twelve years of my life,

119

knowing that I *did* have a father, but knowing nothing about him other than the bastard had done a runner even before I was born and hating him for leaving me and my old lady to fend for ourselves for all those years, and then I spend the last two years getting to know my father, learning to understand him and seeing how things were from his point of view. For Christ's sake, Mr. Christie, learning how to *love* the man! And now the bastard's up and died and I'm going to have to learn how to live without him!'

'Not if the experiment is successful,' I suggested.

Then he did turn to look at me. 'Listen man, if the experiment is successful, that'll be great – but I've got to tell you that I've got a whole load of doubts about all of this – and even if it is successful, then so what? I still don't have my old man to talk to, to hug, to share beers and jokes with. So okay his spirit is alive and well and living forever in heaven, but that doesn't mean squat as long as I've got my jaxie down here. You can't get drunk and go fishing with a fucking ghost!'

The bitterness and the hurt and the sadness clung to his every word like sphagnum moss. Again I found myself frantically searching for the right words, but could not find what was not there. Looking at the scenario from Julian's point of view, there could be no argument or compromise. He wanted his father back, not in some abstract spiritual sense but in the corporeal physical world. He knew that this was impossible and therefore he sought to turn back the clock and change the laws of time. He knew too that *this* was an impossibility, and thus it was only natural that he should rail against the strands of fate and destiny that had placed him in this untenable position, and that just for good measure, had complicated things even further by placing Beth Hammond in his line of sight. Something else that he wanted but knew he could never have. If I had been Julian then I also might have had a quarrel with my God.

'Doesn't the idea of being reunited with your father one day give you any kind of succour or support?'

'Maybe it ought to, and if he does come through to us in these experiments, maybe it will. But right now? No, it gives me no support at all!' He sighed. 'Anyway Mr. C, was there something you wanted?'

'No, not really. Beth was worried about you. Wanted me to look out for you and make sure you're okay. Also, I suppose, if

I'm to write a book about your father and all of this, I need to know how you're feeling right now.'

'Well I guess you've got your answer to that one,' he laughed mockingly, 'and as for Beth, ah hell, she doesn't have to worry. Not about me anyway. I just need a bit of time to get my act together and find the right shape of face to wear – if you know what I mean.'

I told him I knew exactly what he meant, and left him to it, wrapping him in the arms of my deepest sympathy and understanding. Julian Boyd wasn't the only one to lose somebody much beloved to the arms of death.

On the evening of the 18th I locked myself away in my bedroom and tried to get down to some serious writing. Without distractions and without alcohol I wrote about a thousand words. On the morning of the 19th I deleted about half of them but was still left with half a dozen paragraphs that made some kind of literary sense. After breakfast I talked to Beth for a few minutes and arranged to meet her later, then for need of some exercise, I walked up through the village and climbed the crag to the ruined castle on the brow of the hill.

By the time I got to the top I was puffing and panting, but the view was more than worth it. It was a cloudless clear blue morning. The Rock of Gibraltar was a sharply etched thumbnail in the far distance and from this vantage point I had a panoramic view not only of Jimena but also half of the Jimenato valley: there were tantalizing glimpses of the neighbouring white villages of San Pablo, Casares and Gaucin, and despite the season of the year vultures hovered on the thermals above my head. And why not? North Africa was only thirty five miles away as the crow flew! The air was sharp and clean, cutting through the crust of contaminated lungs like a surgeon's scalpel and making me wish that I hadn't started smoking when I was fourteen years old... Then I ruined the good thought by tucking myself down into a windbreak corner and piling tobacco into the old briar. But here I felt warm and safe and secure and at peace. This was my place, the place where my ashes would be scattered to the four winds when my own time came to make a departure from this less than perfect world; this was an epicenter of personal spiritual energy for if Jimena de la Frontera was my *sanctum* and the terrace al El Anon was my high altar, then this

121

ancient monument with its ruined crown pointing like a finger of God into the azure heavens was my *sanctum sanctorum*.

I pulled out the now very tatty notebook and started converting more thoughts into words about Anthony Zander, remembering conversations that we had had, smiling at some of the humour we had shared, and wondering what would make good reading for a third party.

I had half a dozen of the little Dictaphone tapes in my pocket and pulled one out at random and slotted it into the machine...

My voice: 'Can we talk about your work for a while?'

Zander: 'Sure go ahead. What do you want to know?'

Me: 'Well, you've been part of the Hollywood film industry for forty odd years, so who, in your opinion, is America's best actor?'

Zander: 'Hell Mr. Christie, that's an impossible question to answer, and you should know that yourself! You've got different people for different eras... In the old Hollywood studio days, well I guess there was Spencer Tracey and Cooper. I never rated Bogart too much, I mean he was okay, but he was always Bogart wasn't he? I always had a sneaky respect for Kirk Douglas because he always worked at his craft and made a good transition from leading man to character. Sure he was always Kirk Douglas, but at least his performances were believable.'

Me: 'What about today's actors then?'

Zander: 'Gibson and Cruise, I think. Christ, I hate Gibson's politics and his crazy religion, but that's beside the point. The man can act. He's believable. As for Cruise, he's vastly under-rated in my opinion, and he's definitely got his best work yet to do, but dollar for dollar, he makes good movies and his performances never disappoint. The other thing I like about Cruise is that on set he's the same with everybody. There's none of this "I'm the great movie star" crap. He knows it's a team effort and he makes sure you know he knows it's a team effort.'

Me: 'What about Mel Gibson?'

Zander: 'He prays a lot.'

Me: 'Okay, what about actresses?'

Zander: 'Munroe could have been great and Hepburn was great, and when I say Hepburn I mean the Katherine, not the Audrey. Of today's batch we have some very talented ladies indeed. There's Paltrow, and in my opinion, that woman is the finest actress in the world! Her accents and voice maintenance are superb. Rene

Zellweger is absolutely incredible, but man, just wait till she gets into her late forties and fifties! She'll probably take an Oscar every other year is she chooses he scripts properly. I love Nicole, and it's a damn shame about her and Tom, and if there's a classic example of two people who loved each other too much, then they're it – but if you're gonna ask me who the best actress is at this moment in time, then it's got to be Paltrow.'

Me: 'Okay Mr. Zander, what about directors?'

Zander: 'That, believe it or not, is a much easier question. In contemporary terms there are three geniuses. One of 'em is Oliver Stone and then there's Spielberg and the third is Eastwood.'

Me: 'Eastwood? Clint Eastwood?'

Zander: 'Yes sir, the very same Mr. Eastwood. Average actor but absolutely brilliant brilliant director and if you want some evidence for that statement look at "The Bridges of Maddison County" which was a wonderful piece of work, and "Unforgiven" – especially "Unforgiven". These are works which, in my opinion at any rate, exemplify the director's art. That doesn't mean that there were not and are not other good directors, Tarentino is good and I love Ron Howard movies but Messrs. Stone, Spielberg and Eastwood are the best we've got right now.'

Me: 'What about your favourite film?'

Zander: 'Loved "Gone With The Wind" but it was not a good film. Loved "Titanic" and that was a very good film. Loved your Winslet girl but as for Leo, he was completely miscast. They should have used Cruise, and from what I'm told, they had the opportunity to go with Tom but for whatever reason, political or otherwise, they turned the option down. "Apocalypse Now" was probably one of the most *important* films of the 20th century. The story needed to be told. Loved Sheen. Hated Brando. Bit like Orson Welles – so much up the ass of his own legend he forgets that to be an actor you're supposed to actually *act* occasionally and not wander through a script like an automaton trading on a self imagined image of greatness. But as for my *favourite* film, which was, I believe, the question you asked, then it's a movie few people will have ever seen or heard of called "Somewhere in Time" with Jane Seymour and that poor bastard Chris Reeve. That film really got to me.'

Me: 'Yes, me too.'

Zander: 'You know this movie?'

Me: 'Yes, I've got it on my shelf at home. I've watched it more than a dozen times.'

Zander: 'My God, that's amazing!'

And it was amazing in the sense that it was another weird connection between us. "Somewhere In Time" had been a low budget B film that had done bugger all at the box office and yet, having seen it once, I had gone to great lengths to secure my own print. The film had been seminal in my own spiritual evolution and here was Anthony Zander saying it was his favourite desert island movie.

And finally, me again: 'Okay, and just for the record, who's your favourite Bond?'

Zander, laughing: 'My favourite Bond is Timothy Dalton because he was my Bond, but the best Bond is undoubtedly Pierce Brosnan. No one will ever top his portrayal of the character.'

The tape clicked to a finish and I spent an hour scribbling up some notes. A goat wandered around the edge of the ruin, saw me and bleated in surprise. Shook its horny head, rang a bell and ran away with a clinking clank down the side of the hill. I climbed off my bottom and re-lit the pipe which had gone cold. Took in the view for a last time and feeling that I might had done something marginally creative that constituted a reason for my presence in this place, I followed the goat down the hill and made my way back to the hotel.

Julian phoned mid-afternoon to suggest an evening meeting at La Casa Blanca, and I told him that was fine, but that I'd come down earlier and if it was okay with Beth, would borrow her PC for a couple of hours. Which worked out very well, because at the end of a three hour session on Beth's computer I was beginning to feel that I had the shape of this book, or at least the first half of it, even if I didn't have much of the detail or any indication of what might be the content of part two.

Beth brought me some coffee around tea time and asked me how much longer I thought I might be. I told her that I'd like to work on through until about seven o'clock. She said okay and that she'd have a snack supper ready for about seven. I wasn't feeling bossy but I thought that it might be time for a minor executive decision and I suggested that we go up to the village, enjoy a few drinks and have our meeting over a nice dinner somewhere.

124

She looked dubious but I argued my point. 'Look,' I said. 'You could cut the atmosphere in this place with a knife, and while I'm not suggesting for one moment that we go out and party I think we'd all benefit from a few bright lights and a bit of human contact.' I caught the look in her eyes. 'Yes, I know that part of you would rather stay here with Anthony's energy all around you, but Beth, trust me on this. You need to get out of this rarified atmosphere for a while, and even if you feel you don't, I do, and I'll bet you Julian does as well.'

'He's right Beth,' Julian spoke from the doorway behind her. 'We've been locked in our own misery for long enough so let's get out and spread it around a bit.'

'Oh all right,' Beth finally agreed. 'But nowhere too noisy. Nowhere too Spanish.'

I bit my tongue and held back the obvious retort. That this was Campo Spain so how could you *not* end up going somewhere Spanish? But I knew what she was saying and the circumstances were extenuating.

A lot of the Spanish working bars can be basic and raucous, floors littered with the detritus of a long day of busy service, frequently with beer crates stacked against the walls, toilets that don't flush and with working Spanish men yelling conversations above the contrary blasts from the TV or radio. Even some restaurants in the white villages can be very noisy places, and although they may be clean and cosmopolitan in atmosphere, you would hardly describe them as intimate or sophisticated – which in my book is just fine because I like the vibrancy and vitality of the campo watering holes, the sawdust and the occasional burst of spontaneous singing counterpointed by frequent communal roars of camaraderie when someone has told a good joke or a TV football player has scored (or missed!) a great goal.

When I had lived in Jimena I had spent a lot of time in these places writing good poems and bad novels; I'd drunk litres of cheap red wine and had steadily worked my ways through the trays of *tapas variados*.

I had slept away scorching afternoon siestas and then in the early evenings I had played my guitar in Gibraltar for a fair living. But the late nights and the early hours of the madrugada had been mine to call my own and I would frequently not find my bed until well after four o'clock in the pre-dawn grey of the new born day – waking again to face that day on a different footing with the sun edging up into the sky and an alarm clock gently telling me it was something past ten or getting close to noon. The lifestyle, with its loose and informal passing of hours, had more than suited me and I had fallen easily and naturally into the Spanish rhythm of life. That's not to say that those years were always easy because they were not. Nor does it mean that I was always happy because I was not... but at least I had felt *right* within myself and at peace with my inner spirit.

Apart from anything else money went a long way in a Spanish hill village and for a relatively few pounds one could live like a prince. Bar Marylin, which in those days had been known as Louis's Bar after its cadaverous chess playing ex-priest owner, had had a sign up just inside the door. It was a tariff of prices. Beer was two pesetas, brandy was three. You could have a breakfast for eight pesetas and a three course dinner for ten. A bed for the night would cost you a further eight pesetas and stabling and hay for your horse would set you back another ten pesetas. Various brands of cigarettes were available for only one peseta a packet, and glass of red wine or a glass of sherry would cost a mere fifty centimes. And here's the amazing thing. The date on this tariff of fare was August 1963!

Okay I'd been there in the late eighties and by then there had been a few hefty price increases, but it was still a very inexpensive cost of living. The food, whether bought and cooked in a bar or restaurant, or purchased fresh from the counter of the local shops or market stalls, was always simple, but it was always fresh, and of course, totally organic long before some marketing guru had coined the expression to sell more stuff over the tills in overcrowded English supermarkets.

But I had to admit that Bar Marylin or Bar España were probably not the best places to enjoy a serious working dinner with Beth and her half brother; I knew that El Anon was closed that evening for a private birthday party and La Tasca, much as I loved it, would be full of Jimena's ex-pat gossips who, given half a chance, would try to earwig our every word, so in the end we settled on Corrie's bar, or to give it its full and formal name, Café Bar La Lorca.

I used the Casa Blanca house phone to give Corrie a ring and asked her to lay a table in the corner of her small restaurant – somewhere a bit discreet where we could enjoy some privacy. She

126

said it was a done deal. I suggested seven o'clock, she said eight would be better, and so eight o'clock it was.

If you're running a good bar in Spain people tend to forget the silly names their owners give them and they become known by the owner's own identity; La Tasca, for example, is Pepe's Bar. Bar Marylin is Angel's Bar. Jacinto's old place now has a posh new name, but it's still known as Pepa's Bar after the matriarchal Valkyrie who runs the business with an iron fist and hard biting tongue that will flay the flesh off any pour soul that comes within ten centimeters of upsetting her in any small way. Thus, it's little wonder that Café Bar La Lorca is known both in and outside the village simply as Corrie's Bar.

I'd known it in three different incarnations. When I'd first moved to the village it had been El Aquila Bar, a chintzy English gaff run by a tall lanky guy called Long John and his bull terrier breeding wife Susan. Long John had spent too many years in South Africa and couldn't get out of the habit of calling the local Spaniards "kafirs". Needles to say, El Aquila did not flourish and Long John didn't exactly last very long. Long John met his Waterloo on the night when one of the local Bad Boys called Curo decided it was quite reasonable to ride his horse in El Aquila, demanding beer for himself and hay for the horse. John was not amused and produced an enormous ten bore shot gun from under the counter and threatened to blow Curo's head off if he didn't get out immediately. John referred to this totally illegal weapon as his ghetto blaster, and this reference had nothing to do with cheap mechanical machines that played loud music to deafen young ears. This beast of an elephant gun was fitted with a collapsible stock and a fan shaped nozzle at the end of the barrel, which, John assured me, was "good enough to clear a street full of kafir bastards up to a range of fifty yards!"

Curo was a brave lad, but John's ghetto blaster was a bit intimidating to say the least and he beat a hasty retreat, but not until the horse had trashed half the bar and had crapped all over the floor. Thus, Curo, horse, Long John and elephant gun passed into history and legend of the village, but of course word went round like wild fire, and although nobody liked Curo very much, they liked the idea of an Englishman threatening a fellow Spaniard with a shot gun even less: El Aquila was placed under sanction and embargo, John and his wife were sent to Coventry, the Guardia Civil confiscated the illegal gun and fined him about ten grand, and in the end he and Susan, along with their three bull terriers moved on to Marakech where to the best of my knowledge they all lived happily ever after.

Its next incarnation was as La Para, run by a Mancunian called Guy and his Spanish wife Margotti, and to give them credit where credit was due, La Para worked well for most of the people most of the time. It developed into a late night drinking hole for serious drinkers and in its own way it became a successful Spanglish Bar with a hard core ex-pat clientele. In those days I was not the drinker I was later to become, and so I didn't spend too much time there, although Guy and Margotti were good pals and we did share a lot of laughs together.

La Para became the official watering hole for the region's property dealers and estate agents and after a while Guy figured he could earn more cash selling houses than selling beer to other people who sold houses, so he sold the place to a French couple who turned La Para into a high cuisine French restaurant – the only trouble being that in rural Andalucia there wasn't much call for high class French cuisine, and certainly not at the prices the French couple were trying to get away with! The place closed after less than six months. Nuff said.

In its final incarnation as Café Bar La Lorca it really became of age. Corrie stripped out all the rubbish and brought it back to being a simple little Spanish bar with dimly lit corners, Moorish arches and intimate alcoves. In one section there were shelves stacked high with English books (vital for ex-pats living in a foreign land) and in one corner there was a huge overstuffed settee and an enormous wood burning stove surrounded by a stack of logs. Over towards the far end of the room there was a long Moroccan curtain that separated the bar from the restaurant, and the walls of both bar and restaurant were covered with the poems, crudely hand written, some in English although mostly in Spanish, of Federico Garcia Lorca. Soft lights and a sense of mystery made this a very sexy place to be. And then of course, there was Corrie herself.

You walked through the portal from the steep hill outside and the warmth of the ambience rose up to greet you like a long lost friend. But this ambience came only in small part from the décor, the deep pink and amber walls, the soft lighting and the log fire. The better part of it came from the lady behind the bar... Corrie...whose smile could melt the heart of a frozen Eskimo! Corrie who had one of those youthfully innocent faces, enigmatically beautiful and incredibly pretty and, at the same time, wickedly mischievous. Corrie, a thirty something lady with lovely curves in all the right places, and who, most unfortunately for most of the single blokes in the village, was totally in love with her husband Steve and 101% dedicated to their two characterful kids George and Alfie.

And for the record, here's a thing worth remembering. Most wives think that their husbands fantasise over the brigade of skinny super models and scantily clad pop princesses – and they're wrong! If a man is going to fantasise about anybody is it usually about someone real and touchable and someone whose personality is a lot bigger than their ego. Women think that men like skinny women, and they're wrong again. Generally speaking, men like *curves* and we don't like *bones* – and as I've said, Corrie had all the right curves in the right places – and yet it was the lady's face, her voice and her smile, and above all else, her personality that made her so very attractive to the fellers and yet at the same time unthreatening to women. Regardless of sex, Corrie's spirit welcomed you into her presence.

And yet not everyone came to Corrie's Bar, which was just as well, because you wouldn't want everybody. But the people it *did* attract were my kind of people. The writers and artists. The quiet Spaniards. The more thoughtful ex-patriots. If people got drunk in Corrie's bar, they were gentle, funny and philosophical drunks. In the same way that there was not the ubiquitous thump thump thump of mindless junk music, nor was there any aggression: seldom was there an argument or a raised voice other than in laughter and if someone got so drunk that they couldn't stand up, well, there was always the settee to collapse on, or Steve and some other more sober soul would carry the inebriated one home.

If someone asked me – "James, which is your favourite bar in all the world?" then without any hesitation I would refer them to Café Bar La Lorca, Corrie's Bar, on Calle Sevilla in Jimena de La Frontera, in the Province of Cadiz!

As I walked down Calle Sevilla it was raining that light evening Andalucian haze drizzle that is so typical of Southern Spain in the winter months of the year. The cobbles and the uneven flagstones glistened in the moist wetness of the night; long shadows danced from the old antiquarian streetlamps and as usual the wood-smokey tang clung to the other scents of the soft exotic air. Instinctively I slowed my pace, soaking up the atmosphere and savouring the silence of the moment. Again I was reminded of the fact that *this* was my Spain, not the clash of sand and sangria, not the crude noise of the crowded costas, but this simple tranquility of the mountains and the separateness and serenity of this different world and culture.

Here you were what you were not what you professed to be. Here you were judged by what you did and not just by what you said. Here it did not matter whether you were rich or poor, a lawyer or a street-sweeper. As long as you conducted yourself with dignity and paid for your drinks you were accepted into the community. You were judged, not by your wealth or your position in life, but by your honesty and your pride and by the way in which you behaved. There was no artifice and the fakes and the phonies who came to this place looking for redemption and absolution never found it and soon fell by the wayside.

I came up short outside La Lorca jerked back to reality by the immediacy of the moment. Reverie over. Back to the bizarre business with Anthony Zander and his unlikely progeny. I sighed and pushed myself across the threshold.

The progeny in question were sitting on a pair of high stools at the far end of the bar but to get to them I had to run a gentle gauntlet through a dozen friendly and familiar faces. A group of Spaniards, including my old gypsy king mate Rafael and his hard drinking buddy Diego, sat to the immediate left of the door. There was a cry of cheery greeting and I had to reach over to shake Rafa's hand before I was allowed to move on and say hello to Tim Channon and his pretty wife Kate who were obviously well in to their second or third rounds of the evening. Tim was a merchant banker who worked down on The Rock, and in all probability his greatest business asset was his wife. Next I got shanghaied by another Spanish pal called Antonio and I had to fight to prevent him buying me a drink because he was already wrecked and would probably be hard pressed to pay his own bar bill at the end of the night. I had a few words with Barney, my elderly ex-pat musician friend, and Barney, who despite his seniority of years always had an eye for the ladies, was in the company of two Spanish females – Juani who had worked for Garth Odell in the old days, and Carmen, she of the boyish short hair and doe-like brown eyes who tried so hard to speak English and who wrote love poems for no one in particular and occasionally for someone she had yet to meet.

Beyond them and over to the right, leaning on the wall in front of the fire was Corrie's husband Steve, tall, lanky, laconic in conversation with another guy also called Steve and his willowy wife Helen, who were both in the property market. Over on the settee on the far side of the fire was Big Irish Bill and Little Fat Chris, playing a laid back blues duet on two nice looking guitars, and of course, behind the bar, dressed in a chunky grey cardigan and very tight trousers was the ever present and effervescent Corrie. In total there were sixteen people in the bar. I knew them all by sight and thirteen of them by name. More to the point, they all knew me.

I pulled up a stool next to Julian and Beth. Corrie came over and I tried to order a drink, but she told me that there were three already in the pipeline for me – one from Diego, one from Barney and one from Antonio. Which was okay, but I knew I'd have to reciprocate before the end of the evening, and that was okay as well because that was the way things worked over here. Bar bills became horrendously complicated towards the end of the night and a lot of Spanish barmen made a wild guess at who owed what and then slapped fifty percent on to cover their backsides. Corrie never did that and all of us who used La Lorca trusted her word as gospel.

I started on my first brandy and coke, refreshed my friend's glasses, and together we trawled down the limited little menu choosing our food. The drinks flowed freely and we chatted for a while, talking about nothing and by some unspoken Bacchanalian contract, not mentioning Anthony or his passing. It was almost as though, once we had agreed to take our heads off the block for an evening, we were determined to relax and unwind and drink away the tension imposed by death and grieving. Yes, we needed to remain sufficiently sober to talk a little business, but at the same time we strove to put an alcoholic barrier in place to hold our communal sadness at bay.

Julian told a string of Australian jokes in poor taste. They were bad, but we laughed at them anyway simply because we needed to laugh. Beth told the joke about the hedgehog and the loo brush – which is the one joke most women know in various forms and tell with equal degrees of bad timing. For my part I told them about the night Long John had his run in with Curo and of that old price tariff down in Bar Marylin. They both thought I was winding them up on each account, and didn't really believe me until we were joined for a while by Juani (who really wanted to reminisce about Garth) and who, in the process, confirmed the truth of my two tails. The stories were re-confirmed when the two musicians took a break and Little Fat Chris came over to say hello and bum a cigarette (he'd been there in El Aguila that night as well) and then Tim and Kate sidled over to our corner of the bar and before we knew it we were part of a convivial little group that was having a "good time!"

I think this must have taken Beth and Julian a bit by surprise because although they'd been in the village for a number of months they had neither integrated nor socialised and now for the first time since God knows when they were in the business of making a few new friends – and to all intents and purposes, they seemed to be enjoying the experience and it gave me chance to pull back and engage in one of my favourite pastimes of people watching.

The ladies seemed to be paying Julian a lot of attention, which was hardly surprising because it's not every day a girl gets the chance to talk to a Greek God. Big Bill had sauntered over and in partnership with his musical number two, Little Fat Chris, they both tried chatting Beth up. Beth seemed oblivious to it, but she wasn't oblivious to the fact that Julian was getting the eye from Juani and Carmen, and it was obvious (although I dare say only to me) that she was uncomfortable with a few pangs of jealousy. Only Corrie seemed unfased by all of this, but like me, she knew what was going on and at one point we made eye contact and winked conspiratorially...

...Which made feel good about having Corrie as a friend, but then pushed me into a deeper study on the pheromones of sexual attraction. Here I was in the company of three females, each of whom in their own way was exceptionally attractive. I wasn't in love with any of them, didn't want to have sex with any of them, but if I was to be honest with myself, then yes, I suppose that I wanted them to notice and at least on some level, be aware of me.

Maybe it was a kickback from my teens and adolescence when gutted by shyness and a feeling of inadequacy I felt that I wasn't noticed by anyone at all!

Corrie, Kate and Beth Hammond – three beautiful women, yes, but they were also *people!* Was it not possible to find another person attractive without sexuality getting in the way? There are some men that I have loved in my life in a totally none sexual way so was it not possible to experience this same feeling of love for a woman without jealousy doubt and suspicion getting in the way of something that might have had something to do with the need for recognition but had absolutely nothing to do with sex?

I took another long slug from my second (or was it my third?) brandy and coke, and thought "fuck it" which is the kind of thing you think when you get to fifty-sodding-six and you realize with some distress that you're no longer thirty five or even forty four. I looked around my motley companions and realized that apart from Barney who'd gravitated over to our end of the bar, I was the oldest person in the group by a good ten years. Not a happy thought, so I lit a pipe and ordered my third (or was it my fourth?) drink of the evening.

Barney looked rhuemily at the ladies present and sighed into his wine glass. He caught me watching him and tipped me a forlorn wink. 'It's quite terrible when you get to nearly ninety years old and you find yourself still fancying the same women that you fancied forty years ago.'

It wasn't so much what he said but the way in which he said it that made me chuckle.

'I could think of worse things,' I commented dryly

'Really? I can't imagine what!'

'Being fifty six and still fancying the same women that you fancied forty years ago, or even worse, getting to sixty and not having the energy to fancy anyone at all!'

'Oh my dear boy is it as bad as all that? Come, we must have another drink to wash away the creaks of encroaching old age, but James, do put things into perspective. You've got a very long way to go before you fall into my league. All I want really, if I am to be truthful, is to stay sane enough to keep my memories alive. When you're 89 you can't hope for much more than that, can you?'

It was a sobering question and I realized that I didn't know the answer.

What, I wondered, did any of us want? Corrie and Steve wanted to make a success of their lives in Jimena to keep their family away from the blight of Britain. Julian wanted his father back and he also wanted Beth. In that moment Juani and Carmen both wanted Julian. Antonio wanted to be rich and sober, Tim Channnon wanted an absolute guarantee that his pretty young wife would love him forever. Barney wanted his sanity and his memories.

I looked at Beth and I realized that I didn't quite know what she wanted, and then I thought of my wife back in North Yorkshire, and I hoped that she still wanted me. Which brought me full circle. What did I want? I ordered my fourth (or was it my fifth?) drink of the evening, and it wasn't hard to find the answers.

I wanted immortality and recognition, and if I couldn't have those, I'd settle for being half as good as Barney if ever I got to 89 years old.

We ate a good supper. True to her word, Corrie had put us in the far corner of her small dining room next to the window that overlooked the rainslicked Calle Romo which ran parallel to Calle Sevilla. She'd lit a calor gas fire and had worked hard to carry the ambience through from the main bar by putting candles on the table and pulling a couple of small lamps into our corner. There was some nice background music – sounded like Rodrigo's Guitar Concerto – and the noise from the bar was muted to a distant hum. The three of us had imbibed generously of aperitifs to the extent that we were quite cavalier about ordering a bottle of Corrie's very best Rioja, and as the food and wine went down our moods mellowed and our conversation mellowed with it accordingly. We talked freely, but by tacit unspoken agreement, avoided the one subject that was uppermost in our minds. And yet, like water finding its own level the subject came up in its own time and with a degree of typical Taurean inevitably, it was me who blew the gaff.

We'd been talking about the food and the wine and about Corrie and La Lorca and some of the bar's clientele. The conversation moved on to the immortal Federico Garcia and his phenomenal qualities as a writer and a poet. Written on the wall was one of his poems – an English translation – which Julian pondered on for a good three or four minutes, and then, feeling his way, read out loud:

"In the green morning I wanted to be a heart,
a heart ...
and in the ripe evening I wanted to be a nightingale,
a nightingale.
Soul, turn orange coloured,
Soul turn the colour of love.
In the vivid morning I wanted to be myself.
A heart.
And at the evening's end
I wanted to be my voice –
A nightingale.
Soul, turn orange colour.
Soul turn the colour of love. "

He looked at the writing on the wall, quizzically mystified. 'Yeah, well it is kind of beautiful, I'll give it that.' Then he looked at me directly. 'But what does it mean, exactly?'

I shrugged. 'For one thing, it's someone else's translation of the master's work, so it's difficult to form an opinion. But I suppose that all he's trying to do with these lines is to express a mood and a state of mind. He's not necessarily trying to describe anything in a literal sense, he's just trying to make us feel the way he's feeling and make us understand why he's feeling it.' Then like the rising water table it just slipped over the edge of the dam. 'Julian, it's hard to explain, but your father would have known what Lorca was trying to say with these lines.'

And as the cat stretched out of the bag we sat in silence for a second or so.

And then Beth laughed quietly. 'You didn't mean to do that, did you James?'

I grinned ruefully. 'No, I really really didn't, so maybe it was Anthony giving us a nudge and telling us to get on with it.'

'All right.'

Beth pulled a thick green file out of her briefcase and we started the business bit of our evening by going through the procedures Zander had put in place. This was stuff that we had already discussed and I was eager to get on.

'I think it's time,' I said carefully, 'for me to know who our three clairvoyants are.' I saw the flicker of doubt on Beth's face but held up my hand before she could register any protest. 'Yes, I know it's

135

going against the letter of Anthony's brief, but we've already done that a few times already, and this aspect of the experiment is very important. These three people are arriving in Jimena tomorrow and just like you, I've got a job to do here, and it would help me enormously to know who and what I'm dealing with. I was brought into this experiment as an impartial observer, but it must be obvious to you both that the rules and the goal posts have long since been changed and moved, and whether I like it or not, I am now an active particpant.'

'Yes that's true,' Beth sighed, and while Corrie cleared away the dinner dishes and then at my request brought a bottle of Duke De Alba to the table with three *café solos*, Zander's daughter rifled through her cavernous briefcase once more and produced three A4 folders, colour coded green, blue and yellow.

'Can't I just give you these to look at later?'

'Be much quicker and easier if you just read me the bare bones right now,' I suggested, groping for my pipe and tobacco.

'Oh hell, you're not going to smoke that evil thing in here are you?' Julian moaned mournfully.

'I most certainly am,' I replied smoothly. Juilian just didn't know how to do it. If he'd said '*JC would you mind not smoking your pipe in this small dining room*' I'd have accommodated him willingly enough. His rude protest, justifiable or not, simply rubbed me up the wrong way. I was paying for his beer and his flaming supper, so he could like my flaming pipe or lump it.

Beth, ever the mediator, came to the rescue. 'Well, I'm going to have a cigarette with my coffee,' she announced. And then, all innocence and sweetness – 'Would you like a Marlboro, James?'

I caught her eye and raised an eyebrow. She winked and I joined in the conspiracy of smokers.

'Thanks Beth, I'd love one.' I put my pipe back into my pocket and helped myself to the silent killer from the red and white pack. 'Okay, now come on, tell me. Who have we got coming tomorrow?'

She opened the green file. 'All right... Er... From the USA we have Mandy Breck, born June 1957 – that makes her forty six, doesn't it? – lives and works in San Francisco, has an exclusive private client bank, charges $200 for a private sitting... My goodness, that's quite a lot of money, isn't it? – Anyway she does a lot of work with the Hollywood movie crowd and apparently is booked up for months in advance. She's appeared frequently on dozens of West Coast TV shows and has published lots of different books.... Umm, let me see, oh yes, here we are... "How To Develop Your Own Psychic Power" in 1989, "How To Become A Medium" in 1992, "How To Heighten Your Healing Gifts" in 1994, "How To Talk To The Angels" in 1998, "How to....'"

'Write "How To" books,' Julian cut in with perfect timing and we all laughed.

Beth handed me over a 10x8 colour photograph and I found myself staring at the glamorous image of a blond haired woman of indeterminate age. There was lots of soft focus around the edges of the picture and I suspected that the photograph had been airbrushed to remove any odd lines and wrinkles.

'She's supposed to be very good,' Beth offered. 'She's done a number of readings for Anthony over the years and he always spoke very highly of her. Said that she was always very accurate. Of course, she doesn't know anything about Casa Blanca and she doesn't know anything about me and Julian, because Daddy said it was quite a few years since he'd last seen her. She knows I exist, of course, but we've never met, and the other thing is...' Beth bit her lip.

'She doesn't know Anthony is dead,' Julian finished for her with a totally unnecessary degree of verbal brutality. I shot him a despairing glance. Was this some very poor attempt at black outback humour or was it just the anger and the hurt finding release in any way that it could? Either way I could have hit him in that thoughtless moment as I watched the other kind of hurt, the loving kind, cloud Beth's eyes.

'All right,' I snapped. 'Let's get on with it.' Then in a much softer tone – 'Who's next Beth?'

She opened the yellow file. 'Okay, well, next, from the United Kingdom we have David Doubleday....'

'What?' I shouted, rocking back on my chair in surprise and in the process knocking over the brandy glass and spilling its precious amber liquid all over the white linen tablecloth. And then, with a really deep sinking feeling of total dismay and horror... 'Oh bloody, bloody, *bloody* hell!'

'What's the matter?' Beth asked in bewilderment.

'David sodding Doubleday is what's the matter!' I retorted in disbelief. 'Who the hell invited *him* to take part in this? How, for sweet *fuck's sake*, did he ever get on your list in the first place?'

'Wassup James?' Julian asked. 'Do you know the bloke, or something?'

'Yeah Julian, sort of, or something...'

'Well I sent out the invitation and handled all of the arrangements,' Beth said defiantly and defensively, 'but it was on Anthony's instructions. He was Daddy's choice and he was very keen to have him on board. Anyway James, come on, tell us what's wrong with Mr. Doubleday.'

'Yes, in a minute,' I sighed, 'but just as a matter of interest, tell me what you've got in your file about him first.'

'Well he's on TV a lot...'

'So are the bloody adverts!' I almost yelled at her in my frustration. And then, gathering my cool... 'Sorry love, go on...'

'He does TV shows on both sides of the Atlantic. He's got a huge following both in the UK and in The States. He's written a best selling book called "Over The Rainbow" in which he answers many of the questions Daddy wanted us to look at. He's a leading member of the British Spiritualist Movement...'

'Which one?' I asked tiredly.

'It just says BSM.'

British School of Motoring, I thought. Typical of Doubleday doubletalk. 'Okay, what else?'

'That's about it really. I mean, there's some personal stuff here – he's supposed to have done readings for some very important people, including Princess Diana before she died, and he's healed all kinds of illnesses for different people...'

'Got any specifics?'

'No.'

'No, I thought not. Beth, where did all this information come from?'

'Er, some of it from his website, some of it from his publishers, some of it from his own personal biography that he sent us along with an autographed copy of his book, and there was also a big package of stuff that came from the TV company that broadcasts his shows. Anyway come on James, what do you know about this man that we don't?'

138

'Let's put it this way,' I said, speaking slowly and choosing my words with great care. 'I think you're going to find that Mr. Doubleday isn't quite as good as he thinks he is, or anything like as good as his publicity machine says he is.'

'Do you know him then?' Julian interrupted.

'Not personally, no, but I certainly know of him, and one thing's for sure, he's going to know of me, so which ever way you look at it, the integrity of Anthony's experiment is compromised by Doubleday's presence on the team.'

'You telling us he's a con man?' Julian jutted out aggressively and I shifted uneasily in my seat.

'No I'm not saying that exactly, but this man is a media medium and in the world of real spiritualists he doesn't have a very good reputation.'

The truth of the matter was that despite his media popularity he had a bloody awful reputation. It was all right to hold an audience's attention for twenty five minutes on the TV with out-takes and breaks for the adverts, but quite another to hold an audience's attention for two solid hours in a live theatre performance, where if you waffled and got it wrong the house knew about it straight away. One of the mediums I'd worked with, for example, packed them in and held them in, while David Doubleday, on the strength of his TV reputation, packed 'em in at twice the price, but simply couldn't hold them. Times without number I had heard stories of audiences walking out in disgust and disappointment half way through a David Doubleday demonstration.

Unfortunately, it went even deeper than that.

There was an occasion when someone that I knew had written to Doubleday begging him for a message and virtually giving the medium the story of their life. On the evening of the demonstration Doubleday asked if there was someone called Peter in the audience (my friend's name) who had lost a younger female relative in the last few years, and then proceeded to deliver a highly detailed message, ostensibly from the spirit world, but basically regurgitating all the information my pal had provided him with in the letter!

And then there was the incident with a séance that Doubledasy had been leading. It had been somewhere up in Scotland, quite early in his public career. Someone had tripped the light switch at the wrong time to reveal Doubleday manipulating a floating tambourine with a contraption made up of very fine fishing line and a small rod. How he lived that one down I'll never know and if the press had ever got hold of the story they would have crucified him.

What worried me greatly was that if Doubleday had been vetted and accepted by the Zander clan, what did it say about the skill and integrity of the other two clairvoyants, and come to that, what did it say about me?

This Mandy Breck, for example, seemed to be an American clone of her British counterpart, and while they might get on famously telling each other their favourite TV anecdotes, were they up to the challenge that Zander had set for them? Frankly, I was beginning to wonder. Deep breathing James, keep your mouth shut. Get a grip.

'All right, we can't do anything about Mr. Doubleday at this late hour, and I suppose, if he was Anthony's choice, the man might yet surprise me. I'll try to keep an open mind and give the guy the benefit of the doubt.'

'But James, he's been on the telly,' Julian protested.

'So has Lassie,' I countered.

'But if he's been on the box, then he must be *some* good, mustn't he?'

I marveled at Julian's naiveté, but didn't pursue the argument. 'Let's hope so,' I said, none committally. And then, 'Okay Beth, who's our third person?'

Beth furrowed her brow and read from the blue dossier. 'Edith Schiff, born in Salvan, Switzerland, August 1915...'

'1915?' I echoed with a degree of incredulity. 'How old does that make her, for Heaven's sake? Eighty nine?'

'Eighty eight,' Beth corrected. 'She was a founder member of the Second Chapter of The Golden Dawn, was on first name terms with Dione Fortune, studied with a young Edgar Cayce, and for a very short time was associated with Aleister Crowley.'

'Good God!' I exclaimed

'Who's this Crowley guy?' Julian put in. 'D'you know anything about him?'

'Yeah, a few bits and pieces,' I answered dryly, and gave him a potted history of the occultist who at one time had been dubbed by the British press as "The Wickedest Man In The World." To be fair Crowley had done some good work and great research in the 20's and 30's but after that he lost the plot completely and went slightly – and then totally – off his head. He claimed to be able to

140

communicate with both demons and angels and saw himself as the second coming of the Antichrist.

'It actually gets even better,' Beth said. 'She moved to Austria in 1936 and became marginally involved with The National Socialist Party.'

'The bloody Nazis?' My gob was smacked again... but somewhere in the deep recesses of memory an odd little bell was tinkling away. I must have read something about this woman at sometime in the distant past, or I'd heard of her somewhere. No more than a passing reference perhaps but enough to register a small flag in the filing cabinet of the mind.

' – Yes it would seem so,' Beth carried on. 'By then she had acquired the reputation of being a very precise medium and a very accurate seer. Lots of the Nazi bigwigs – and they were quite interested in this sort of thing, weren't they? – were very taken by her. Apparently she was a very good looking woman, but she seems to have fallen out of favour quite early in the war... Suspected of spying for the British and spent three years in the concentration camp at Belsen. After the war she went back to Switzerland and has lived in the same house in Martigney since 1947.'

Oh tinkly tinkling little bells – Edith Schiff? British Intelligence, World War Two? Belsen? Of all the concentration camps available in Nazi Germany, it had to be Belsen?

'Beth, just run me through your source material, will you?'

'Some of it came from the internet – she doesn't have her own website, but she's cross-referenced on about a dozen other sites, and there's a book that Anthony read years ago, written by her son Richard. Anthony said it was out of print now, but he was incredibly impressed with it, and although it is a number of years ago, I remember that he went to some lengths to get in touch with the son, but I don't know whether he ever did or not. The lady herself has written a number of articles for various magazines, and has published a couple of papers on physical mediumship and post mortem survival, but nothing recent, I'm afraid. The last one was back in 1974.

'To tell you the truth James, we didn't really expect a reply to our letter. Both Julian and I thought she'd probably be dead by now and even if she wasn't, the chances of her being willing to travel all the way to Spain at the drop of a hat were pretty slim, but she was the first person to respond positively to our invitation and when I spoke to her on the phone she said yes straight away and she seemed very spry and on the ball. It was almost as though...' Beth struggled for the right words, 'it was almost as though she'd been waiting to hear from us and was surprised that *we* were surprised by her acceptance of our offer.'

I replenished my spilt brandy glass and let my brain digest the information. I quietly fretted about David Doubleday but there was bugger all that I could do about him. Mandy Breck's promotional material made her sound like a tacky seaside fortune teller, and however good she might have been once, Edith Schiff was almost ninety years old and was probably, despite Beth's impression, well in her dotage. And yet, and yet, these were the three mediums Zander had chosen from dozens of likely candidates, and so to some extent, should I not respect his judgment? I grinned ruefully because it didn't seem that I had much choice one way or the other!

We talked for a while longer about the arrangements for the following day. Beth would drive the Cherokee and pick up Edith Schiff and Mandy Breck who were flying into Jerez airport within an hour of each other, albeit from different points of origin, and it was agreed that Julian and I would drive up to Malaga airport in the hire car to pick up David Doubleday. All being well, we should be able to rendezvous back at Casa Blanca by tea time with our various cargos. Although they would be staying in the guest rooms there was no way in which we could isolate them and hold them prisoner for the duration of their stay in Jimena (which is more or less what Zander had wanted us to do) so we decided we might as well take them all out to dinner and give them a familiarization tour of the village on their first night, and then get down to the schedule of the experiments first thing the following morning.

'...Which brings me to the last item on the agenda,' Beth said cautiously, 'and James, this is where we need to ask you a big favour.'

'Okay, go for it,' I said, no idea of what was coming down. 'What do you need?'

'Well, according to Anthony's instructions, I'm supposed to act as co-coordinator, but I really have no idea how to go about doing it all, and Julian doesn't have enough terms of reference, so we wondered if you would mind doing it?'

'What do you mean by co-coordinator?' I asked.

'Oh you know, tell them what they've got to do – and I suppose tell us what *we're* supposed to do for that matter, and just generally, well, sort of take charge...'

I suppose I should have seen it coming, but I hadn't. Not that it mattered. 'Yeah, okay, leave it with me. I'll look after that side of things as best I can.'

They both looked relieved and Julian was about to put his two-penneth in but at that point there was the sound of breaking glass from the bar next door and a roar of masculine laughter. I realized that I was tired and more than a little drunk, and as far as I was concerned, it was time to pay the bill and go our separate ways. Anything else that needed to be sorted out could be sorted out in the morning. Almost on cue Corrie popped her head through the curtain to ask if we needed anything, and I told her no thanks, just *la cuenta*. Beth and I argued about who was going to pay, and although she was a lot richer than I was, this was my patch and I had my pride, and so I won.

We made our exit through the now very crowded bar and walked out onto a wet Calle Sevilla. Beth and Julian headed for the jeep and I strolled down to the main square: I needed some air to clear my alcohol dulled senses, and it was pleasant and comforting to loiter beneath the umbrellas of the interlocking orange trees that circumnavigated *El Paseo* on three of its four sides. It was comforting yes, but I felt very ill at ease. A West Coast fortune teller, a late octogenarian who'd had links with Alaister Crowley and the Nazis, and David Sodding Doubleday, who was in my opinion, despite my earlier words to Beth and Julian, an outright fake and a fraud! It did not bode well, and all of a sudden I saw this whole experiment with death ending up as a shambolic disaster...

And that made me feel really bad because Anthony Zander expected and deserved something so much better than what he was likely to get. Not for the first time I found myself wishing that Harry Andrews or someone else that I knew was part of this junket, because that way we'd have been guaranteed some sort of positive result. By then Harry Andrews was back in the States and my other ace in the hole, Stephen Holbrook, was in Wakefield and probably wouldn't have touched this project with a ten foot barge pole anyway, so like it or not, it was down to me.

And right then I didn't like it at all. As much as anything, just to put my mind at rest, I put a call through to Harry in America and brought him up to speed with what was happening. He'd never heard of Edith Schiff, but he was familiar with Breck and Doubleday, even though he didn't know either of them personally. Like me he was surprised to find that David Doubleday had been invited along.

'How did he end up with the job?' he wanted to know.

'You tell me,' I retorted. 'Suffice to say he's got some really nice glossy PR blurb, and by the sounds of it the people who've invited him have simply read the blurb and gone with the reputation.'

'Ummm," Harry pondered thoughtfully, the line crackling from the other side of the world. "All I can say James is just be a bit careful how you go, because at the end of the day, I don't think David's going to be much good to you. I mean, we both know what happens when a TV reputation gets put to the true test. Looking sexy doesn't do you much good when you've got to come up with some hard factual proof of post mortem survival.'

'Hey Harry, you don't have to tell me that. You're preaching to the converted. Who're you talking about, by the way? Doubleday or Breck?'

Harry laughed. 'Both of 'em, I suppose. You've never actually met Doubleday, have you?'

'No.'

'Well in that case, if I was you, I'd just keep my trap shut about everything, and see how he gets on.'

'Fine. Do me a favour though, will you, and do a bit of digging? See what the consensus of professional opinion is on your side of the water and in particular see if anyone knows anything about this Edith Schiff lady. Give me a ring back tomorrow if you come up with anything and if I don't hear from you, I'll assume that you've drawn a blank.'

'All right, I'll do my best, but I can't promise anything quickly. I'm up to my eyes in it and I leave for Japan next week, but I'll give you a ring either way before I leave. How's your lovely wife, by the way?'

'Dunno.' I chewed my bottom lip moodily. 'She's not answering the phone.'

'Probably just missing you a bit too much.'

'Yeah, well, probably.' I retorted, earnestly hoping that he was right.

144

Fourteen: *Malaga – Jimena, Sunday 21st December*

Once upon a time it could take as long as four or five hours to get from Jimena to Malaga airport, especially in the summer months when the Costa del Sol was full with its usual influx of sun seeking tourists. The N340 wound its way through Estepona and San Pedro, Marbella and Fuengirola, Benelmadena and Torremolinos, and there was no respite from the long queues of turgidly moving traffic. Then, mostly with the money flooding in from the EU they had built the new motorway through the mountains and although you got hit by the ubiquitous toll booths every ten or fifteen miles, it still cut the journey time down to a straight seventy minutes, and those of us who used the new route paid the tolls gladly.

It was a cuttingly clear morning, coolish but with a cobalt blue sky that almost hurt the eyes and not a cloud in sight. We cruised at a steady eighty kilometers, not talking much but enjoying the magnificent scenery, and both glad to be out of the claustrophobic constraints of the village. Julian seemed to be much more calm and at ease than he had been at any time since his father's passing, and I suppose it was the due process of grief working its way through his emotional system; I'm sure that he was still hurting the way in which we all do when we lose someone or something precious and important to us, but the rage of vitriol and fury eventually subsides into a deep and lonely ache that we nurture and hold within ourselves. The hurt does not get any less, but the nature of the beast does change to allow us to get on with our daily lives. True, a part of our spirit is closed off – the psychological doors are closed against the horror of what we have experienced (and in many cases continue to experience for many ongoing years yet to come) but the human psyche has its own self defense mechanisms and it has many tricks up its sleeve to dull the pain and divert attention. Maybe spirit itself in the form of a Higher Spiritual Authority has some hand in the process, and on that December morning we were provided with a glorious God-given day that would have been hard for us to ignore. Not for the first time in my life I thanked God for Andalucia.

As we drew closer to the airport I gently suggested that it might be a good idea if Julian took the reigns of this first meeting with David Doubleday. 'You make the introductions and do the talking, just introduce me as James, but drop the Mr. Christie bit, and if it's

145

okay with you, I'll sit in the back on the way home and you can drive.'

'Okay by me Mr. C, but d'you mind telling me why?'

'Yes, I just want to get some feeling about this guy without him knowing that I'm doing it.'

Julian looked interested. 'Hey, you can do that?'

'Sort of.'

'Can you do it with everyone you meet?'

'You can try.'

'Do you always succeed?'

'Definitely not!' I cast him a wry glance 'For example, I tried it with you and made a real hash of it.'

'Forget it James. We all screw up sometimes, and I didn't think much of you when we first met either... Hey, wow, look, they named the airport after me!'

We turned off the 340 on to the slip road that led us into *Aeropuerto de San Julian* and parked up in one of the car parks. They'd built the airport back in the early 1960's – along with thirty other airports dotted all over Spain that were exactly the same in every detail. A German architect had helped bring Spain's newly developing tourist industry into the 20th century and these unimaginative blockhouse buildings were cathedrals of homage to Teutonic conservatism and Latin poverty. But Malaga had grown and evolved with the influx of business and the influx of money and although the blockhouse schematic was still in evidence, there were softer lines and increasing semblances of sophistication: it might not have been another Heathrow but it could certainly give Manchester a run for its money.

We walked through to the arrivals hall and we were right on time which was more than could be said for David Doubleday! His flight was delayed by an hour so we went and had an awful cup of coffee in the bar and kicked our heels. Julian was in a talkative, inquisitive mood and went through a litany of questions about clairvoyance and mediumship, some of which I could answer, others which I could not. What this did do, however, was make me very aware of how little Julian knew about the subject, other than what he'd read in the last few months and the bits that he'd picked up from his father and sister. And in some ways, I realized, this might be no bad thing.

'Have you,' I asked casually, 'ever had a reading from a psychic or a clairvoyant?'

'Nope, never. Never knew anything about it until I met Anthony and Beth. Not the sort of thing I was interested in... It isn't that I'm skeptical or anything, although I've got to admit that some of the things that Anthony and Beth used to go on about do seem a bit way out and far fetched... It's just that I've never been exposed to any kind of psychic or paranormal experience, so, just like Beth said last night, I don't have any terms of reference.'

'Okay, well the thing to do is tell all that to David Doubleday, ask *him* all the questions you want, and I'll listen very carefully to his answers and tell you later where I think he's gone wrong.'

'You really do have a downer on this bloke, don't you Mr. C?'

'Yes I suppose I do – and it's a shame, because I've never met the man, and only know him by reputation. I've got to tell you that I'm not very confident about his abilities, but I don't want to say any more than that. You're a fresh mind and a fresh ear; you'll listen to what he has to say without any of the preconceptions that I might have lingering around in the back of my mind, so you are better placed to judge him than I am. I've just got to try and be open minded, and remember, as Beth reminded me last night, that he was Anthony's choice, so maybe this is the power of spirit moving in some circuitous way that I don't understand.'

'Yeah, but you're supposed to be the expert, so if you don't understand what's going on what chance have the rest of us got?'

And I'd heard those words a few times before, hadn't I? The very words I'd berated a few clairvoyants with over the long years of searching for answers that no one seemed to have!

'Julian I take a dim view of "experts" – they're just people who know a lot about very little. As for me, I'm no expert in anything at all. The only thing that I've had that you haven't had is exposure and experience, but I don't think that means much. When I was your age I thought I knew all of the questions and most of the answers, now thirty years on, I realize I don't know half of the bloody questions and I don't know any of the bloody answers!'

I paused thoughtfully, and then used this opportunity to put something in place. 'Look, over the next few days we're going to be in situations where the three of us, you me and Beth, are going to be on the receiving end of anything and everything these clairvoyants might want to tell us. Me, I'm a cynical old fart, I've heard every cliché in the book, and one thing I can do is spot a phony at fifty yards. I'll know when someone has got something genuine or when they're groping for it or just making it up as they go along. Beth is a very intelligent girl, and I *think* she can be fairly objective in her analysis, but on the other hand I think that she wants to hear from her father so much that she might be persuaded by evidence that I would find questionable or wanting... And therefore, it's just as well that Anthony has been very clever and canny by putting his codes and controls in place. But you, well, as I said, you're the fresh head and the fresh ear, so when you're sitting with these people keep an open mind, but don't give anything away: don't give them any information at all. Let *them* tell *you* what *they* know.'

'Mr. C, I don't quite know what you're trying to say...?'

I sighed and groped for my pipe. He was making me put into words something that I would have preferred to hold in my soul.

'Look Julian, I believe in life after death, and I believe that it is possible for there to be some form of communication between the two worlds. I believe these things partly because I have had some evidence to suggest that it might be so, but mostly I believe because I *want* to believe... No, more than that actually, I *need* to believe! Therefore this experiment that your father has set up has become far more important to me than either he or I might have imagined possible when my name came out of his hat and I said yes to his offer, because although I've had all kinds of evidence over the years, I've come to a point in my own life where evidence is not enough and just like your Dad I want some hard incontrovertible *proof*... But I certainly don't want to go through what your father has put himself through to find it.

'Our three mediums are going to try to provide that proof, and this is where my experience gets in the way. I have known *hundreds* of people who believe that they can give proof of life after death, who call themselves mediums and clairvoyants and who believe that they are genuinely in touch with the spirit world. The trouble is that for every one of them who can, there are dozens who can't who *think* they can and scores of people who can't and who *know* that they can't but who would like people like you and me to *think* that they can.

'It gets complicated sometimes because there are a few people who have some sensitivity and some psychic skills and who have the occasional gift of precognition, but this is a long way short of and something very different to being a spiritualist medium! In their

148

ignorance because they honestly don't know any better, they'll call what they've got clairvoyancy or mediumship, and not only are they deluding themselves, they are deluding the poor buggers who come and sit at their tables in search of some enlightenment or guidance.'

'So how do you tell the goodies from the baddies?' Julian asked.

'I was just coming to that. The ones who are okay won't need to ask you any questions.'

'Questions? Like what?'

'Ooooh, questions like "I've got someone here with a tummy problem, so do you know anybody who's had a stomach ache recently?" Or "I'm getting a strong connection with the letter J so do you know who John is, dear?"'

'Millions of people called John,' Julian observed.

'My point exactly! So when you're sitting with our two whiz kids and our wonder-granny, and they're trying to prove to you that they are in touch with the spirit world in general and Anthony Zander in particular, just keep your mouth shut and don't help 'em at all. Don't even ask them any questions until after they've shot their bolt because the very nature of the question can feed them information that they can regurgitate to make their case. One thing's for sure, I'll be watching their every move and listening to their every word. They are not going to be able to pull the wool over my eyes and if there is a phony among them, if I have my way, they'll be going home early.'

'And you think Doubleday is a phony?'

'Let's wait and see.'

'Ah come on Mr. C, that's not good enough!'

'Let's wait and see,' I said again.

'Well that answers *that* question!' Julian exclaimed. And then in a more thoughtful tone – 'Hey, this experiment might actually turn out to be a bit of fun!'

Fun? No, somehow I didn't think it was going to be "fun" at all.

They called the Gatwick flight and we made our way back to the arrivals gate. Doubleday wasn't difficult to spot. Inevitably smaller than his TV image he still cut quite a picture. Mid forties, medium build, reddish ginger hair swept back in a bouffant with some grey at the temples and a wispy Bill Cody moustache. He wore a pale cream Armani suit with an Abercrombie raincoat over his shoulder, and was dragging a leather Antler wheelie case and a set of golf clubs.

'Golf clubs?' Julian mused. 'When does the silly sod think he's going to have time to play golf?'

'Now, now,' I soothed getting in stride with his humour. 'Be kind. He might have some unexpected free time on his hands after tomorrow.'

Julian laughed. 'Mr. Christie, you can be a right bastard!'

'Just call me James," I pouted, and Julian laughed again – a merry forgotten laugh, and in that split second I had a glimpse of the man that Beth saw and found some deeper understanding of her problem with her half brother. Sweet Jesus, talk about "the love that dare not speak its name" – at least that was legal and socially acceptable these days!

Julian was very good. He greeted David Doubleday in his usual effervescent way and he introduced me as the company's interpreter and Mr. Fix-it. I nodded a greeting and shook Doubleday's hand – small hands, well manicured nails, but roughish skin and very slightly clammy. Doubleday said he was pleased to meet me in a cheerful voice that had a mid-Atlantic resonance over Geordie roots and vowels. I hoped that he would continue to be pleased to have met me and couldn't blame a man for having been born on Tyneside.

Julian hoisted the golf clubs over his shoulder and with a conspiratorial wink in my direction, led the way back to the hire car. I slid in behind the driver's seat while Julian got in behind the wheel. Doubleday took the front passenger seat, so I was able to view him from a three quarter rear angle. He had a minor problem with dandruff and said "I say" a lot..

'I say, what fabulous weather after England – I say, so good of you chaps to meet me – I say I can't wait to find out more about these experiments you people have set up...' and 'I say, I hope I'm not going to be a dreadful disappointment to you!'

I hoped so too.

Giving nothing away, Julian went into his Opus Australia routine and had hardly spoken half a dozen sentences before Doubleday was talking about his own Australian experiences which revolved around a "phenomenally successful" tour of The Antipodes two years previously and how the audiences had been so "wonderful and welcoming."... And while Julian did his best to make David

Doubleday feel welcome in Spain I sat quietly in the back of the little Seat Ibiza and wondered.

On the surface Doubleday seemed confident enough, but that clammy hand and his ability to out-talk Julian hinted at an inner nervousness. I was able to watch his eyes through the rear view mirror and on more than one occasion I saw his watery blue peepers cast a furtive glance in my direction. If I could see him then he could see me. Best then, I thought, just to close my own eyes and go with the flow of the conversation, which sounded like a good idea except that I went a little too far with the flow and fell asleep. The hum of the engine, the drone of the conversation, the warmth of the sunshine belting through the Ibiza's windows, all conspired to dispatch me to the Land of Nod and I only jerked back to the realm of reality when we came off the smooth black top of the motorway and started bouncing along the country road towards San Enrique, by which time Doubleday was snoring with his head resting against the window, and Julian was yawning fitfully.

We pulled over to the roadside just after San Martin de Tessorillo and I took the wheel for the last few miles back to Jimena.

'Oh, I say!' Doubleday woke up. 'We've changed drivers have we? Are we nearly there? Could do with a pee... Didn't really get chance on the plane or at the airport.'

'Ten minutes?' I asked, knowing that it would be at least twenty.

'Oh yes, I think I can hang on that long.'

Which was good.

There is some mischief in us all, and where there is mischief there is malice – albeit in varying degrees. I didn't know Doubleday, I only knew of him. What I knew of him I didn't much like and therefore I didn't want to like him in the flesh either. This, of course, was totally unfair, for in good conscience the man seemed to be reasonably affable and inoffensive; he had done nothing to hurt me personally and if he seemed a little nervous and on edge, then maybe he had a right to be. After all, he was coming into this situation relatively blind, no doubt influenced to some extent by Zander's money, but still taking a few things on trust. Was this ego? Was it a subliminal desire to prove something, or was it, I wondered, just plane loneliness?

Whether you are good at your job or bloody awful, the psychic profession is an isolated and insular world; you may have any number of professional contacts and clients, but there isn't much social intercourse or camaraderie with colleagues and contrary to expectation it is not a profession in which you make friends all that easily. The psychic is the modern day shaman and the seer and he (or she) tends to live apart from the general crowd and clamour of humanity. Sometimes viewed in fascination, but equally viewed with varying degrees of suspicion and distrust, the novelty of being just a little bit different from your fellow men can soon wear thin and become a burden rather than a delight.

As we negotiated the bottom end of the village and started the last short run along the riverbank, Zander's voice echoed into my mind *"Be charitable, James, be charitable!"* Okay Anthony, I thought, I would try to be charitable – and in that moment it crossed my mind that David Doubleday probably didn't have that many friends and deserved a better chance than the one I was giving him.

'I say, this looks splendid,' he exclaimed as we turned into the courtyard of La Casa Blanca and parked up next to the Jeep. 'Er, before we do anything else, d'you mind if I go to the toilet?'

Once we'd got our three clairvoyants in one place we were hard pressed to know what to do with them. Zander had not written the pauses into his script, so firing from the hip, once we'd got them sorted out with their accommodation, Julian piled them all into the Jeep and took them on a familiarization tour around the village while Beth and I went up the Anon and sorted out a table for an early dinner. And when it came down to it, it was a pretty strange dinner.

The six of us sat around our table like half a dozen stuffed puppets; all of us, me included, were feeling nervous and self conscious – how to start a conversation with three strangers? Where to steer it? What to say? What *not* to say? Obviously we had performed formal introductions back at the house, and while each of the mediums had known they were to be part of a three handed team they had not known until that moment who the other team members were going to be... And interestingly enough it was clear from those first few minutes of initial contact that none of them had ever heard of either of the others. Which was a bit odd, for despite the insular nature of a clairvoyant's life, reputations were familiar and were usually followed with a degree of interest. I was in no position to ask at this late stage in the game but not for the first time I did wonder *exactly* what procedures Anthony Zander had gone through in his selection process.

The conversation was stilted to say the least and I figured that the best thing to do was to get some alcohol into these people as quickly as possible. Wine was brought to the table and I saw it as a personal quest to make sure it flowed freely. I didn't have too much of a problem with Mandy Beck and David Doubleday, but Frau Schiff informed me that she did not drink wine and would prefer a bottle of schnapps.

The octogenarian's English was very good, but the accent was pure Hollywood. TH's became Z's and W's became V's, and that was only the half of it! And thus: 'Herr James I do not drink ze vine, zo can you pliz ask for a bottle of schnapps?'

Great, I thought! A clairvoyant Granny with a booze problem. Harry Andrews please come to Spain NOW! All is forgiven!

Our waitress that evening was a lovely Spanish girl called Consuela. She had an enormous pair of breasts and wore the most ridiculously tight tea shirt you could possibly imagine. We were old mates back from the early years in Pepe's bar. I gave her a nod and she bounced over to the table and brought her ear down to my lips.

'Do we have any schnapps?' I asked in Spanish.

'Sure. There is the stuff from Archers mixed with peach juice for the tourists, or Gabriel has a bottle of 100% proof from Warsaw stashed under the bar which I can bring you if you want...'

I cast a glance in Granny's direction, and – no, I had the feeling that the Archers simply would not do.

'Better bring me the stuff from Warsaw,' I said in resignation.

'You want the whole bottle?'

'Yeah, the whole bottle.'

'Okay, how many glasses? Six?'

'No, just one.'

'*Mierda,* James, you'll be flat on your back! That stuff is lethal.'

'It's not for me love,' I muttered. 'It's for the old lady. She doesn't like our wine.'

'*Mierda!*' Consuela said again with a tone of awe in her voice. 'You sure about this James?'

I nodded.

'Shit! Okay, back in two minutes.'

Edith Schiff.

Well, she may have been eighty eight years old, but she didn't really look it. Sixty eight or maybe seventy eight, but definitely not eighty eight. She was as skinny as the proverbial beanpole. Not an ounce of surplus flesh on her lean frame. Her hair, dark grey, not silver, was pulled back in a tight bun, accentuating the hawk like features of her face. High forehead, seamed with leathery wrinkles, a beaky Roman nose, high Slavic cheekbones and parchment tight skin. She had all her own teeth even though they were far from straight and tended to be badly stained by tobacco tar and nicotine. Her eyes were unusual, neither one colour nor another, but a strange shade of golden amber; tigers eyes, as sharp as razors and as hard as stone. Those eyes were bright and alert, and missed not a nuance of our conversation, stilted though that conversation may have been in that early stage of the evening.

She was tall, at least 5'10", with absolutely no indication of the usual stoop that comes with age to most people getting on in years. She wore a severe black dress with a high collar and long sleeves, and there was a notably absence of any make up or jewelry. She reminded me of a ravening black crow, and then when the schnapps arrived and her eyes lit up with some pleasure, and she leaned across to take the bottle and tippled the colourless liquid into the shot glass, the sleeve of the black dress pulled up above her wrist to reveal the pale blue residue of tattooed numbers on her forearm – and then I was reminded of something totally different.

I stared at that tattoo. I simply couldn't help myself. It may have been rude and insensitive but some magnetic spell wove its curse across my eyes and I could not shift them from their gaze for love or money. And of course, Frau Schiff was well aware of my scrutiny. The tiger's eyes glinted with cynical amusement.

'You know vhat zat is, of course?'

'Yes I do – but it's not something you see very often – these days.'

'Jah, you are right. Many times I have zought of having it removed but alvays I have said no at ze last minute. Zose numbers, vhat is left of zem, remind me of my greatest humiliation in zis life, and also my greatest triumph.'

'Your *triumph*?'

'Jah. I survived.'

Suddenly, and without any kind of warning, I warmed to this elderly lady. She was old, no doubt about that, but at the same time she was ageless. Tough as old boot leather with a bizarre and mysterious history – *Alastair Cowley and The Nazis?* – she was nobody's idea of the kindly old Grandmother; you didn't want to mess with this woman, and she carried with her a dynamic energy that manifested itself it the form of a powerful presence that hinted at something deeper than just wisdom and knowledge. If she'd had some connection, *any* kind of connection, with Crowley then she must have had some knowledge of magick – and when I use that word I deliberately spell it with the additional letter k to differentiate between what I'm talking about and the guy in the tuxedo pulling the rabbit out of the hat. Apart from anything else, anyone who could chain smoke her awful brand of cigarettes and drink 100% proof schnapps neat without batting an eyelid, and who was still quite obviously going strong at nearly ninety years old, had to have the constitution of a bull elephant.

As if to prove my point she poured a liberal shot of schnapps into the glass, inhaled the fumes as though assessing a fine wine or precious brandy, then downed the shot in one, slamming the empty glass back down onto the table top in a Cossackian gesture of defiance and satisfaction.

'Not so bad,' she acknowledged with an appreciative inclination of the head. 'Jah, is very good!'

Then she proceeded to pour herself another shot and several more after that.

Mandy Breck was a complicated contradiction. She had a bright and bubbly personality and she laughed a lot – although not always with her eyes, which maintained some degree of detachment, constantly measuring her environment and the impact of her words. I wanted to think of her as some twittering peroxide blond bimbo, but she failed to fall into that preordained pigeon hole and I suspected that many a good man who'd made the mistake I was trying to make, had come a cropper at her hands.

Her hair was naturally fair and streaked with highlights that may well have come out of a bottle, but it would have been a flaming expensive bottle! It was thick and lush and fell around her face in haloes of natural curls and waves – a grown up Shirley Temple. Her bio. said she was forty seven, but she didn't look it. At first glance you might have guessed late thirties, but I supposed that was the point of all the make-up she was wearing; if you looked beyond the cosmetic veneer then the crow's feet and laughter lines were evidential enough. I suspected that she might have had some lightweight cosmetic surgery, in which case she'd spent her dollars well and had not been robbed.

She had big baby blue eyes and full rouged lips over brilliant white teeth; she was carrying a few extra pounds on a Munroe-like body and she wore lots of expensive jewelry and a heavy musky perfume that wafted across the table every time she moved. Her voice was pure California – honey sunshine tones with long drawn and rounded vowels... *"Oh Gaaad, Ah just gotta tell you guys Ah just lurve this restaurant and Gaaad Ah lurve this waahn we're drinking..."* But it wasn't totally unpleasant and despite my earlier reservations her presence at the table was quite amusing. Her overt sexuality was funny rather than sensual, and I got the impression that although she'd taken a lot of trouble over her appearance – she was the kind of lady who'd put on some lipstick just to go to the loo – she didn't take herself too seriously. Not in the femme fatal role anyway – but from her conversations with her dinner companions it was clear that as a clairvoyant she did take herself extremely seriously. She was clever, using the royal "we" rather than the singular "I" and she tended to talk very carefully about what she had "done" rather that what she actually thought. She was in an unusual situation... The same situation that Edith and David were in, but she was genuinely self confident and the circumstances didn't phase her in the least. I reckoned that if Edith Schiff was here out of curiosity and if David Doubleday was here to try and prove something to someone, then Mandy Breck was here purely for the money. Of course I could have been wrong. I'm not a clairvoyant – but I do have some psychic sensitivity and I do have some perception when it comes to reading people cold, and right then I'd have wagered a case of good brandy on my reckoning.

Poor David Doubleday didn't know which way to turn. He had Mandy Breck on his right and the svelte and beautiful Beth on his left. He was obviously attracted to both women but couldn't very well chat them both up at the same time (although he did try manfully.) To complicate matters his jaw dropped and his eyes nearly popped out of his head every time Consuela leaned across the table to serve him; he was a totally predatory male spoiled by choice and I dare say that he spent the better part of the dinner subconsciously planning his future conquest with one of the three women. In his perfect world he would have had all three, but in his conscious mind he probably thought he had a better than even chance of pulling one of them and he'd go for the first one who gave him any indication of interest. Right then he wasn't getting buying signs from anyone, but in his party-going frame of mind, that was something that was going right over his head. He wasn't drunk, but he was certainly putting back enough Rioja to neutralize his shyness and bring out the effusive part of his character. *This* was the Doubleday we saw on the TV screens and certainly *not* the Doubleday I'd met a few hours earlier at Malaga airport.

At least, I mused wryly into my own glass of wine, it disproved the rumour that he was gay. If he'd been at all that way inclined he'd have been concentrating on Julian, who sat opposite him. As it was, Julian was on the receiving end of Mandy Breck's attention, and the only recognition he got from David came in the form of a few glances of envy and exasperation because it was Julian, rather than David, who was hogging the masculine limelight... Clairvoyant males all seem to be slightly effeminate, and maybe it's because they are much more in tune with their feminine sides than are the rest of us, but for heaven's sake, this does not make them all homo sexual!

On more than one occasion a few people have thought that Harry Andrews is that way inclined... The theatrical flamboyance, the flying flame red hair, the lightly timbered voice... But if anything Harry is homophobic; he wouldn't recognize a gay if one was chatting him up at close quarters, and he is totally dedicated to his gorgeous wife and two wonderful children. But rumours are rumours and rumours are born in the fabric of hearsay and speculation and become an unofficial truth by the power of repetition and speculation. So a lot of people, me included, were very wrong about Doubleday's sexual orientation – and, I realized, if I could be wrong about that, I could be wrong about a whole load of other stuff as well.

The wine and the schnapps and the Anon's superb cuisine were all excellent ice breakers and by the time that Consuela brought in the deserts, everyone was on convivial first name terms and we were having quite a little party. Beth and Julian and myself had to be very much on our guard; nothing could be said or divulged that could give our guests any insight into the nature of the forthcoming experiments, so although we drank, we did so relatively sparingly. The only person not to get into the party mood was Edith Schiff. The Swiss psychic may have been enjoying herself but she didn't say much and never initiated a conversation. She sat at the head of the table steadily murdering The Warsaw Express without any visible sign of ill effect. She chain smoked white tipped Caporal cigarettes (much to Julian's disgust) but as she sat next to an open window and took care to blow her smoke and doff her ash out into the courtyard, there wasn't much that he could have said in protest, even if he had dared to – and I use the word "dared" quite deliberately because Edith Schiff was both intimidating and taciturn in her presence at the table. Indeed it was Frau Schiff who was primarily responsible for bringing our dinner to a slightly premature end.

There was a lull in the conversation at which point Edith cleared her throat, and in that one small gesture managed without much difficulty, to get our attention.

'Ve haf all had a gut dinner and for zis ve must zank our hosts. Ze qvestion is, who *are* our hosts and vhat exactly do zey vant from us for all ze money zey are paying us to be here?'

I'd known that sooner or later someone was bound to bring this up. Beth had asked me to deal with it when it did but I'd suggested that it would be much better if the initial response came from her. I didn't mind taking over the following day when it came to the practical mechanics, but she *was* the lawyer and it was she who had invited these three people, four if you counted me, to this table.

Beth leaned forward slightly. 'You are here,' she began, trying not to sound too formal – *and from somewhere there came the sound a lightly tinkling wind chime* – 'at the invitation of The Hammond Foundation for Psychic Research. My name is, of course, Elizabeth Hammond, and, er, as you can imagine, I am part of the family that has put the foundation and the foundation's program of experiments together.'

The Hammond Foundation actually existed to the extent of there being some expensive headed notepaper and a New York office address. Other than that it was purely a front for Zander and his family to carry out their stratagems without interested parties knowing that Zander was in any way involved. It was interesting that my letter from Beth had come on the AZ monogrammed notepaper while the mediums had had their correspondence on The Hammond Foundation stuff. It was petty and trivial but when I'd found out about this I had been extraordinarily pleased. Egos of the world unite.

'The purpose of these experiments is to prove incontrovertibly that there is life after death, that it is possible to communicate with spirit and that it is possible for spirit to communicate with us in a two way dialogue...' Again the tinkling of unseen wind chimes – 'and to this end we have brought the three of you together as the world's leading clairvoyant mediums, to help us find that proof.'

Mandy and David preened like a pair of peacocks. Edith inclined her head slightly, acknowledging what she perceived to be a divine truth.

Beth: 'I would like to stress at the very outset that in no way are we trying to put you or your gifts to the test...' Did I sense a subtle sigh of relief from David and Mandy? '...but that we hope to utilize your gifts in our pursuit of hard evidence and the truth.'

'Pah!' There was a note of scorn in Edith's voice. 'Vhat, iz ze truce? Truce, like so many zings, iz subjective. Vhat constitutes ze truce about anyzing? Von man's freedom fighter iz ze ozzer man's terrorist. So vhat vill ze 'Ammond Foundation accept as its truce?'

Mandy and David said nothing but waited with baited breath, for as any psychic or clairvoyant would agree, Edith had a very valid point. As they waited for their answer you could have heard a pin drop, but there was no pin to be dropped – and for the third and final time I heard the wind chimes, but there were no wind chimes to chime.

Beth didn't lose it in the least, but her answer came from the lawyer and not the bereaved daughter. 'The Hammond Foundation is funded by The Chase Manhattan Bank of New York,' she said evenly, weaving the web of a lawyer's lie – it was the same as me saying that James Christie Productions and Mage Publishing were funded by The Royal Bank of Scotland just because we had a couple of accounts with that particular bank. 'And it is through this association that we have been able to pay you your rather generous fees. We feel that the payment of those fees entitles The Foundation to determine the parameters of truth and objectivity. We have our own criteria of measurement and assessment and as I have said, you yourselves are not on test or trial. We have been assured that you are the very best people in your field and with your help we intend to prove the reality of something which has hitherto been regarded as improvable. We are not looking for evidence of post mortem survival but hard tangible proof – and our experiments have been designed to find that proof.'

'Er, yes, but I say, what happens if we don't find that proof?' This, as you might imagine, from David Doubleday.

'Then our experiments will be deemed to have been a failure and we pack up and go home. You will have been paid your fees and you will not in any way be held responsible for the failure of the experiments. The Foundation will be out of pocket, but we hope we will have learned something. Basically we'll go back to square one and reassess our criteria and our methodology.'

And that reassured everyone, including Edith, for even she knew that he who paid the piper invariably called the tune.

Shortly after that Consuela presented us with the bill. Beth paid and people got up to leave. It was early but it had been a long day,

160

especially for our three guests. After the usual round of goodnights I was left alone at the cluttered table. Consuela brought me a coffee and a brandy and started clearing away the mess while I sat quietly with my thoughts and favourite pipe.

'You okay now?' she asked when she had finished.

'Fine thanks.'

'You need anything else you call be from the kitchen.'

And off she went, leaving me in the ambient silence of the now empty restaurant. I closed my eyes for a while, not in tiredness but in a relaxed mnemonic replay of the evening's conversations. There was some distant clatter and chatter from the kitchen and upstairs in the bar someone with good taste in music, probably Gabriel, was playing Eva Cassidy's first tragic album. I listened while she worked her way through the tracks and it was only after she had sung her incredible and inimitable version of "Somewhere Over The Rainbow" that I got up from my seat and started quartering the restaurant. I was looking for wind chimes.

Within the dining room and its immediate environs there were no wind chimes, but outside in the courtyard garden I did find an old rusty set hanging from a small bay tree, about six or seven feet from the French windows. I scraped the stem of my pipe along the hollow tubes of metal, and the chimes sang out their dull song, a rusty arpeggio pitched somewhere slightly lower than middle C. These were not the chimes I had heard earlier. Those chimes had been far lighter, more lyrically tremulous and pitched at least an octave higher than these old things that I was tampering with now.

So I went back inside.

The chimes that I'd heard, not once or twice but three times, had seemed to come from somewhere behind me, but when I looked at my placement at the table I'd been sitting with my back to a thick internal wall. Sound bounces and does not always travel in straight lines, but even so there has to be a source – and as far as I could ascertain there was no source for the chimes that I had heard, which begged askance of the question – had anyone else heard those chimes or had it only been me? And indeed, had I really heard them at all or was it a flight of fancy? A flook and twist of the imagination?

I sat down and thought about it for a while, replaying the movie in my mind. I'd heard the chimes three times and had assumed that there had been some wind chimes within earshot. It had been a still silent night, no breezes, no sudden drafts and I had registered the sound as paranormal coincidence, imagining Anthony's spectral hand brushing the hollow pipes to create the faerie music. But even spectral hands cannot brush against earthly wind chimes if those wind chimes do not exist.

All of a sudden this seemed to be important. I checked my watch. Beth & Co. had been gone for thirty five minutes or so but it was still only eleven o'clock and while Messrs. Doubleday, Breck and Schiff might be settling down for the night, I was certain that Beth and Julian would still be up and awake.

Impulsively I pulled out my mobile and keyed in Beth's number. She answered immediately.

'You lot all right?' I asked.

'Yes, I think so,' she answered cautiously. 'They've all gone off to their respective rooms, but I think they're probably still awake. Why? Is anything wrong?'

'No, not really. I was just checking. How about you and Julian?'

'Yes I think we're okay...' That same hesitant tone.

'You only think so?'

'Well, I'm with Julian now, in the kitchen having some tea, and we've just been talking, and James I know this is going to sound a bit silly, but there's a bit of an odd atmosphere in the house that wasn't here earlier...' She trailed off lamely.

'Does Julian feel it too?' I wanted to know.

'Not as strongly as I do, but yes he does, but neither of us quite knows how to describe what we're feeling. It's sort of like a tension in the air...'

'I wouldn't worry about it too much,' I said reassuringly. After all, there were strangers in La Casa Blanca who would have brought their own energies with them, psychic or otherwise, and it was only natural that the house's vibration altered slightly to accommodate them. You know what it's like yourself – a friend or a couple of relatives come to stay for a weekend and for a while your home doesn't feel quite like your own home. After they've gone and you've waved them off at the door everything settles down to being the way it was before. That's what my reasoning mind said, anyway.

So cut to the chase. 'Beth, the reason I phoned is to ask you an odd little question... When you were talking earlier at the Anon, you know, when you were going on about The Hammond

Foundation and putting Mrs. Schiff in her place – well done, by the way – did you happen to hear anything unusual?'

'Like what?'

'If I tell you your objectivity will be impaired, so give me something off your own bat first. Just think back an hour, do a replay in your head and see if you can come up with something.'

'Umm, all right.' There was a short silence, and then – 'No, not really. I mean there was some back ground buzz from the kitchen area and there was some music filtering down from the bar, but I can't think of anything else.'

'Do you remember any wind chimes?' I asked lightly.

'Wind chimes? Umm, well yes, I think I did, actually a couple of times, I suppose. At least, as I say, I *think* I did. Why? What's significant about that?'

'Do me a favour,' I avoided answering her question. 'Just ask Julian if he heard any wind chimes.'

Beth: 'Julian, James wants to know if you heard any wind chimes back in the restaurant when I was making my little speech?'

Julian (in the distance): 'Wind chimes? No don't think so. Not that I can remember anyway.'

Beth: 'Julian says not.'

'Yeah, so I heard. But you're sure that you did, right?'

'Pretty sure, yes. Why?'

'Oh nothing important,' I sidestepped the issue. 'Anyway, look, you guys make sure you get a good nights sleep and I'll see you both very bright an early in the morning.'

So Beth thought she'd heard chimes but Julian was sure he hadn't. I'd have been happier if they'd both heard something or if neither of them had heard anything. No point in asking the mediums – that moment was lost. Bugger. I should have made a point of asking at the table while everyone was still present, shouldn't I? Of course I bloody well should, but that moment was lost as well!

I sat in the semi-darkness, hunched and brooding. I knew I had an early start the next day but I also knew that if I went to bed sleep would be elusive. There were too many thoughts banging around in my head and when I closed my eyes my mind filled up with bizarre and implausible images. Edith Schiff staring at a crystal ball which reflected pale blue numbers and saying "Vee haff vays of making you talk"... David Doubleday looking sweet and innocent and saying something like "No I didn't hear a wind chime, and what's a wind chime by the way?" Mandy Breck uncurling from a table covered with Tarot cards where she'd been doing a reading for Julian and telling him "Aaaah just lurve playin' around with Australians." The wind chimes tinkling away with Zander's voice singing along "The bells are ringing for me and my girl!" Julian and Beth holding hands in the moonlight with music from The King and I playing in the background and me singing "Hello young lovers, you're under arrest."

Then things got really spirally and as I viewed where I was within the framework of my own life, I started to slide down what my wife calls the "slippery slope" into an abyss of darkness. Too many issues, too many ifs and buts, and absolutely no "clairvoyant" vision of my own future. No, no, I didn't want to go there, not tonight or at any other time – although I knew there would come a time when I had to go there either wielding a sword or carrying an olive branch to sort out the ache in my chest and the cancer in my soul.

Enough.

I snapped my eyes open and went up into the bar. Gabriel was still serving a few late customers and although there were a few familiar faces I wasn't in the mood for company or conversation so I took a drink out on to the terrace and leaned on the parapet looking out over the roof tops of the settling village. It was an odd kind of night, very dark, no moon and few stars, cool, but absolutely still with no breeze. I turned up the collar of my jacket and shivered; I wasn't really cold, but I still felt uncomfortable within myself. The tension that Beth had described as being present in La Casa Blanca seemed to wrap itself around me, tilting the village of Jimena slightly out of focus and making it feel like an alien place. Not exactly hostile, neither was it friendly, just dark and sentient, waiting for wheels to turn and cogs to fall into place. Lovers would have found no sweet repose in the pueblo's streets this night for it was a night wherein the shadows were too dark and dangerous and that other kind of secret tryst held sway – the sort which are full of conspiracy and where whispered conversations fall just below the threshold of human hearing.

I leaned out over the parapet of the balcony. Below me was a narrow cobbled alley that climbed up to the right and connected with the bottom of Calle Granadillos, which in turn struggled upwards at increasingly difficult angles towards the castle. Down to the left the alleyway connected with Calle Consuelo which linked the high barrio of the village with the lower part; another wickedly steep hill that demanded its price from residents and visitors alike. Little wonder so many of the elderly population had problems with their feet and with their backs, for living in an Andalucian hill village exacts a high physical toll on the human body once you get past a certain age. And yet many feet must have trampled these tortuous streets for twenty five hundred years and longer, for there has always been a Jimena. Before the Romans there had been the Iberians, and after the Romans there had been the Christians and then the Moors and then the Christians again until both cultures had finally mixed into the single bloodline of Al Andaluz. Generation upon generation had made their home in Jimena, for he who controlled the village controlled the trade routes from the coast up into the Spanish interior and no advancing or retreating army could move with impunity with the Jimenato thorn in its side.

So Jimena certainly had its ancient history, and no less dramatic was its modern history, for it had suffered a bloody civil war, the subtle scars of which still remained, and if not in the architecture, then in the psyche and distant memory of its people. Jimena was an old place, its history striated in the bedrock of its foundations, and as such it emanated its own vibration of power and sentient awareness, not unlike Glastonbury in the UK or, albeit on a grander scale, Karnak in Egypt. It was a Geminesque energy, sometimes bright, delightful, filled with the balm of laughter and the soothing essence of healing; but just like the mask of Janus, this place had its other darker, more mysterious and much less obvious side that was not all sweetness and light. This darker side seldom touched the transient tourist and very rarely would any Jimenato admit to its existence, although it dwelt deeply within the collective psyche and subconscious. But for the educated spirit that stayed a while, touched tasted and pushed and probed, the pagan magick made itself felt beneath the pale veneer of Catholicism.

I was suddenly reminded of Edith's Schiff's words – "my greatest humiliation in life and also my greatest triumph" – and her words made a connection, for so it was with me and this place called Jimena de la Frontera; it had been in this village fifteen years earlier that I had experienced my greatest humiliation and also my greatest triumph. Perhaps that was why these narrow streets carried such a

165

weight of importance within my consciousness; perhaps this was why there was such a magnetism that drew me ever back like an elasticated umbilical cord, not wanting to let me go or pass beyond that one moment in my life when, instead of running from the battle and the challenge, I'd met it full face on, had fought hard – and had won!

Anthony Zander had chosen a very good place to die. Although nothing more than a pin prick in the map of southern Spain, Jimena was an epicenter of a spiritual tornado that moved you on a breaking wave of self knowledge from Alpha to Omega. Stonehenge may be nothing more than a pin prick on the map of southern England, but the psychic presence of those standing stones reverberates around the whole of the British Isles. You don't always find your answers in places like Stonehenge and Jimena, but if you pause and can learn to be still, you do begin to discover the nature of some of the questions you should be asking.

I finished my drink and went back to my room – had a quick wash and cleaned my teeth, then rather than getting into bed, stretched out fully clothed, clasped my hands behind my head and stared up at the ceiling willing sleep to take me as and when it would, not caring too much one way or the other whether it did or whether it didn't. It was seven minutes to midnight and I reckoned my phone would be ringing before one a.m.

The text bleep shrilled at five minutes to one. RU UP it said in the new cyberspeak that was inexorably replacing the English language. I didn't bother texting back. I just rang the number.

'Hi Julian. What's up?'

He sounded cagey. 'Sorry to disturb you, mate – were you asleep?'

'No.'

'It's just that there's some weird shit going on down here and both Beth and I kind of wondered...'

'What kind of weird?'

'It won't sound much if I tell you over the phone but quite honestly, Mr. C, we're a little bit spooked, so...'

'All right, I'm on my way.'

'Thanks a lot mate,' he sounded relieved. 'See you when you get here. We'll put some coffee on.'

'Fine. Just make sure that Beth makes it.'

I got up off the bed and threw a few things together – tooth brush and clean underwear – then made my exit through the old hotel. Gabriel sat in the little office adjacent to the front door, cashing up for the night. He looked up with a raised eyebrow.

'There is a problem?'

'No, not with me,' I explained. 'But with some friends in the village.'

'You will be back later? You have a door key?'

'Yes, I've got a key, but I don't think I'll be back later.'

'Okay, buenas noches Señor.'

I drove through a very silent and totally deserted Jimena. No soul stirred, no dog barked. Christmas was only three days away and by some tacit and unspoken communal agreement, the Jimenatos were getting in a few early nights before the festive season began. From the moment the bars and restaurants opened on the morning of December 24th there would be a constant round of parties and family gatherings that would go on more or less without respite until the end of the Three Kings festival on January 6th. For now the Christmas lights and decorations that adorned every street and square cast deep shadows that seemed rather more threatening than festive. A sense of tension increased as I drove down the long winding hill past the Guardia Civil barracks and on towards the iron bridge, for now the lights receded and the night became darker and even less hospitable. The Seat's headlights cut a swathe forwards, but where the night encroached at the periphery of the beams, the blackness was positively stygian. Pockets of mist drifted across the Hozgarganta and eddied up through the trees and over the reeds to obliterate the narrow camino. It was all vaguely reminiscent of a scene out of an old Hammer horror movie, and while part of me wanted to break out in a fit of giggles, there was another less cheerful part of me that was becoming just a little bit cold sweaty. I wondered what the problem was at La Casa Blanca. Weird and spooked were evocative words, but meaningless when used out of context. If the context was a pitch black night with wraithlike entrails of mist and a feeling of inner emptiness in the solar plexus, then weird and spooked started to make a lot of sense.

By the time I reached La Casa Blanca the mist had eddied out apart from a few lingering wisps that clung to the reeds. Turning into the short drive I could see that a lot of the lights were on – and that Julian and Beth were standing out on the verandah waiting to greet me. Parking in my usual spot next to the Jeep, I cut the engine and climbed out into cool, and down here by the river, rather damp night.

'Okay you two, what's happening?'

In partial answer Beth threw her arms around me neck and gave me a massive hug and a big kiss on the cheek. 'Oh James, thank you so much for coming!'

Julian slapped me on the back. 'Good on you Mr. C.'

It was nice to feel welcome and wanted, no matter what the circumstances. But I still needed to find out what those circumstances were. So I asked again – what was going on?

'Better come on inside Mr. C, then you can tell us!'

'Beth?' I asked

'I don't know James, I really don't, but like Julian says, just come in to the house and walk around a bit and tell us if we're imagining things.'

Okay, that was fair enough, so with most of my objectivity intact, I walked into La Casa Blanca – and I felt it straight away.

Felt what?

Ah well, there are only so many words within the framework of the English language and even the finest wordsmith in the world would be hard pressed to string any of them together coherently to

168

describe the brisance of tension that seemed to hang in the very air. It was a sparkling and tingling thing that you couldn't see, but you could certainly feel it brushing against the skin of your face and around your hands, and in a different dimension, you could sense it, lightly touching the outer synapses of the mind. Therefore whatever this was, it was working on two distinctly different levels, both the mental and the physical. Neither Julian nor Beth had told me what to expect, and as I was obviously experiencing what they had been experiencing, there was an independent three-way corroboration of the fact that something was happening within the confines of La Casa Blanca.

As I moved slowly through the house, the energy subtlety changed.... It was particularly strong in the reception lounge, Zander's interview room and also in his bedroom. It was pleasantly powerful in Beth's study-cum-office, but less tangible in her bedroom and also in Julian's bedroom. In the kitchen there was but the faintest trace and in the corridor that contained Miguel and Maria's room and the guest bedrooms that contained our three clairvoyant guests, it was virtually none existent.

This in itself was interesting, for logically one might have expected the epicenter of this strange energy to emanate from the mediums' quarters, especially if it was one of the mediums (two of them or all of them) who were indirectly the cause of the phenomenon. By virtue of the fact that this was where the psychic palpitation was at its weakest there was an obvious conclusion to arrive at. Although this energy might have been sparked by the mediums' presence in the house, it did not come directly from them but from an external source: the greatest concentration of energy was balanced between Zander's bedroom and Beth's study, and therefore it seemed logical to assume that this was an energy directed specifically towards Beth and Julian and for their benefit. Of the source and cause one could only speculate, but my best guess was that it came directly from their father.

As I came towards the end of the grand tour a huge grin began to spread across my face and there was that familiar sting of salt moisture behind the eyes with the ever present lump in my throat. This energy was lifting and enervating, it was light, lovely and beautiful and it made me want to laugh out loud with sheer delight.

'James what is this?' Beth asked with a note of anxiety in her voice. 'We've been half scared to death and you arrive and walk around grinning like the Cheshire cat that's just fallen into a vat of cream and swallowed a canary.'

'Can I assume,' we were back in the kitchen now, 'that all three of us are aware of this tingling sort of "we're being watched" atmosphere?'

'Oh yeah Mr. C, we're aware of it all right and I'm damn glad to learn that you're aware of it too, because for a while back there I thought it was just us!' Julian sounded positively relieved. 'If you hadn't arrived I was going to wake up one of our mates in the guest wing!'

'All this is,' I said comfortingly, 'is your father popping in to say hello. He's probably excited about what's going to start happening tomorrow and he's impatient for it to begin.'

'Are you sure?' Beth didn't sound too sure herself.

'Look, Beth, don't be afraid of this... Just reach out with your mind and think a minute. Does this atmosphere seem in any way threatening or dangerous?'

'Well no, not really, but I've never felt anything like this before. And neither has Julian.'

'You've never lost a father before,' I said as gently as I could, 'and we're all a bit scared about things we don't know anything about. Listen up the pair of you, I promise you there is nothing nasty or negative happening here. Quite the reverse, this is absolutely fantastic!'

'There's some other stuff Mr. C.' Julian cast a glance at Beth, and then looked back at me a bit sheepishly. 'There's been some problem with the lights. Here in the kitchen but more so in the lounge and Anthony's bedroom. They keep flicking on and off – all by themselves.'

He sounded so serious and worried, and I just couldn't help myself. I burst into a peel of laughter – but neither Julian nor Beth saw the humour and Julian glowered at me, assuming I was laughing at him.

'Look, let's have some coffee,' I suggested, looking at Beth hopefully, 'and I'll try to explain a bit how this works.'

This was where the experience with my clairvoyant friends stood me in good stead. Times without number people like Harry Andrews and Ossie Rae had encountered situations wherein house lights, and for that matter a load of other electrical appliances, seemed to be controlled by unseen hands. Always, without fail, they attributed this to a visiting spirit attempting to make contact. This is not so far fetched as it sounds, for in truth some very serious research has gone into this phenomena; the theory being that whatever constitutes spirit, it is in part made up from some sort of electrical energy, or at least carries with it some element of electrical discharge. Therefore it seems entirely logical, even if the science is a bit weak through lack of hard data, that a spiritual electrical discharge could quite easily have an interactive effect on a temporal electrical discharge. On a purely personal level, I've been interviewed half a dozen times over the years for this or that radio and TV show, and on at least half those occasions there have been malfunctions with various bits of electrical equipment which have left technicians scratching their heads and muttering curses under their breath along the lines of "well nothing like *this* has ever happened before!" Spirits and electricity may go hand in hand but clairvoyants and electricity usually don't.

I remembered and recounted the tale of a mate of mine called Mick Reed who had been booked to provide an evening of clairvoyance in a well known York venue. He'd walked out on to the small stage, and had said 'Good evening ladies and gentlemen...' and the fire alarm had gone off. Not a nicely ringing little bell, but a honking great klaxon! The bar manager had flipped the switch and re-set the alarm, and again Mick had tried to start his evening. 'Good evening ladies and gentlemen...' and the klaxon had blasted across the room for a second time making it impossible for Mick to make himself heard. Again the bar manager had tripped the switch, and suspecting possible sabotage, I'd moved to the back of the bar area to make sure nobody was playing silly buggers. Mick had tried a third time, and a fourth time, and a fifth time to get started, but he never once got past "ladies and gentlemen" before that damned klaxon drowned him out. The audience thought that this was all quite hilarious and were rocking in the aisles with mirth while Mick, stoic Geordie that he was, battled on calmly waiting for the problem to sort itself out, which it did on the sixth attempt to start the demonstration. I was there and I can tell you that no temporal finger triggered that alarm and Mick would tell you the same thing himself!

I explained all this to Beth and Julian as best I could but they still didn't seem totally convinced. Again they exchanged that secretive glance that I'd noticed on more than one occasion now, and then, quite out of context Beth said:

'Julian, go and see if it's still there, will you?"

If what was still where?

'Yeah, right,' Julian nodded and marched out of the kitchen door.

'Where's he off to?' I asked, perplexed.

'Be patient James. He's just gone to check something.'

Julian returned within fifteen seconds. 'Yep,' he confirmed. 'It's still there!'

'In that case,' this was Beth addressing me, 'James, you'd better come and have a look at this!'

'Okay, lay on MacDuff. You lead and I'll follow.'

We exited the kitchen and presumably retraced Julian's footsteps along the side of the house until we came to the back lot with the copse of trees – which, of course, was where we had buried Zander three days before.

Immediately I could see the cause of their nervousness. Sitting in the little dell between the two Spanish oaks and hovering just above the mound of earth that was Zander's grave, there was a thick layer of mist. Pale, opaque and unmoving other than in minute eddies caused by inconsistencies in the atmosphere, in its own right it created a startling effect and with the connotation of its location it was, I suppose, enough to send the shivers up anyone's spine.

'Have you been out of the house and upon along the river in the last few hours?' I asked, and when they shook their heads and replied in the negative, I told them that I'd just driven down the camino from Jimena and that there were at least a score of mist patches just the same as this between the iron bridge and La Casa Blanca.

'It frequently happens like this on a still night after a hot day. The lights going on and off in the house and that lovely atmosphere that met me when I walked in, well, I'll lay that at your father's door, but as for this little patch of mist, this is just Old Mother Nature doing her thing. Now come on back into the house the pair of you, and let's see if that coffee is ready yet.'

When we went back into the kitchen the coffee was just about perking – and the tingling sensitive atmosphere was all but gone. Nothing more than a trace memory in the ether. And with the absence of that energy, perhaps combined with my few words of reassurance, Beth and Julian began to relax. We took the coffee pot through into Beth's study, which as far as I was concerned was the softest and most homely room in the house. It was now pushing two o'clock in the morning, but nobody, least of all me, seemed in the least bit tired. We put on some music, Samuel Barber's gorgeous Adagio, and just sat talking until the big hand was on the twelve and the little hand was on the four. Beth and I smoked by the small log fire and Julian sat by the open window; there was a welcoming atmosphere of camaraderie, and as Zander's children talked ever more openly about their lives and different experiences, I felt a gently pervasive sense of peace and place.

These two people had become, and whatever happened, would always remain very important to me. I felt the emotion of love for them, and it was that gentle unassuming unconditional love that I had found so very hard to understand as a younger man. In reciprocation there was a deep sense of satisfaction born of the knowledge that I had been accepted by them and that I had their trust, their respect and their affection. Perhaps their affection was not that important, although it meant a lot to me, but their trust and their respect counted for a lot at a time in my life when other people who knew far me better were doubting my trustworthiness and my integrity. Right then, in that duende moment of being "part of" Beth and Julian could have asked me any favour, set me any task, and I would have denied them nothing.

Around four o'clock we called it a night. We talked very briefly about the format of the following day – the same day really but later on – then Julian and Beth departed for their separate bedrooms and I stretched out on the chesterfield in front of the fire's last dying embers. Sleep didn't come all that easily. I'd drunk a lot of coffee, but on top of that my mind was full of clashing thoughts and ideas. It was clear from their reaction to the early phenomena that neither Beth nor Julian had had very much first hand experience of practical spiritualism: I knew this to be true of Julian but was a bit surprised that Beth had been so spooked by a few lights going on and off and by an "atmosphere" which in all truth had been totally benign and suffused with so much love. All right, there had also been that mischievous patch of mist, but even so, it had been natural and explicable, and I would have expected common sense and reason to have overcome any initial jitters...

...Which, of course, was easy for me to say, and also somewhat hypocritical, for there had been too many times in the past when I

173

had been unnerved by a lot less than anything that had happened thus far at La Casa Blanca!

Like most psychics I am very susceptible to any kind of atmosphere and there have been a few instances when I have walked away and backed off very mega quickly when I've come across something I haven't liked. Scaredy Cat Christie running a fast mile away from things that go bump in the night – yes, well maybe, but we'd all do well to remember that there are some things that go bump very nicely and other things that go bump very nastily and until you know which bump you're dealing with it's better back off and be on the safe side! To function as a psychic, even on the most basic level, one has to have some degree of imagination and as any artist or suspicious lover will tell you, imagination can be the greatest gift or the darkest curse.

My mind turned to the following day. This would be the day that Zander's experiment would begin, and damn it all, I was excited about that. I was excited too by the prospect of putting our three mediums to the test, for despite Beth's placating words in the restaurant, although not on trial, they were to be tested, and the results would separate the psychics from the clairvoyants. I knew that I wouldn't be able to prove it but I felt certain that Zander would be there, waiting to come through: in my opinion he'd already made his presence felt in La Casa Blanca, and it had been a beautiful presence.

Sleep snuck up on me eventually, and my last waking thought was about wind chimes. La Casa Blanca had lots of wind chimes dotted around the house, in the main reception room, in the master bedroom, out on the patio and along the verandah. There was even a wind chime here in Beth's study. I suspected that I could brush against any one of them and that I would hear the same tinkling chimes that I had heard a few hours before in El Anon.

Many of us have an entirely false image of ourselves. In my own mind's eye I see myself as being stocky and compact with a wise face and warm compassionate eyes. In reality I'm a fat little man with a crumpled physiogamy partially concealed by a whiskery beard and moustache, and my eyes, rather than being warm and compassionate, tend to blink more on the myopic watery side of tiredness.

I will sometimes see myself as dark and mysterious, which is a pretense; an act designed to cover self doubt and uncertainty. Occasionally I think I am the life and soul of the party, full of spontaneity and humour, and usually this is when I'm a little bit drunk, totally tactless, and hell bent on telling the same jokes I've been telling for the last twenty odd years or more. Sometimes I see myself as the loner, and that part of my self assessment is correct for I have always been forced apart from the crowd, ever since the scarring horror of my schooldays when the educational authorities were insistent upon forcing a square peg into a round hole. Personally, I've always enjoyed playing with the team, but over the years there haven't been many teams that have wanted me playing on their side – the fat kid at school, last to be chosen, with this sad trend carrying on through teens and into adulthood.

One thing I have never seen myself as being is The Leader. It has always been so much easier to be the follower. Sometimes the counselor, sometimes the court jester, but never the king. Occasionally you get thrust into a role that you do not play naturally well, and so it was with my role as director of experiments pp Zander, Boyd and Hammond. Beth should have done it, but felt that she couldn't. Although I would have preferred not to have been pushed into the position, I *could* do it – so I ended up doing it.

On the morning of December 22nd I gave two briefings, one before breakfast exclusively to Beth and Julian, and one after breakfast to the three readers.

To Julian and Beth: 'Part one of Anthony's experiment means us each having a reading from each of the three clairvoyants, and whatever you do, do not give away any information. Don't react to anything they say, don't tell them anything, don't deny or confirm anything. They have to work stone cold. If they ask you a direct question – which they probably won't after I've talked to them later on – just smile and shake your head. At the end of each session, when they've shot their bolt, just thank 'em very much, but still keep quiet. We'll assess what they've had to tell us later on, and compare notes from the tape recordings.'

After Maria and Miguel had served a light breakfast it was time to tackle our three guests. As we sat around the kitchen table drinking coffee, apart from Edith who had asked for tea (not Vodka, thank God!) I put my professional hat on and made my pitch.

'Well, I'd just like to say that I hope you all had a good night's sleep and I'd like to set out a tentative programme for today. We've put together a plan whereby over the day each of you will do a reading for each of us. That means you'll have three readings to do, and we thought we'd keep the pace and tempo nice and easy with one reading in the morning, one reading in the afternoon and one reading in the early evening. We'll have a break for lunch and a stroll along the river, and this evening we can either dine in the village as we did last night or we can have something here, whichever you would prefer.

'Now I do need to emphasise something that Elizabeth mentioned last night and say again that you and your individual skills and talents are not being tested in these experiments,'.... well that remained to be seen! 'but because the whole aspect of clairvoyance and mediumship is, if you like, being put under the microscope, we do need to impose some gentle conditions. One is that neither Elizabeth, Julian nor myself is allowed to give you any information or help you in any way, and the other point, which I need hardly mention because I know you wouldn't do it anyway...' like hell they wouldn't! '...is that I have to ask you to regard each reading with the utmost confidentiality and not to discuss the readings with each other until the experiment has been formally concluded. I hope that will be all right for you?'

There were nods of agreement and acquiescence and I was aware of David DD staring at me quite intently. Was he now putting two and two together?

'We have,' I rounded things off, 'put a special room to one side for the readings, although if any of you feel uncomfortable in that room, you are welcome to choose your own space, and I do need to tell you that the readings will be openly tape recorded. I hope no one has a problem with that?'

And I said it in such a way as to make it abundantly clear that if anyone did have a problem with that then they were going to have a problem. Most clairvoyants and psychics do not have and should not have any problem committing their words to tape for the sake of reference and referral. Those that do have a problem are either the fakes or the phonies or they are the few who are so much up their own backsides with their own sense of self importance that they don't think their clients are worth this small consideration.

'I do not mind haffing my vords recorded,' Edith said, 'but I haff not got a tape recorder.'

'Oh please don't worry,' I said as sweetly as I could. 'We have several.'

'Oh Ah always use a tape recorder for mah readings,' Mandy exclaimed brightly.

'Yes me too,' said David.

Yeah I thought. I'll bet, but only when the cameras were in focus.

The room that we had set aside for the sittings and the séances was the reception room in which I had first met Zander. We had placed a fair sized round table in the middle of the room with two opposing chairs; on the table itself there were a couple of pale blue candles in delicate glass holders, and a small posy of fresh flowers. Also, slightly to one side there was a smart new table top tape recorder.

In one sense the room was bright and cheerful while in another is still contained the ethos of Anthony Zander's presence. Everything was brilliantly clean and there was a quality of peacefulness and calm. And yet, to tell the truth, there wasn't much energy.

A couple of months previously I had been visiting the Arthur Findley College at Stanstead Hall in Essex, which is the home of the British Spiritual movement. I'd been attending a memorial service for the great English medium, Doris Collins. My host for the day had been the indefatigable Eric Hatton who had given me a lightening (and I suspect illicit) tour of the building. One room had stuck out in my memory; a long high vaulted lounge, softly lit and sparsely furnished. In fact, the only furniture had been a small round table covered by a plain white cloth with two high backed chairs facing each other. This was set in a very generous bay window, on a small dais raised a couple of inches above the rest of the room. Above the table there had been a highly hung and very old chandelier.

From fully twenty feet away that table and the empty space above it literally hummed with raw expectant energy. It was here, I realized, that most of the hard hands on work at Stanstead Hall would be done. This wasn't just a séance table it was a portal between two worlds and...

'We have to go, I'm afraid,' Mr. Hatton had called from the doorway, and with deep regret I'd turned away from the object of my attention. Damn it, I'd wanted to sit at that table, reach out and make contact with ambassadors from an afterlife...

Our table at La Casa Blanca looked attractive enough, but was completely devoid of that Stanstead Hall vibration. I had a gut feeling that this room was not the right place to conduct the sittings, but this was the room that Zander had specified, and this was the room that Beth and Julian had set up. So, we'd go with it. At least to start things off.

We didn't exactly draw lots. It was more of a hasty thrash out in the kitchen. Beth would start the day with a reading from David, Julian would follow her in with Mandy, and I would follow on with Edith. In the afternoon I'd have Mandy, Julian would have David, and Beth would go with Edith. In the early evening I'd have David, Beth would have Mandy, and Julian would be at the mercy of Frau Schiff.

We'd scheduled one hour per reading per person and reckoned that this should give everyone plenty of free time; there wouldn't be any pressure, and the day, thank God, was bright and blue and pleasantly warm so if people wanted to sun themselves on the terrace or take a walk along the river bank they could do so without becoming housebound or bored. Miguel and Maria would provide a buffet table from one o'clock onwards and people could help themselves to whatever they wanted whenever they wanted it. By tacit agreement we agreed that we would not discuss the contents of the individual readings until we got together at the end of the day.

During the first part of the morning I busied myself reading through the files and PR material appertaining to the mediums, trying to memorise as much as I could, and almost before I knew it, the day was climbing towards noon and my appointment with Edith Schiff.

I found her sitting in the reception room leafing through a Spanish magazine. We were still ten minutes early but she informed me "zat the ozzers haff finished" so we went straight through into the reading room.

Here in the last two hours David had read Beth and Mandy had read Julian, but the room was still open and calm with no trace of residual energy one way or the other. Edith and I sat at the table.

'I vant to smoke,' she announced, 'so eisser ve go somevhere vhere ve can haff cigarettes or you find me an ash tray, and zen ve do some vork together, Jah?'

Julian would do his nut, but the easiest thing to do was to find her an ashtray – and of course, it also meant I could smoke my pipe. Out of deference to Mr. Boyd I did open the French windows half a foot and was rewarded by a gentle breath of oleander – and the lyrical tinkling of a wind chime! I'm not sure if Edith Schiff registered that wind chime but I sure as hell did. Either the breeze was in the right direction or Anthony Zander was standing by waiting to come through.

The old lady sat stiffly in her chair. She smoked one of her Caporals while I fiddled with the tape recorder. Then stubbing the cigarette out she closed her eyes and reached forward and took both of my hands. Her breathing slowed to a regular but very shallow pattern. The seconds ticked away and became minutes, and then...

'I haff lady, very old, sitting on garden bench surrounded by red flowers. She is dead many years and I sink she is Grandmother. Mother's mother not father's mother. She says nothing but vatches you viz great love and kindness. She is calling your name but is not your name. Your name, I know, is James, but she is calling you "Kitten" or somezink like zhat. Zis lady has two names but I don't zink I know vhat zey are but zey sound like Elsa...? Jah, Elsa, Elsa, Elsa, but I get nozzing else except she is telling me zis is a very good name for some reason and zere is a connection viz Malta?

'Now zere is a very fat man sitting in a caravan. I zink zis iz ze kind of man who prefers ze company of ozzer men, razzer than ze company of vomen. Zis man has zick dark hair and his teeth are very very white. Zis man has died also many many years, and now Christmas is important anniversary. Zis man vork in ze theatre, but also very powerful working wiz vorld of spirits. Zis makes sense to you please? He cooks somezink and zen he dies...Zer man has name like Osvald and he vants you to know zat vhenever you vork

179

on zer stage he stands by you even vhen zhere is only small audience of von person. Can you tell me zis is true, yes or no?"

We had the rules in place, but rules are sometimes made to be broken and this Swiss psychic was blowing me away. 'I'm not supposed to help you,' I said quietly, 'but so far all you have told me is correct.'

'Good,' she chuckled without opening her eyes. 'Von day I make a good medium, jah? Okay now ve vait, ve vait... and Jah here is a man who has died in a motor car... No...Nein!' she interrupted herself. 'He has not died in ze car but has been crashed and injured badly in ze car and is taken to ze hospital vhere he fights so hard to live because he did not vant to die... Zhere are two or zree hours vhile doctors fight very hard to save zis man but is too late and injuries too severe, and if zis man had lived he vould have been... ah... jah, had zis man lived very much damage to bose head and body. Zis man not related to you, but is goot friend and I zink you miss him much. He has great humour...' Edith cackled joyfully. 'Jah, very naughty man viz great humour. Names.... Names.... You vill vant names for proof, so name von is Sam and name two is John and name zree I cannot get but maybe has somezink to do viz salt? Zer man has message vhich is simple. He says to zank you for your friendship... And also be careful viz ze number 340... You understand, please, James?'

'Yes,' I croaked through the lump in my throat and the tears in my eyes.

'Goot, goot, now please to be calm, somevone else vaiting to come through, so ve vait, ve vait, ve vait...'

Outside the wind chimes tinkled and my spirits lifted like a rocket to the moon. For God's sake, it was going to happen. Zander was going to come through!

'I haff voman here who zings songs and valks viz a bad bad limp.' My heart fell through my bowels with a chill of arctic ice. 'She is fat lady viz black hair, who does not zink you vill expect to hear from her or zat you vill vant to talk vis her but she is here anyvay to send you her love and to say she is sorry about saying she vanted to hunt you... Nein nein nein, not hunt you, *haunt* you! Zer lady says her name is Joy or maybe she zays her name means Joy, and also she zays she is your mozzer who has died vhen you vere gone somevhere. I zink zis lady and you not alvays goot friends, but truce is, zis lady teaches you many many zings and even now she is zere for you if you should need her.... Also she says she vas very afraid to die but as soon as ze actual moment came everyzink vas all right and now she is safe viz Jesus... Now ve vait, ve vait, ve vait...'

We vaited, sorry, waited, but nothing else came through, which was just as well because by then cynical Mr. Tough Guy Know It All James Christie was pretty well emotionally wrecked.

This had been a devastatingly accurate reading, and although no mention had been made of Zander, Edith Schiff had proven her worth as a medium beyond reproach. Everything that she had told me had been pertinent and relevant. She had connected with my Grandmother, who always in my mind's eye, I saw sitting surrounded by wallflowers. My Grandmother's name was Elsie Maud Elsiegood, and Edith's multiple "Elsa's" were good enough for me on that count, and if Elsie Maud thought that her name was a good name, then who were we to gainsay her? Malta, of course, was meaningless, but Malton, which was very close phonetically, was meaningful in the extreme. I had been born in Malton, over in the east riding of Yorkshire and during the first few years of my life, while my mother had been on the road with her show business career, my grandmother had functioned in loco parenthis. The name "Kitten" was meaningless, but Kit was a familiar family nickname and my grandmother would frequently turn this into "Kitta" if she was feeling particularly sentimental.

The fat man in the caravan needed no introduction. She had been describing Ossie Rae, even down to his sexual preferences, who had earned his living partly as a drag artist and partly (and much more importantly) as a spiritualist medium. In fact Ossie was the greatest medium I'd ever known and in the early years of my exploration into the occult world, he had been my guide and mentor. Ossie had indeed had thick black wavy hair, but didn't have a tooth to call his own in his mouth. What he did have was a set of brilliant white dentures that he only ever wore on stage, and they were so whiter than white that they positively shone like beacons across the footlights.

Once, when I was very young, still at school, I remember, we were doing a pantomime in a Godforsaken little theatre in Bishop Auckland. Nobody had any money, we hadn't been paid, the panto wasn't due to open until Boxing Day. To save cash the cast of the show had camped out in the dressing rooms over Christmas, and I recall Ossie trying to cook a Co-op Christmas pudding over three candles.

He'd been at it for more than an hour, when in total exasperation he'd exclaimed "I'll go to my bloody death cooking Christmas pudding!" – and twenty years later to the day, that's exactly what he did do. He'd been cooking the pud in his delightful new home in Ferrybridge, and half way through the procedure, had collapsed with a stroke. He'd been dead by the time they got him to the nearest hospital, and thus his own prophesy had come melodramatically true. As a man who breathed the fragrance of tabs and greasepaint it was logical that he should be with me whenever I walked on to a stage, and even when I had an audience of only one person (in a reading situation) it was even more logical that he should be sitting there watching over my words. If it hadn't been for him I would never have set foot in the world of spiritualism.

The guy who had died as a result of a dreadful car crash (on Spain's notoriously dangerous N340) had been Sam... Christened John, but known as Sam. His last name was Sellers, and although I was reaching for it a bit, the last time I looked you did keep salt in salt sellers. Truly, Sam had not died in the crash, and although his medical team had fought like hell to save him, he passed from this life on the operating table. Later, the surgeon had told his grieving widow that if Sam had survived the crash he would have been in a wheelchair, paralysed from the neck down, with the grave possibility of brain damage to boot. Sam was a rakish rogue with a joie de vivre par excellence, a wicked wicked sense of humour, and a man of great physicality. In a wheelchair he would have been a member of the living dead. This man and I had been good friends, and Edith was right, I missed him terribly. He was a man with the great gift of laughter: he could walk into a wake of Jehovah's Witnesses and within five minutes would been telling jokes, cracking great ice packs of reserve and bringing even the most conservative and austere of gatherings to fits of joviality and humour.

Edith's coup de' etat, however, was in bringing my mother through in this reading. She was indeed the archetypal fat lady of the theatre who sang for her supper – in her hey day the soprano who could shatter the wine glass with a sustained top E above C. And Edith had been dead right, I had not expected to hear from her and had no desire to talk to her on either side of the grave. My mother's name was Joyce, not Joy, and after a very bad car crash in the 1950's when the surgeons at Barnet hospital had virtually rebuilt her ankle with steel plates, she'd always walked with a pronounced limp. Up until being about fourteen I'd worshipped my mother as much as, and indeed if not more than most sons loved their mothers, but after that everything had started turning increasingly sour.

Here was a woman who had taught me to independent since the day that I was born and the moment I had begun to exercise that independence she had striven to restrict and control it. True enough, she had taught me many things – how to stand on my own two feet and how to act the part of confidence even if I wasn't feeling it, but she also taught me elitism – *Dahling just remember that there are only two kinds of people in the world! There are people like us who are the performers and there are other people who pay to come and see us perform* – and my God, it had taken me half a lifetime to unlearn that dangerous and destructive lesson, by which time I had paid a very high price for the benefit of my mother's teachings. The other thing she was responsible for, although to give her her due she might not have been consciously aware of what she was doing, was to instill in me the deeply rooted psychological thought that women who bring love into your life always end up leaving you in pursuit of their own emotional needs and agendas. When you've outlived your usefulness your ejection from a loved one's life is always so easily justifiable.

Throughout my late teens and twenties I did my best to get along with the lady, but as I moved into my thirties she moved into her sixties and the first subtle signs of Alzheimer's began making their presence felt in many tiny little ways, unnoticeable at the time, but recognizable for what they were a dozen years later with the benefit of retrospect and hindsight.

The "haunting" that Edith had mentioned was specific to the last great argument between mother and son. The mother was not getting her own way and in a rage of vexation threw a bowl of cornflakes at the son, missing his head by inches and showering him with milk and bits of cereal. "You're not supposed to do what you want to do, you're supposed to be here when I need you! I only ever had you so I wouldn't be lonely in my old age!"

Yes she actually said that and there wasn't anything that the son had wanted to say in return. So he'd turned and made towards the door and his last sad exit from his mother's house – and life.

"You come back," the stricken mother had howled after him. "...Or I promise you that as soon as I'm dead I'll come back and haunt your every waking moment."

I didn't know whether or not she'd succeeded in that ambition, but there were times when I knew she'd tried. She'd died in 1989, lonely, fragile and scared, and ever successful in making me feel guilty. And that made me feel angry for in my deepest heart of hearts I knew that I had nothing to feel guilty about.

So we waited.

There were no further spiritual links but Edith did have some observations to make. 'I zink you are a very complicated man. Many different jobs and careers. You are in ze theatre vonce as musician or actor or both, you make pictures and you write vords in books and poems, and right now you do not know vhat shall happen next vis your life. Many problems, many qvestions, many doubts, many vorries about ze heart and ze mind. Zo, I tell you, not to vorry. Everyzing is taken take of. You understand?'

No I did not understand but by then my elastic was pretty well stretched so I simply nodded in agreement, happy to take her word for it. I escorted her into the kitchen and thanked her very much for her efforts on my behalf. I made her a pot of tea, then took myself off for a walk, not down by the river where I was in danger of bumping into someone, but up the mountain at the back of the house where I managed to get lost among the boulders and buttresses of rock.

Found a spot in the sunshine.

Sat down.

Lit a pipe and let my mind wander back over the past forty or fifty minutes. Then let it wander back over the past forty five years.

Many people flock to clairvoyant demonstrations in the desperate hope of a message from a loved one. They may have lost a beloved mother, a revered father, an adored child or a worshipped wife or husband. They will sit in a crowded hall or theatre hanging on to the name and thought form of the person they most want to hear from. Frequently they will cry when they get a message and they usually feel like crying when they don't.

I've often joked that I have never had a message from the other side because I am the least likely candidate to receive one. In truth, I have never lost anyone who has been that close to me. Certainly my Grandmother, Ossie and Sam were of some seminal importance in my history, as indeed had been my mother and a couple of other friends who hadn't made it to middle age before the ferryman had demanded his coin. But in no case had there been that passionate bond of love that facilitated spiritual contact in the first instance – or that would make me want to hear from them anyway. Therefore I found it hard to believe that any of them would want to communicate with me.

And yet Edith Schiff had forged those four links and although I suppose she could have pulled in something from a couple of long departed uncles and although she could possibly have pulled something in from Garth Odell, she'd gone for the strongest bonds that she could find, even if those strong bonds were relatively weak. But here was the anomaly! I had wanted to hear from Anthony Zander, and more than anyone else, he had been uppermost in my thoughts. From Anthony, however, there hadn't been so much as a murmour, and thus in proving her credentials as a clairvoyant Edith had scored ten out of ten but in proving that Anthony Zander had survived death, she had scored a big zilchy zero.

Mandy Breck sat me down at the table which she had covered with a deep red velvet cloth. Each corner of the cloth was weighted down by a different piece of crystal... Top left, amethyst, top right, clear quartz. Bottom right, rose quartz, and citrine at the bottom left. They were lovely pieces, quite beautiful in their own right and they would have been expensive. This was not the sort of stuff you'd be able to buy on the high street but only from a specialist dealer who knew the true value of what they were selling. Then, once we'd got comfortable, she pulled out a pack of Tarot cards and I thought ...Oh no, not the bloody Tarot!

...Which was a bit ungracious of me given that I'd earned my living for the better part of twenty years by turning over Tarot cards for a never ending queue of clients looking for divine guidance and the answers to the same old questions...

Am I going to find happiness?

Am I going to keep the happiness I've found?

Does he/she really love me?

Is he/she being faithful to me?

Can I get away with being unfaithful?

Should I get a divorce?

Should I get married?

Should I change jobs?

And so on and so on and so on... All perfectly normal and valid questions, frequently answered in depth and with profound perspective by the various spreads of the 78 symbols that make up the Tarot deck. But to the best of my knowledge there is no spiritual entity present or instrumental in the provision of these answers. It is more of a mind thing rather than any kind of spiritual connection. In their defense Tarot readers would claim that studying the cards opens the psychic mind, and so it does – but here again the psychic mind and the medium's clairvoyant soul are two different things. The Tarot reader will bleat that it is all the same thing – which just goes to show how little they know about the forces they are dealing with.

And herein lay the rub. Yes, I had read the Tarot for half of my adult life, but I was neither a clairvoyant nor a medium. In my simplistic assessment if you were a genuine spiritualist you didn't need craft tools like a pack of Tarot cards to focus your clairvoyant faculties! Yet here was one of the "world's top mediums" resorting to a pack of Ryder Waite to make contact with the Great Beyond. It didn't hang right and although I said nothing I was immediately on my guard – which is not to say I wasn't interested in hearing what Mandy Breck had to say. The problem was that I could probably read the cards better than she could do it herself.

We went through the selective process of shuffling and cutting the cards, first into two packs, then into four, and finally into eight. After making my final choice Mandy took the much reduced deck and turned the symbols face up on the table. Eight cards in total. The Lovers. The Devil. The Two of Swords. The Tower of God. The Eight of Cups. The Queen of Swords. The World – and finally, The Fool.

A random chance selection but if I was doing a text book reading for an imaginary third party that just happened to be me, those eight cards made perfect sense and told a true enough tale of what was relevant in my life at that point in time.

The Lovers indicated the fact that emotional issues were uppermost in my mind and would hold sway over all choices and decisions. The Devil represented duplicity, distrust and a fundamental inability to break free from chains that anchored me to the past. The Two of Swords referred to the pressure of having to make impossible decisions under duress wherein there were great issues of principle involved that would have long term ramifications in an uncertain future. The Tower indicated that there were great forces of fate and destiny involved and suggested it would be unwise, even impossible, to go against what the gods had pre-ordained. The Eight of Cups prophesied a deliberate walking away from that which was old and familiar and well past its sell by date in favour of something new and wonderful, but that this walking away process would not come without pain and regret. The Queen of Swords signified the presence of a powerful and influential woman in my life who was a force to be reckoned with and who was determined to have her own way – someone who could bring me great pleasure if she was appeased and profound carnage if she was not. The World was telling me that like it or not, it was time for my world to change and The Fool advised me that it would be foolish to resist the inevitable.

As I say, if I'd been doing a reading for me on the basis of those cards, this would have been the bedrock upon which I would have built my projections and psychodramas. Obviously Mandy Breck saw those same cards in a somewhat different light.

'Oh James,' she cooed, 'I can see that you're a really sweet guy…'

Sweet? I was as sour as next year's gooseberry!

'…and that you're really sensitive and highly psychic in your own right!'

Yeah, well, okay, maybe…

'I can see that you've got lots of different skills and talents but they all seem to clash and get in the way of each other so no one talent can really shine through the way you'd like it to…'

Fair enough, that was half clever.

'I can see that you've done quite a lot of traveling in your time but you still haven't been to half the places you'd like to go to…'

True, as far as it went.

'You've had lots of different jobs and lots of different relationships, but you've been with the same person now for ten or twelve years and I'd say that although you've had your ups and downs it's basically a good relationship, although a few things have been shaken up a bit in the last few months. So, this might not seem to be such a good time for you emotionally, but it's an important time for getting some pretty awkward issues sorted out…'

187

Impressive. She was now getting my full attention but this was no more than a Tarot run would tell any experienced reader...

'I get the impression that you're a highly educated guy, probably real good with numbers and sums, and really into computers and all kinds of modern technology...'

Wrong, wrong and very wrong!

'You like good food and fine wine...'

True, but who doesn't?

...Mandy rolled on for half an hour, mainly churning out a range of "cold reading" clichés and character traits. She was mostly right in what she said, but she presented her information in such a way in which it would have been difficult for her to be wrong. 'You've been very badly hurt in the past!' Yes, but haven't we all? 'I want to link you with stomach troubles and problems with the back!' Fine! I sometimes suffer with gall stones and my wife has a bad back – but how many people do you know that this could be equally applicable to? 'I've got a younger man here who I think might be your son. Things are good between you now, but there have been problems in the past.' Fairly correct, but again hardly the stuff of revelation.

There were a dozen other things that she could have said to give her statement more authority but instead she went on to talk about a daughter and all the problems I'd been having with her, which was an absolute nonsense for I had no daughter.

'You'll be changing address soon,' I was told, which was, of course, unproven, as was the prophesy that 'a couple of years from now you're going to be earning a lot more money!' Which was reassuring but was nothing less than what most people would like to and might expect to hear in a reading such as this...

At no time did Mandy mention names or dates or give any in depth information. There was no trace of anything remotely spiritual, and there was no mention of Anthony Zander. It had been a psychic reading with an awful lot of generalizations, and if this was genuine clairvoyance from one of the world's leading mediums, give me Madam Za Za on Scarborough sea front any day. Mandy had used a number of cold reading techniques that might have impressed a client coming in off the street, but alas, it did very little to impress me. The Tarot had been there just for show, for at no time was there any reference to either the cards or their meanings, so all in all, considering her reputation, I was very disappointed by her efforts.

By the time I got to the sitting with David Doubleday I was not in a good mood. My head was thumping and I was feeling grumpy and tired. As for David, he seemed quite relaxed and confident and he certainly looked the part of the mystic; dark green shirt with a Russian collar and blouson sleeves, hair slicked back and gelled down, a distinct whiff of expensive cologne. To his credit there were no cards or any other form of occult paraphernalia, just him and me sitting opposite each other across the table.

'I need a minute or so to tune in,' he said, 'and although I'm not going to read your palm or anything like that, some kind of physical link is helpful, especially in the opening stages of the sitting, so I wonder if we could just make light finger contact...?'

I extended my hand, palm down, across the crisp white linen and very gently he rested his fingers on top of my own. He closed his eyes and slowed his breathing. It was a warm evening, I was tired, thought what the hell, and closed my own eyes. Some time passed – to tell the truth I might even have dozed off for a minute, and was only brought back to reality when David broke the link by pulling his hand away from the finger tip contact. I opened my eyes to find him studying me with a direct, but never-the-less uneasy look.

'I'm very sorry,' he apologized. 'I'm not getting anything at all of a spiritual nature. I've got a mixed up jumble of psychic impressions, but that's not what all this is about, is it?'

'No,' I agreed, mentally applauding his honesty. 'But why not just give me what you're getting anyway. It might help to open something up.'

'Er, all right...' He didn't sound too confident, but he closed his eyes again and re-established the finger contact. 'Er... some of this is really rather peculiar and I don't pretend to be able to understand any of it, but I'm getting really heavy feelings of claustrophobia and waves of tiredness and really deep depression... I'm also getting a tight feeling, it's like two bands of pressure, one around my head and one around my chest. Then there's a picture of a beautiful old sailing boat on a navy blue sea – I can smell the salt water and hear the creaking of timbers and the rushing sound of the sea, and everything here is so fresh and clean... and still with the sea, but something very different – it's night and you're standing on the battlements of a white castle and you're throwing something as hard as you can into the waves below... I've got a picture of Scotland now, kind of like looking down on a map from way up in space... A lot of Scotland is black and cold and barren but then there are other parts which seem to be on fire.... Peculiar, really peculiar... Now I've got a picture of Majorca, again like looking down from space and over Majorca there's kind of like a clown's face, superimposed over the landscape... And there's a load of stuff here about cars. I'm seeing a white sports car but it's hard to describe because it keeps changing shape and there's something to do with tractors and butterflies in the rain, and I've got you writing in lots and lots of notebooks and as you're filling up these notebooks you seem to be in a lot of pain.... There's a very old man with thinning hair and he hasn't got any teeth and you're really frightened of this old man, and I can see cats and dogs and lots of different magical symbols, there's lots of bright lights and really loud classical music.... I keep getting a feeling of being high up and looking down on... well, nothing at all... It's like you're standing on top of this really high cliff and you're wondering whether you should jump off it or not and I've got images of pyramids and ancient temples in the middle of sandy deserts.... There's a lonely little boy weaving his way through these pictures and, like, over his head, there's the sound of women's voices arguing and quarrelling... Got a man in a dinghy and a lady in a wheelchair and there's a giant pair of scissors cutting through telephone wires and there's this constant noise like a dozen babbling voices all yelling in your head at the same time...'

He delivered this monologue in a fast flat tone, hardly pausing for breath or punctuation. Now he stopped, and pressed his fingers against his temples. 'My head hurts,' he said simply. 'I need to stop now for a minute.' And then 'I say, I wouldn't like to be in your head for any great length of time.'

'That's exactly where you've been though,' I muttered uncomfortably.

He looked up at that, obviously interested. 'Did any of that make any sense to you at all?' he asked hopefully.

'It all made perfect sense,' I confirmed. 'Like I said, you've just been on a virtual mini tour of my brain.'

'Oh I say,' he said. And then, 'My goodness!'

He sounded genuinely relieved and surprised, and no more surprised than I was myself. No, there had been no spiritual link, and no, there had been no lurid prophesy, but oh yes, the man had definitely slipped inside my mind and every single thing he had said had found its mark and made its connection. This was neither spiritualism nor psychism, but pure old fashioned mental telepathy and the fact that he himself had had no control over the process made it all the more impressive. Furthermore, that he had verbalized thoughts and mental images that (a) had not even been in my conscious mind, and (b) had been presented to me in such a way that I knew exactly what he was talking about, even if he didn't, gave me very grizzly food for thought. There had been no help, response or reaction from me, so the "cold reading" theory was blown completely out of the window and although his mediumship was still suspect, I found that I was having to look at David Doubleday with some fresh perspective and respect.

'Let's take a break,' I said. 'Pressure off. Come on, let's go outside and sit on the verandah. I'll have a smoke and you can pull another rabbit out of the hat.'

'Did it really all make sense?' he asked again as we settled into a couple of the ubiquitous cane chairs.

'Yes,' I said soberly. 'It most certainly did but it wasn't clairvoyance in the true sense of the word.'

'No,' he agreed. 'It wasn't. I don't know what it was really.'

'Just as well then that I do.' I lit my favourite briar. 'But anyway, you can't get away with just that. The Hammond Foundation is going to want a bit more for its money.' I puffed smoke rings up into the shadowy dark space above our heads, aware of the early evening sun casting its dappled light across my face. 'So go with the flow, David. Take your time, and pull in whatever else you can pull in.'

'Fair enough. Can I have your fingers again?'

'Sure.' I reached over and this time placed my finger tops on the back of his hand. I closed my eyes and enjoyed the last rays of the sun before it disappeared behind the mountains.

'Who's John?' he asked.

'A name that I know,' I answered.

'Well who's Jo, Joan, Joanne or Joanna?'

'I know the name of Joanna.'

'Ummm,' he fell silent, and then let his cat out of the bag. 'This is very difficult,' he said. 'You know, what with you being a close friend of Harry Andrews' and being in bed with the Mage Publishing people.'

'I'm not really in bed with anyone,' I said shortly, on the one hand dismayed that the gaff was blown and on the other hand mildly amused by the incestuous implication of being in bed with myself. 'Anyway, how do you know I'm me?'

'Oh well, er, I thought I recognized you at the airport yesterday, and then this morning when I was waiting for Julian to come for his reading I was browsing along the bookshelf and I saw your two books, and the penny sort of dropped. Just checked the photographs in "Out Of This World" to be sure, and of course, there you were, so to speak...'

I'd be a liar if I said I hadn't foreseen the possibility of this occurrence, but now that it was upon me I still didn't quite know how to deal with it. So I told it like it was, and if that caused a problem, then it was going to be his problem and not mine.

'Look David, here in Spain I'm just like you. I've been contracted to the Hammond Foundation to do a specific job of work, and while it's a different job to the one you been asked to do, we're both pretty well in the same boat.'

'Yes, but what exactly is your job?'

'To take part in, observe objectively and to report dispassionately on the result of the Hammond Foundation's experiments on the subject of clairvoyance and post mortem survival,' I answered directly.

'Then we're not in the same boat at all!' he exclaimed. 'For example, I won't have any control over what you put in your report, will I?'

'No you won't,' I conceded. 'Just as I will have no control over what you say to Julian Boyd, Beth Hammond and to me.'

I could see that he didn't like it one little bit. 'I'm not very happy with this,' he said plaintively.

'No, I can see that you're not.'

'Do Edith and Mandy know what you're doing?'

'Yes of course they do,' I retorted. 'Beth made my role in the proceedings quite clear at dinner last night. You were there. You heard what she said.'

'Yes, but do they know who you are?'

'David, I'm just a jobbing writer with a commitment to spiritualism.'

192

'No James that's not right! You work with a lot of professional mediums and you write books about them!'

'Yes, but what difference does that make?'

'It impairs any objectivity you might claim to have because you'll be comparing us to them!'

'That's crazy,' I sighed, wishing I'd doubled up on that morning's dose of Prozak. 'That simply isn't my job at all. Nobody will be comparing anybody with anybody, and least of all with any of the mediums I'm connected with in the UK none of whom have any role to play in this business. They weren't even invited. Just as Beth Hammond told you yesterday, this is not any kind of personal test or point scoring competition. No one is on trial here. It's just an experiment.'

'But we all think that there's more to this experiment than we've been told!'

Ah, so they'd been talking among themselves, had they?

'That might be true,' I soft pedaled, 'but just because the Hammond people are playing their cards close to their chest at this early stage in the proceedings doesn't mean that anyone is trying to trick you or deceive you. That would be totally counterproductive. The Hammond Foundation wants this experiment to work! They want a publishable and a positive report that can be held us as squeaky clean and totally objective. They want no whispers of collusion and they don't want any of their evidence to fail under hard scrutiny, and as far as I know that's the only reason why the experiments are being conducted in a modular way.'

'So what exactly is it that they're after?' he asked. 'I mean obviously you must know. You're on the team, so to speak.'

'I can't tell you that, and in any case, it's not my place to tell you. That's got to come from Beth... But I'm pretty sure you'll find out before the experiments are over.'

He looked dubious and doubtful. 'Listen,' I said, with some growing exasperation. 'If The Hammond Foundation told you it wanted to achieve direct contact with Jesus of flaming Nazareth, how long do you think it would be before you and Edith or Mandy started getting visions of some lovely bloke in a white robe wearing a halo and sandals?'

'Now you're impugning our objectivity,' he complained.

'Honestly David, no offense meant, but surely you see my point?'

'Well yes,' he managed a conciliatory grin. 'I suppose so...' And then he suddenly blanched. 'My God! That's not what you're trying to do, is it?'

'What?'

'Make contact with Jesus Christ!'

He was so deadly serious that I had to laugh. 'No,' I said, falling neatly into his trap. 'We are not trying to make contact with Jesus.'

'But you are trying to make contact with someone specific, aren't you!'

His eyes gleamed with his little victory and I kicked myself for being so stupid. 'Well that might certainly be a part of the Hammond experiments,' I admitted, thinking that perhaps this little bit of information might light a small fire under our clairvoyants' backsides, 'but it is by no means the whole of it....'

The light was beginning to fade and out of the corner of my eye I could see Beth hovering at the far end of the veranda. 'Look David,' I said, anxious now to terminate this conversation, 'let's call a halt here. Neither of us is in the right frame of mind to take things any further this evening, so let's start afresh and have another crack at it tomorrow. And do please let me put your mind at rest about what we have been discussing.'

I started to get up, but he reached out and put his hand on my arm to forestall me. 'Hang on James, I'd like to get one thing crystal clear between us before we go any further.'

'Okay,' I sat back down in my seat and took note of the hard glint in David's eyes.

'The bottom line is this,' he said. 'If, when you write your report or whatever it is that you're going to write, and you're writing about me and you're saying nice things, then feel free to use my name, but if you're not going to say nice things then you better make sure you don't use my name or anything like it, or my lawyers will be getting in touch with you and The Hammond Foundation – pretty damn quick, I would imagine! I simply will not tolerate anything being published which is in any way even slightly critical, defamatory or detrimental to my reputation!'

So there it was. The bumbling "I says" were gone, the kid gloves were off, and I was seeing this man's other persona, one based on ego and ambition and ruthless determination to preserve his media position. I was tired and I didn't feel like a fight, but at the same time I was curious to discover just how deep his paranoia went.

194

'What if,' I tried to make my voice sound reasonable, 'I just write the truth as it happens? I mean, take our earlier conversation, for example. I could say totally honestly and accurately that in my first sitting with you there did not appear to be any clairvoyant activity but that you did provide a stunning example of mental telepathy that was highly relevant to me both consciously and subliminally and that I was extremely impressed with what you were able to do?'

That seemed to mollify him and he mulled it over for a few second. For half a minute I thought I'd got him, and then the moment, like so many moments in so many similar circumstances, was lost and gone for ever, never to be retrieved and inevitably determining the course of a future pathway that would always bring difficulty and regret. Offer someone the free mile and instead of accepting gratefully, pride, ego and prejudice get in the way and they demand the bloody motorway!

'I want full editorial rights,' he said.

'You what?'

'On anything you write about me, I want full editorial rights. If I like what you say, it can go in. If I don't, it stays out.'

I dearly wanted to tell him to fuck off. I was sick to my stomach of people telling me what I could and couldn't do and Doubleday was pushing me to my line in the sand. Even so, I took a deep breath, and tried to keep my cool.

'David as a matter of course you would be given a copy of the first draft. At that time you would be most welcome to make any comments or reasonable requests with regard to anything I might have written. The same courtesy would be extended to Edith and Mandy, and for that matter to Beth Hammond and Julian Boyd. I'm not out to offend anybody and I don't want to make enemies, but as a matter of principle, and common sense, you can't have any editorial rights. And that's final.'

'Right,' he snapped. 'If that's the case, what's to stop me from packing my bags and leaving right now?'

'Absolutely nothing,' I kept my voice neutral. 'But if you did, I imagine you might be in breach of contract with The Hammond Foundation and therefore your fee might be forfeit. As far as I'm concerned, I'd just do the job I'm being paid to do and would report the details and the circumstances of your departure and I would have no qualms about publishing the substance of this conversation we're having.'

195

'It would be your word against mine!'

'Not quite...' I reached forwards and picked up the Dictaphone from the table. It had long since run out of tape and had stopped recording, but he didn't know that.

'Has that thing been on all this time?' he asked incredulously.

'Of course it has,' I lied innocently.

He glowered at me. 'I'm not happy about this,' he said.

'Yes I know. You told me that before... And I'm sorry about that, I really am, but there's not much I can do about it. What I suggest you do is talk to Elizabeth Hammond. She's in charge, not me.'

'That's exactly what I'll do!' he said.

And that's exactly what he, or to be more precise, what we did – and basically, Beth sorted it. David would not get his editorial rights, but he would get his first draft and if he didn't like what I wrote about him, I agreed to change his name and disguise his identity. I think the only reason he went for it was the fact that Beth did point out that he would be in breach of contract if he pulled out of the experiments prematurely and therefore his fee, minus traveling expenses, would indeed have to be returned. But I think he must also have been aware that it would have been tantamount to a declaration of war, with the UK rather than Spain as the battleground.

Beth functioned as the diplomat rather than the lawyer, smoothed waters and feathers, pointing out that we were still in the early stages of the experiments and how valuable David's contribution was perceived to be. He postured and preened and I decided there and then that I was *not* going to use his correct name in this book. Later on that same evening, after a five minute bull session with Julian, we came up with the name of David Doubleday... And any detectives out there intent on provoking a court case that I'd prefer to avoid, you can start detecting now.

Miguel drove Mandy Breck and David Doubleday into the village for what Mandy described as "an independent night out on the town, and hey, don't worry about us, we'll get a taxi back when we feel like coming home." Miguel's pretty young wife Maria prepared a light supper for Edith Schiff which she took in her room, and Beth, Julian and myself convened in Beth's comfortable (and with my presence, increasingly untidy) study. It was the first time we'd had chance to meet privately all day and I suppose we were all anxious to hear how the other had got on with their sittings.

'Well,' said Julian as he opened a bottle of wine, 'that was a regular crock of shit, wasn't it?'

Beth looked at him disapprovingly, but I laughed (easily) in his direction. 'Did you think it was as bad as all that?' I asked

'None of 'em got anything right – leastways, not for me they didn't!'

'Beth?' I looked in her direction and raised a questioning eyebrow.

'There was some interesting stuff,' she began cautiously. 'But nobody got any kind of link with Anthony. Not even a sniff.' She paused, unable to hide her frustration and obvious disappointment. 'I must confess, I had expected more from them.'

'First things first,' I suggested. 'Let's listen to all the tapes and see if there is any common ground in the readings.'

Both Beth and Julian seemed uncomfortable with that idea.

Julian: 'Christ James, we'll be here for bloody hours!'

Beth: 'Is that really necessary James? Can't we just give you an ad verbatim report?'

On the one hand I could see why they both might have preferred to keep the contents of their tapes to themselves, but on the other hand this was not a time for coyness.

'Look, you can keep your fingers on the pause buttons if you want to, but if we're to assess just what came down here today, and if I'm to write up a report about it, then I'm sorry guys, it's time to spill a few of the beans... and if we're here 'till midnight, then sorry Julian, but that's what I'm here for, remember.'

And so, laboriously we went through the six tapes and we were there 'till long after midnight and long after one o'clock when

Mandy and David made their noisy return. At first it was a stilted process but then we got into the swing of it and with the help of some good wine we even managed to create a mood of camaraderie that for a while bordered on fun. Certainly the humour was cynical and saturated with sarcasm, but somewhere along the line we got our second wind and by two o'clock we'd got it down and done.

The single dominant factor was that not one of the three mediums had picked up any link at all with Anthony Zander. Not even a half reference, a hint or an innuendo. Mandy had felt that Julian, just like me, was a 'really sweet guy' and that Beth was a 'really sweet girl' and although she was nominally correct in their character evaluations and current states of mind, had been way off the mark with most of her remarks.

With Julian she had been correct in saying that his life had changed radically in the last couple of years and that there had been a number of unexpected long distance journeys, she also deserved some brownie points in suggesting that he had some career links with medicine. Arguably she was also on the ball in suggesting that this was a crossroads period in his life where personal emotional relationships were concerned and that what he did in the following twenty months may well have a profound influence over the following twenty years... But in Julian's opinion, and mine too for that matter, she was way off the mark in suggesting that he was battling with his own sexuality. Her vision that he might have some future links with the film industry was purely speculative, and looking the way that Julian looked, she didn't have to work too hard to put two and two together and come up with seven.

In Beth's case Mandy was even further off the mark, making reference to a long and happy relationship in the past, two non-existent children, Beth's determination to be a good mother and her antipathy towards career ambitions. Correctly, Mandy spoke of a very happy childhood and a strong family background, got it completely right in suggesting that she was a 'Daddy's Girl' then got it completely wrong in speculating that she was thinking of taking up a new career as an artist in which all of her "fabulously gifted creative tendencies could be focused on beautiful things."

In Beth's own words: 'James, I don't have an artistic bone in my body!'

In some ways, surprisingly, David Doubleday did rather better, and Julian, without terms of reference, had been far too harsh in his criticism. David correctly tied Julian into a city or a place that began with the letter P... and Julian had studied and worked in Perth, remember. He also said that Julian's finances had changed radically in the previous couple of years through a will or a legacy, and he went on to say that although Julian was following the same profession he had been trained for, the nature of his work had changed dramatically in the past eighteen months and was due to change again in the next few months to come. David had also made reference to a lady in Julian's life called Margaret or Marjorie, and in my opinion that was close enough to "Maggie" to score valid points. David also linked Julian to the USA, saying that it had either been important in Julian's life or was destined to become important. But then he lost the plot entirely and talked at great length about Julian's connection with some form of military organization – "either army or navy but definitely not the air force..."

And in Julian's own words: 'The only link I've ever had with anything of a military nature is to march in protest against its existence on this planet!'

And yet if you'd paid David your thirty quid or so for a High Street psychic reading he'd have earned his fee – and likewise with Beth.

He accurately spoke of her involvement with an orthodox profession – at first he thought it might have been in architecture and then changed it to law. He accurately spoke of one failed marriage that hadn't lasted very long and confirmed that she was without children. He accurately (in my opinion at least) ascertained that she was at some kind of emotional crossroads in her life, and then went on to speak about a feeling of unfairness and injustice within her deepest thoughts and emotions. He did not mention funerals or deaths but he did speak of emotional loss and of Beth's difficulty in adjusting to it. To his credit he mentioned Beth's dual home status, disqualifying Spain as one of those locations, and also to his credit he spoke of Beth being confronted by major romantic choices and decisions that she didn't know how to cope with or how to handle. Very astutely (again in my opinion) he made it very clear that Beth and nobody other than Beth was holding all the cards and it was what she decided that would govern the outcome of the situation.

So no, neither Mandy nor David had made any mention, directly or indirectly, of Anthony Zander or of Zander's presence or role in any of our lives, but in Beth and Julian's case, and I suppose to a lesser extent in my case also, they had provided creditable sea-side readings: Beth was quite right in having expected more of clairvoyants who were supposedly at the top of their class, but credibility hung on that single word 'supposedly' and not for the first time I found myself wondering how Zander had gone through his selection process.

The real enigma of the day was Edith Schiff.

In my case Edith had impressed me greatly with the links she had brought through. That I had not expected any messages from the people I'd had my messages from did not in any way invalidate the fact that I'd had the messages, and as I've said, Edith provided enough detail to prove her claims of genuine contact with the spirit world. And yet for Julian and for Beth she had got nothing. To my amazement, it transpired that she hadn't even bothered to attempt a reading for either of them! To both of them, after having sat in silence at the table for five going on ten minutes, she had said virtually the same thing...

Words to the effect of 'I am zorry, there is nossing for you at zis time. Ve must try again later.'

Beth, on tape: 'Are you sure, Madam Schiff? I mean, there must be something, surely?'

Edith: 'No, nossing at zis time. Ze time is wrong.'

Julian, being Julian, had given her a much harder time. 'Like, what do you mean, there's nothing?'

Edith: 'All ze doors and windows to ze spirit vorld are closed.'

Julian: 'Yeah, well lady, you're the expert, so can't you open them?'

Edith: 'Not as zis time. Ze time is not right.'

Julian; 'Er, so when do you reckon will be the right time? Later on today, tomorrow, next week, next year?' On the tape recording Julian's sarcasm and scorn are ill concealed.

Edith: 'Ze spirits say vhen is right time, not me. Ve try again later.'

Julian opened a fourth bottle of wine. Good lad, he was learning fast.

'Like I said, Mr. C – a whole crock of shit, and especially from Auntie Edith, who never got a Goddamn thing for either me or Beth.'

200

'But,' I said pointedly, 'she got a helluva lot right for me.'

'Why do you think that is?' Beth asked. 'I mean, do you think it might be because you're psychic and we're not?'

I shrugged. 'Could be. Maybe...' And then, realizing that I was copping out – 'No, bollocks to that. Beth, I don't know why she didn't pull anything through for you, but I'll tell you this, I'd rather have Edith's honesty than David's psychic vibes and Mandy's cold reading techniques. Maybe we should just take her at her word and accept that for you, for whatever reason, the time was not the right time and that maybe tomorrow or whenever will be the right time. This has only been the first day of the experiments and we've got a long way to go yet.'

Julian stifled a yawn, and both Beth and I followed suit. 'So what's the agenda for tomorrow?' he asked.

'Don't think there's much point in me sitting with David again – rather unfortunately that energy is now completely contaminated – and unless you feel otherwise, I don't see much point in either of you guys sitting with him again either, or with Mandy for that matter, but I do think Edith should be given another opportunity to see if she can get anything for you. So, after their night on the town tonight, let's give David and Mandy the morning off. You two have sittings with Edith, and then in the afternoon, we'll all sit around in a séance circle and see if that generates anything.'

'What if nothing comes through in the séance?' Beth asked.

'Then we'll get together tomorrow evening and discuss plan B.'

'Er, just refresh my memory,' Julian interrupted. 'Like, what exactly is plan B?'

'Dunno,' I admitted. 'We'll figure it out when we get there.'

Eighteen: *Tuesday 23rd December – the first séance.*

It's all very well saying "Oooh let's have a séance!" – But it isn't as easy as that. For one thing, you've got to be sure that the person conducting the séance knows what they're doing, and as it was once pointed out to me, it takes about six years to train a good medium – one year to learn how to bring something into the circle and five years to learn how to get rid of it again afterwards, especially if the something that you brought in wasn't exactly to your liking.

It isn't just a matter of knowledge and experience, although they are important factors. The key ingredient is spiritual authority, and that was something I didn't have. Beth and Julian didn't have it, and I didn't think that either Mandy or David had it either. Therefore, when it came to deciding who should lead the séance, Edith Schiff was the only candidate – and she refused point blank.

I'd found Edith in the garden, just before we sat down to a communal breakfast, and I'd started off by asking if she would mind sitting with Julian and Beth again.

'No, off course I don't mind, but James I haff to tell you zat I don't know if anyzink vill come of it. Yesterday zey vere bose blocking me by pushing me to say zings zey vanted to hear but vhich I could not zay. Zo, ve read again zis morning, but kindly tell zem to expect nossing and to keep zeir minds open. I am sure zere are messages for zem, but zey vill only come through vhen ze time is right. Herr Julian sinks I can make ze time right but I am only ze conduit not ze initiator.'

Then I'd asked her if she would lead the séance that afternoon, and she'd shaken her head. 'No, I am zorry. Zis is not for me to do at zis time.'

'Well I can't do it,' I'd told her frankly, 'and if you won't, then that leaves either Mandy or David and to be absolutely honest with you, I don't have much confidence in either of them!'

'Jah, I can understand vhy,' she'd said sympathetically, and was there, I'd wondered, just a glimmer of mischief twinkling away at the back of her eyes? And then, after a long pause, she'd added – 'Use ze American. She vill bring somezing through. It might not be vhat you vant, but it vill be something.'

So with my tail between my legs, I'd gone off and propositioned Mandy, and Mandy had leapt at the chance to play the role of the

202

leading lady. As for David, I wasn't sure whether he was miffed not to have been asked, or just heartily relieved.

Breakfast was a bright enough affair, lots of chatter and bonhomie, with the warm morning sun bouncing in through the open windows; Miguel and Maria did everyone proud by serving a full English breakfast and although David and I didn't get into any in depth conversations the atmosphere between us was relatively cordial and without any of the previous day's tension. Everyone seemed reasonably pleased with the light schedule of the day – David elected to walk into the village and Mandy was happy to join him on the premise that she had some shopping to do for the afternoon's event. She said she needed some candles and some herbs and incense and I resisted the temptation to point out that we were supposed to be having a séance and not some kind of late Wiccan celebration of the solstice.

There was no point in rubbing salt into the wound of my misgivings, so instead I tried to be helpful and told her where she was most likely to find the things that she was looking for, and while the subject was open and everyone was present, I also thought it an opportune moment to ask her if there was anything special she needed from us.

'Hey guys, no not really,' she mused out loud. 'If you can just come to the table with open minds and some degree of calmness, I guess that's all I can ask of you. Me personally, well speaking for myself, I'll be meditating for an hour or so before we start, and if any of you are into meditation, it wouldn't harm for you to chill out and find your centres. Yeah, that would be so cool...' Then directly to me, she asked: 'What time do you want us to start, James?'

Without even thinking about it I told her four o'clock. I don't know why. The time was there on my lips even before I had time to think about it. I also knew that by four o'clock the sun would have gone and that it would be raining. Don't ask me how I knew, because I just did. The same energy that said that four o'clock would be a good time to hold a séance also told me that the weather was going to change by the mid afternoon, and I doffed a mental cap to my old shepherd friend Miguel, wondering whether or not he ever "chilled out" or was able to find his "centre".

As La Casa Blanca's Miguel cleared away the breakfast things and David and Mandy trouped out of the door arm in arm in search of whatever they were looking for – maybe candles and herbs, maybe something entirely different – I caught Edith's eye and we exchanged a private smile; this old lady may have been well into her eighties but she did not miss a thing.

As if on cue, as soon as David and Mandy had gone, she turned to Beth and Julian. 'Come, maybe ve vill haff ze sittings now, but not in zat cold vhite room of yours. It iz a beautiful day, so let's go out and zit in ze sunshine. Zere I can smoke, and if there iz anyzing 'appening, I can tell you. If not, zen I can't. You,' she turned abruptly to me, 'you come too viz your little tape recorder if you like. Who knows, you might be off zome 'elp.'

Julian opened his mouth to say something then caught my warning look and kept it shut. We followed Edith out into the sunshine – and truly, it was a glorious morning, at least eighty degrees Fahrenheit and not a single cloud in the azure blue sky – and allowed her to place us round one of the small coffee tables on the verandah. Miguel was right behind us with a fresh pot of coffee and four large cups.

Edith reached across and patted his hand. 'Gracias Señor Miguel, cuando se pueda, hay un cenicero por favour?'

My eyebrows shot up in surprise. This was the first indication we'd had that Edith spoke any Spanish, and if her accent was anything to go by, her Spanish was probably better than her English.

'Si Señora Schiff, ahora mismo…' he actually beamed at her and I found myself wondering what private conversations they might have had out of our earshot. Both Miguel and Maria had been on Zander's payroll and although they might not have had all the details of what was going on, they certainly knew enough to give the game away.

He went in search of her cenicero (ash tray) and using the need for a loo as an excuse I scuttled off after him and caught him in the kitchen just before he re-emerged onto the verandah.

'Just a minute Miguel,' I rested a hand lightly on his arm and used my very best Spanish, 'please don't be offended, but I need to ask you if Señora Schiff has been asking you any questions about La Casa and what has been happening here?'

He looked at me blankly for a second, then realising the implication of what he was being asked, shook his vehemently. 'No Señor James, absolutely not! We have spoken only of the weather and of the food and of La Señora's passion for Spain!'

'What about Maria?' I asked.

204

'No, I don't think Maria has spoken to Señora Schiff at all!'

'Okay Miguel, thank you... But if Maria has spoken to Señora Schiff I need to know about it and if La Señora does ask either of you any questions, I need to know about that too.'

'Si Señor, I understand perfectly, but please believe that Maria and I have said nothing and will say nothing. These were Señor Zander's instructions and we have kept our promises to him...'

There was a whole different dimension to this conversation that I was not privy to, but it was pretty clear that Miguel and Maria had had an independent understanding with Anthony. Miguel's eyes told me that not only was he not lying, he was also appalled at the thought of betraying his late boss's confidence. Liking this young man a lot, I shook his hand and thanked him very much – and then I did go to the loo just in case the session with Edith turned out to be a long one. By the time I got back to the table, Edith was puffing away merrily and Beth was looking at me somewhat anxiously over the old lady's shoulder. The significance of Edith's lapse into Spanish may have gone over Julian's head, but Beth had certainly twigged the possible connotations, and as I gave her a gentle nod of reassurance, she visibly relaxed.

As it happened the session with Edith did not turn out to be particularly long, and although she was not specific about anything, some of the things she did come out with were illuminating and gave the promise of better things to come.

She sat opposite me, with Julian to her left and Beth to her right, and this tableau reminded me of Zander's death bed, and even more so, when she reached out and took both of their hand in her own.

'I know,' she said 'zat ze two of you haff a vere special relationship. And also I know that ze two of you also haff a vere special relationship wiz 'im,' she nodded down the table towards me. 'I also know zat zere are many zings zat you are not telling us about zese experiments, but zis is not me being clever it is me listening to ze vords of Mr. Doubleday!' She cackled, the cackle became a cough and she looked at her cigarette accusingly. Then she stubbed it out and immediately lit another one.

'Vhat Doubleday says is not important because already I know zere are zings ve are not being told, and vhy should ve be told? Ve are psychic, no? Ve are supposed to vork it out for ourselves or viz some help from our guides and helpers!'

Edith's tone softened and her eyes closed in repose. 'Sure, I know zat zere is somvone special you all vant to hear from, and sure Mr. Doubleday has told zis to bose me an ze American, but I did not needs his vords to know zis for myself. I do not know who zis person is, or vhat zey mean to you, but I do know zat zey haff not been in ze vorld of spirit for very long and now is not ze time for zem to make ze contact you are all vanting to receive. I do not make promises zat can not be kept, but zis I do promise all zree of you! Zere vill be contact, but only vhen ze time is right, and until zhen you must trust each ozzer and love each ozzer.' She opened her eyes and held up Beth and Julian's hands, looking at them each in turn; 'Ze bose of you haff much talking and arranging to do before zings can be right for you, and you,' she looked directly down the table and bored me to the soul with a deeply penetrating look, 'you must do more for your wife and if you do not talk to her today on ze telephone you make vere sure you talk to her tomorrow because tomorrow is a vere special day. In fact, I make you promise to make ze telephone call wizzin ze next twenty four hours, jah?'

Mindful that the following day was my 11th wedding anniversary, something that Edith could not possibly have known, I made the promise willingly and gladly and with an open heart.

Between them Mandy and David had done a lot to create the right atmosphere within 'the cold white room'. Now there were profusions of flowers all over the place and the white table top had been covered with Mandy's deep crimson cloth. There were six place settings, each with a small white candle, while a much larger white candle burned in the middle of the table. The curtains had been drawn, and much to my personal satisfaction, the windows closed against the light but persistent patter of rain that fell against the glass. As sure as God created Andalucia in Heaven's own image, the weather had begun to change in the early afternoon; by one o'clock the morning's blue brightness had been replaced by a gray haze, and by three o'clock the rain had started falling out of a leaden sky.

We filed in and took our places; clockwise Mandy, Edith, Myself, Beth, Julian and David. Mandy seemed either agitated, excited or nervous, and I wondered just how many times she'd done anything like this? I'd have been a hundred times happier with Edith at the helm, but obviously Frau Schiff had her own reasons for sitting this one out. Against that, it was she who had told me to "use the American" so we would see what we would see.

'Okay guys,' Mandy chuckled self consciously, 'I guess this is going to be one crazy séance, after all we haven't just got one medium at this table, we've got three, so I guess anything could happen really. Nominally, I'm head honcho for this session, so I'll start things rolling – and I know that my way of doing things might not be everybody's way of doing things, but I can only do what has worked for me in the past, and if none of you guys mind, I'd like to start by saying a couple of short prayers, starting with The Lord's Prayer. Now I have got to tell you that I am not a very good Christian, but these are really power words that offer great protection, and if you wanna say them with me that would be cool, but if you don't that's okay – but if you can go with the flow of the emotion, that would be really really helpful. Okay? Now the other thing is I want us all to hold hands, and whatever happens, I don't want anyone of you guys to break the circle. That's really important, because the circle is not only our joint strength, it also represents my personal protection. Got it, okay... Our Father...'

She did a passable job of reciting The Lord's Prayer, quoting the old King James version rather than the more modern New English. She was quite right in her declaration that these words were "power" words and it has to be said that some words are more powerful than others.

After The Lord's Prayer Mandy offered a few words of her own – although where they originated was anybody's guess: could have been Dean Koontz's "Book Of Counted Sorrows'" or Mandy Breck's own "How To Invoke A Spirit".

'Oh spirits of the other world,' she incanted dramatically, 'we sit at this table at this time and in this place and implore you to lower your cosmic consciousness to our level of attunement. We beg you to come in peace and love, and always remembering we are protected by the angels themselves, grant us the gift of communication. Oh spirits, if you are present here this day, we beg you, give us a sign....'

Oh I'm sorry, but I had to bite down on my tongue so hard to stop myself bursting into a fit of the most hysterical giggles. Oh spirits if you are here, knock once! If you are not here, knock twice!! Mandy may have been well intentioned, but these words, unlike the powerful mantra of The Lord's Prayer, were sheer gobbledegook, and therefore it was not altogether surprising that after Mandy's dramatic petition to Higher Spiritual Authorities all she got for her trouble was the soft and soothing sound of the rain silkenly kissing the window pains.

'Oh spirits,' Mandy beseeched a second time, 'if you are present, give us a sign...'

And out of the blue I found myself thinking of crop circles.... And you, sitting there propped up in bed, or on the bus or the train, or snuggled up in an armchair might well ask why is Christie thinking of crop circles at a time like this? And actually the answer is very simple. Seventy percent of crop circles are faked. A few of them are faked by young farmers who have a weird sense of humour but most of them are faked by government employees dressed in dungarees who want you to think that they are all faked. Why do they want you to think this? Because thirty percent of crop circles are NOT faked and governments the world over have no explanation for them.

It's a bit like UFO's. Official government policy is that they don't exist. People like the American and Russian Presidents know very differently, as do most (although not all) policy making politicians in the western world and a few (a very select and extremely influential few) captains of international finance and industry. People who know me might say something along the lines of "Oh hell, he's off on one of his conspiracy theory crusades again," and I bare them no ill will for their poor opinion of me. Suffice to say that the evidence is there for anyone to assess, and as for me I've done my homework and have come to my own conclusions, based on fact, not fiction. I'll do battle in my corner with anyone who wants to give me an argument.

So what's the connection between crop circles and séances? Well I think you could relate it to the percentages. Thirty percent of them are genuine, conducted by serious searchers of contact with a world of spirit while seventy percent are faked by lesser mortals who either want to impress their followers or who genuinely believe they are in touch with the world of spirit when in fact they are having two way conversations with their own egotistical imaginations.

I wasn't exactly sure what category Mandy Breck fell into, but I had my opinions and suspicions.

And then the table lurched violently to the left of the room, knocking over two of the candles and snuffing them out.

And I had to reassess my opinions of Mandy Breck's powers of mediumship.

Her head had lolled backwards, and her eyes had rolled up leaving nothing but the whites staring out of the heavily made up sockets.

'Splish.' she said in a little girl's voice. And then... 'Splash. Splash. Splash.'

Her head jolted forward and her eyes (thank God) returned to normal... But her voice was distant, sounding as though she was talking more to herself than to the circle of people gathered in convocation. 'Three little boys. There are three little boys. Not so little, maybe twelve or thirteen. They dive into the river. They die in the river. They never surface. Their bodies are found in the reeds. They have not died from drowning, but from some kind of poisoning. Splash, splash, splash, in they go, one two and three, never to return except in this moment...'

Immediate assessment.

She was talking about the three lads who had died beneath Torre Muere from methane poisoning. Question. Were they really here making a connection through Mandy's powers of mediumship, or had Mandy heard the story in the village and was using it now to convince her colleagues (and her audience) of her prowess?

Edith's eyes were closed, her chin resting forwards on her chest. Her breathing seemed ragged.

'Whoops!' Mandy giggled and again her head angled backwards and her eyes rolled until only the whites were visible. 'Rod Stewart!' she moaned in fake fan extacy. 'I love you! I love your music!'

The head (and the eyes) came back to normal.

What the hell was normal?

'I got Rod Stewart here singing "Maggie May" at the top of his voice, so someone here knows "Maggie" in spirit, or maybe it isn't Maggie but May, or what the heck, a name like that anyway, and now I've got this crazy thing with a kangaroo, so maybe this link is for Julian 'cos he's the only guy here who comes from Australia and...'

Edith made a noise. It could have been a snigger or a grunt or a cough. Her head was lower, her breathing heavier.

'Whooah,' Mandy went off again with the head and the eyes thing and this time there was a long pause of pregnant silence before anything followed the whooah; when it did, it was in a lower tone of voice. 'Uh huh,' she said. 'Uh huh. I'm lonesome tonight, and you aint nothing but a hound dog and ah just caint help falling in love with you, Priscilla, an ah just want y'all to know that it wasn't Colonel Parker's fault an' that really baby I do love you tender and ah surely have died and ah'm with the Lord in His most glorious heaven.'

The head and eyes thing reverted and 'Oh My Gaaaard,' Mandy squeeled, 'I've just been talking to Elvis!'

Edith said something that sounded like 'einvloegensossen' – or maybe she was suppressing a Swiss sneeze?

Not for one minute did I think that Mandy was talking to Elvis Presley. I accept that she might have thought that she was, but that was a different thing entirely. Out of the blue I had a memory of a lady that clairvoyant Mick reed and I had met in Bridlington. Her name was, well, I'm going to be kind and call her Betty. She'd approached Mick just before his demonstration and had said she wanted to put some of her 'psychic cards' of the audience's seats. Mick and I had both looked at her 'cards' that had been hand written on cheap brown paper cuts. "Betty" said the logo. "Psychic to Elvis. Privet reedings by appoint. Only £15 phone..." The lady had been more than a bit upset when we'd very gently but firmly told her that no, sorry, but she could not put her cards on our customer's chairs. For nine months thereafter this lady phoned Mick every two or three weeks wanting to know why he was so mean to her and inferring than he was envious of her superior gifts. Those words "psychic to Elvis" locked themselves into my mind and I found myself shuddering with mirth; so dearly did I want to burst out with a huge guffaw of laughter, but this was not the time or the place and having to assume that Mandy was doing her best, I bit down on my tongue so hard that my temporary denture came loose under the pressure.

I was all too well aware that my levity was probably ruining the ambience of something that we should all have been tasking very seriously so I bit down even harder drawing every shred of self discipline to the surface.

Edith coughed and uttered an expression that sounded like 'sherbonkenfarht'

…and that nearly set me off again but I willed myself into the order and maintained the silence.

Not that I needed to have bothered because that was about it. There were no more tilting heads and rolling eyes and messages from rock musicians, and although we sat at the table for at least another half an hour, the three 'messages' from Mandy was all that we got.

A little while later, after the circle had been dissolved and we were all enjoying a nice cup of tea Mandy seemed highly delighted that these three messages had come through. David enthused over her talents, Beth and Julian were full of questions (which Mandy gladly answered) and Edith took herself off for a late siesta. Me, I just said 'thank you' and 'very interesting' and other than that, kept my mouth shut.

Nineteen: *Tuesday 23rd December – second séance*

On the evening of the Tuesday we took our three guests out for a typically touristy Spanish dinner up at Bar La Tasca. The original Bar La Tasca had been next to the taxi rank at the bottom of Calle Sevilla, and it had been little more than a series of interlinked cubby holes serving tapas and very basic (but good) Spanish food. It had done well, and indeed it had done so well that its owners had closed it down and had opened a much bigger and swankier place down on the corner of El Paseo. Certainly there were still the old bullfight and flamenco posters and rustic Andalucian décor, but very little else remained of the atmosphere and the ambience of the original place, for here there were clean tiled floors and a big spacious dining room. There was air conditioning and hygiene certificates and Costa del Sol prices and a Spanglish menu aimed at keeping the ex-pats happy. The owners had cynically exploited their market and the new La Tasca became Jimena's official English bar, full of Brits in search of the "real" Spain but not wanting to risk eating anywhere that didn't serve egg and chips with the paella and who were loath to get their shoes scuffed in the sawdust.

Pepe and Victoria, La Tasca's owners, were very nice people and they worked damn hard at their business of making ex-pats feel at home in a Spanish environment. There was some grumbling among other bar owners and acidic comment that Pepe would do anything to sell a brandy to a Brit, but people are generally envious of other peoples' success and in Jimena I don't suppose things were different to anywhere else in this respect.

When we arrived Victoria made us very welcome and provided us with a quiet corner table in what was a very busy restaurant. She and Pepe had gone to town and probably a bit over the top with the Christmas decorations and although the service was a little on the slow side (which was a blessing in disguise because it stretched the evening timewise) the food was excellent and there was a heavy ex-pat presence which made our English speakers feel a little more at home. The atmosphere was brightly cheerful, although in certain quarters, mine especially, somewhat slightly forced.

Mandy was full of herself – as far as she was concerned she'd led a successful séance and had actually had some short contact with The King. The undeveloped connection with the name that sounded or might have sounded like "Maggie" and the undeveloped connection with three dead Spanish boys seemed to count for nothing, and in my opinion the Elvis link also counted for nothing. There'd been no evidence. There'd been no message. There'd been nothing tangible, other than a fine example of the American's inflated sense of self importance. I'd come to the conclusion that if she was a genuine medium then my name was Walt Disney!

It had been a travesty of a séance and considering the fact that two other mediums had been at the table I felt that I had the right to feel bitterly disappointed; furthermore, on Beth and Julian's part I also felt cheated. Somewhere deep down there in the old Taurean gut some anger, some *not very nice* anger was beginning to stir. I wore my professional smile and tried to join in the conversation, but it was something of a façade. My thoughts were elsewhere, and although it would be wrong to say that I started planning my own agenda, some alternative ideas were beginning to form at the back of my mind.

Six people around a table gives an uneven conversational pattern; it was crystal clear that David was trying to make out with Mandy (and to all intents and purposes was having some luck in the process) and for the better part Beth was trying to make polite conversation with Edith Schiff. Certainly there was some cross talk but this was where the dialogue was more concentrated. This left Julian and I at a conversational loose end, and thus, although we joined in when applicable, we found that we were mostly talking to ourselves.

'You don't seem brilliantly happy, Mr. C,' he said at one point and in a very low tone.

I flashed him my brightest smile. 'That's because I'm not,' I said cheerfully.

'Oh now I find that really interesting,' he leaned across the table and matched me smile for smile, 'because that makes two of us!'

'Of course it makes three if we're speaking for Beth as well.'

'And I think we are speaking for Beth, aren't we?'

'Absolutely,' I sounded really enthusiastic. 'I think we most definitely are!'

'Yeah, but the question is, can we do anything about it?'

'Not right now,' I laughed as though he had told me a joke, 'but later on possibly. I think the secret may well be in remaining sober.'

'Ummm, in that case I think I'll have a shandy,' he sounded sad and philosophical.

'Why don't you make sure that Beth does as well.'

'Right, Mr. C, I can do that!'

'And while you're at it, ask her if she's got a scrabble board.'

'A scrabble board?'

'A scrabble board.'

We had sat down to dinner quite early in the evening and therefore it was inevitable that by ten o'clock we were done bar the shouting. By that time the noise levels in La Tasca had reached an incredible level of decibels and our table conversation had diminished as we ran out of things to be polite about. We (and especially me) needed to get out of this environment, but it was still too early to go home and call it a night, so there was some humming and hahing about what should happen next.

David and Mandy wanted to do the other bars, and surprisingly Edith elected to go for a walk around the village. This put Beth in a quandary, for on the one hand nobody wanted to impinge on David and Mandy's burgeoning "thing" but equally we couldn't leave an eighty odd year old lady to wander the slippery cobbles of Jimena all on her own.

'You're crazy,' Edith exclaimed. 'I may be old but I'm not in my dotage just yet, zank you very much. I am perfectly capable of looking after myself. I shall be fine and vhen I am tired of valking I shall get a taxi back to ze house. Now go on ze zree of you, you get back home and get on vis your vork.'

I looked at her sideways, wondering if she knew what work I had in mind. She met my gaze. 'You haff made zat phone call ve talked about?'

'No,' I admitted. 'I'll do it first thing in the morning.'

'Zee zat you do. Now good night. I see you later on or if not, I see you in ze morning.'

Mandy and David had already buggered off in the vague direction of El Anon, and now Edith marched off across the glistening El Paseo heading towards Calle Sevilla.

'Tell you what,' Julian mused after her. 'She's a game old bird, and there's no arguing that!'

'No,' I agreed as we climbed in to the Cherokee 'She doesn't miss a thing. I hope I'm half as good as she is if ever I get to her age.'

Julian turned on the engine and set the wipers sweeping from side to side. As he pulled out of the square Beth leaned forward from the back seat. 'What's all this about a scrabble board?' she asked.

'Have you got one?' I countered.

'Yes, I think so, but why?'

I laughed shortly. 'Well one thing's for sure love, and that is we're not going to be playing scrabble!'

If you go on to the internet or read any one of half a dozen authorative books on the subject, the general consensus of opinion is that the Ouija board made its first public appearance in the 1890's at the height of the spiritualism's latter day renaissance in Europe and America.

This is incorrect.

The concept of the ouija board, sometimes called the planchette (from the French, meaning 'little plank') is much much older than modern American or European history and to all intents and purposes it emerged around the late 10th Century in the Moroccan city of Oujda. While it is true that the city of Fez boasts the oldest university in the world, (circa 5th century) Fez was the center of secular education while the significantly less well known and very much older Oujda was the capitol of philosophical thought and spiritual learning, and more to the point, of spiritual and occult experimentation. Ali Al Hadin studied there, and before you say "Ali Who?" consider this name very carefully for it is a name you know well, albeit in a totally different context.

Nah, that's not right, is it? I hear you say when you work it out for yourself.

Damn right its right, and if you don't believe me, do your own bloody research!

Well hang on, what about that Genie of the lamp business? I hear you wonder.

Right, well forget about "Genie" and think about "Djinn" and you might be beginning to get a tiny glimpse of the ancient truths not widely available in the libraries or the consciousness of the western world.

It was in Oujda that mystics would gather, and in search of contact with their spiritual ancestors and their spiritual selves, they would sit around a table circumnavigated with letters of the ancient Arabic alphabet and two key sigils designating the positive and the negative. There would, within the center of the circle, be a highly polished stone resting on a slickly polished surface; little fingers would be rested on the stone, questions would be asked, and the answers given by the manner is which the stone 'moved' around the circle of letters.

It was a secret lore, not available to all who sought enlightenment and initially, much like the original Tarot cards, unique to the world of Araby. With the dimming of Arab influence in Europe (circa the 12th and 13th centuries) the knowledge receded into the Arabian underworld, muted, but very definitely not forgotten.

There was a powerful emergent interest in occultism in France at the very beginning of the 18th Century, which, in certain circles was quite open; indeed, France seems to have become the repository and the epicenter of a pan European revival of arcane philosophy and heretical thought, certainly initiated in Italy by Lorenzo and the magnificent Medici family, but refined and developed by French adoption and extrapolation. It is clear that La Planchette was used in séance and necromantic ceremonies as early as 1710, and as the arcane teachings of Arabia gained a consolidated hold on French philosophical thought throughout the 1700's it is little wonder that Napoleon Bonaparte sent a French expeditionary force to Egypt in 1798! Perhaps he went there to find a few treasures and to rob a few graves, and then again, perhaps he had an entirely different agenda... The same agenda that took the Nazis to Egypt (and a few other far flung places) in the early and mid 1930's.

For something with such provenance in history, the ouija board has had extraordinarily bad press, and deservedly so.

Would you give a loaded gun to a child? Hell no, of course you wouldn't! But on the other hand, would anybody raise an eyebrow if you gave that same loaded gun to an expert marksman about to take his place for the Grand Prix at Bisley?

And so it is with the ouija board. It's easy for anyone to play with, and therein lies its great danger – but in the hands (and control) of the professional it is little more than a professional tool.

Look, remember my earlier words? It takes six years to train a medium? One year to bring a spirit into a circle and five years to get rid of it again afterwards? Yeah well, the ouija board gives the impatient their much desired short cut and encourages people to play with paranormal forces beyond their ken and control. And therefore when played with by the wrong hands it is hardly sdurprising that things sometimes go disturbingly wrong!

I must tell you the truth here – I do not like the ouija board, but I do know how to use it. Talk to Harry Andrews. He knows how to use it too, but he doesn't like it that much either. Too many things can go wrong. Too many things have *gone* wrong and it is little wonder that Mother Church pounces upon the planchette with the same degree of glee you might find in a cat pouncing upon a canary.

We convened in Beth's study. Without any shadow of doubt, since Anthony's passing, it had become the epicenter of energy within La Casa Blanca. I'm sure it had something to do with the warmth and the intimacy of the room, the soft ambience, the muted, but never-the-less radiant colours that were so much at odds with the rest of the house, but more I think, you could put down to the lady's presence in this place: it was a space that I shared occasionally, and Julian, I suspected, shared quite a lot, but it was still quintessentially her space and her place, and all that was right and good about the woman permeated through the atmosphere.

We drank coffee, thankfully Beth's brew and not Julian's, and for a little while, were content to be quiet, listening to the gentle fall of rain as it brushed against broad leafed plants and pattered on the pantile roof of the verandah. We'd been in for about forty, maybe fifty minutes when the jiggling of a car's headlights announced Edith's return from the village: we heard car doors slam, and because I had asked her to be there, Maria, Miguel's wife, was present to welcome the octogenarian back to the house and to make sure that she had everything she wanted before she retired for the night.

Five minutes later Maria came and knocked on our door to tell us that La Señora had retired, and if it was okay with us, she was also going to turn in for the night.

'Well,' Julian said in his usual matter of fact tone, 'that takes care of the old lady! I wonder what's happening with our two love birds?'

'They won't be back tonight,' I said.

Beth's eyebrows went up half a centimeter. 'James, how do you know that?'

'Dunno,' I shrugged my shoulders. 'But I bet you anything you like that I'm right.'

'Hey Beth, don't take his bet,' Julian laughed quietly. 'Mr. C is on a role!'

I didn't quite know what he meant, but he was right. My common sense, not that I'd ever had much, was now definitely on the back burner, and my other sense suggested that I was being governed by hunch, instinct, intuition, or some spiritual force beyond my comprehension. In my mind's eye I saw Mandy and David checking into El Anon, taking the last (and smallest) room available, and basically re-writing the Kama Sutra from page sixty nine backwards between now and the first light of dawn. It would have been easy to find out. One local phone call. If I'd been asked to make it to prove a point, I'd have made it, but for myself it really wasn't necessary.

'What did you guys think of this afternoon's séance,' I asked, conversationally.

Beth sighed. 'Not much,' she admitted.

'Not anything!' Julian said emphatically, leaning forwards, and seemingly eager to hear what was coming next. 'Why, Mr. C? What did you think of it?'

'I thought it was a bit of a disgrace,' I said neutrally. 'The Elvis thing was a load of old bullshit and although she might be given some credit for coming up with your mother's name and for mentioning the tragedy with those three kids who died in the river, she did not develop any of the links and in the latter two cases she could so easily have picked up the information from external sources. Torre Muere is a place of legend in Jimena and David Doubleday had already tied you in with the name of Maggie, and I somehow don't think David and Mandy have too many secrets at this stage in the game. In short, I was very disappointed and if she did pull in any kind of spiritual energy it was incredibly light and tenuous.'

'Praise the Lord,' said Julian in mock supplication. 'I thought I was going to be out on my jaxie with this one!'

'Yes, well, you're not,' I told him.

'The question is, what do we do now?' Beth sounded totally crestfallen. 'This is all going so horribly wrong. Nothing seems to be working at all!'

'Well my love,' I said gently, and I suppose rather teasingly, 'up in my part of the world we have this philosophy that says "if tha wants summat done proper, do it thee bloody sen."'

'Which means what, exactly?' she asked, frowning slightly.

'I guess he means,' Julian offered, 'that if we want to talk to Anthony, we'd better have a go at it ourselves, because if we leave it to these three international whiz kids, we might be waiting until next bloody Christmas before anything comes through.'

'In one,' I confirmed. And then, 'So, if you're up for it, have we got a scrabble board or not? And while we're at it, I wouldn't mind a few candles lit in various places around the room, and if you wouldn't mind Beth, would you bring that small office desk lamp over here, just to light up the table for me...'

So now the room was very softly lit in the glow from half a dozen pink candles and a single low wattage table lamp. I took the scrabble pieces out of their canvas bag and lay them clockwise around the table in a large open circle starting with A and ending up by placing the Z next to it on its left. I took two small squares of paper, wrote YES on one and NO on the other, and placed them inside the circle to the far left and the far right. Finally I took a clean wine goblet from the shelf and put it in the middle of the circle face down.

'What we do,' I said, pretending to rather more confidence than I actually felt, 'is to very lightly rest our forefingers on the base of the upturned glass. We reach out in our minds to make contact with the spiritual energy that we believe is waiting to make contact with us from the other side of the veil, and that energy will move itself through our fingers to spell out any message it wants us to receive... This is how it's supposed to work in theory, anyway, and really, we should have a fourth person present, not part of the circle, but simply taking notes of where the glass moves to and how it moves. Needless to say we don't have that fourth person, so we are all going to have to be each other's judge and jury and be sure in our minds that neither we, nor any one of us, are pushing the glass in any particular direction. The secret is to relax and to go with the flow of anything that comes down here, and if you do feel the glass moving beneath your finger, for heaven's sake, don't either of you panic and pull you hand away, because that will ruin everything.'

'Isn't this just a little bit dangerous,' Julian asked, from his position on the sofa next to me.

'Julian, it could be if we were just playing at poltergeists, but we're not. We're trying to make contact with your father, and therefore in a way, we're lighting a specific beacon for a specific spiritual entity that all three of us want to hear from. Keep your mind open and your heart pure, and I promise you we'll be okay.'

'What do you mean, keep your heart pure?' he wanted to know.

'Did you love your father?' I asked.

'Of course I did!' he retorted indignantly.

'Fine, then just keep that thought in mind for the next wee while, and that's what I mean about keeping your heart pure. Now, let's start by closing our eyes and thinking about Anthony, about who he was, and what he has done, and what role he has played in each of our lives. Let's be very mindful of how much we need to hear from him for all of our different reasons, and guys, trust me, if things go awry I'll break this circle and close it down faster than you can say your Daddy's name, but I want you to know I feel safe about trying this, because right now, while I've got no faith at all whatsoever in our three so called professionals, I still have plenty of faith in the idea that Anthony will find a way to come through to us as long as there is a way to be found.

'Now then,' I paused, looking down at the table, 'if this damn glass moves, let's all try to remember where it actually moves to and what it spells out, and needless to say, whatever you do, don't push the glass. Either it's going to move or it isn't, and what we need now is just a tiny little bit of faith.'

'If we only have to have one finger on the glass, I can take notes as we go,' Beth suggested. 'Would that help?'

'Sure, that would help a lot, but try not to let it get in the way of what we're trying to do.'

We were quiet for a while. I deliberately let the room and the atmosphere settle down. The rain outside became more insidiously persistent, and although there was some tension between the three of us, it was a quietly positive thing born of determination and not desperation.

I did not feel like being dramatic, and there was no real need to be dramatic, but as the spoken word sometimes carries much more weight than the silent thought form, I felt it was necessary to speak, rather than just to think.

'Anthony? Are you here please? We need you to be here?'

Silence. Nothing.

'Anthony,' and I know it sounds stupid, but I tried to make my voice conversational, as though he was sitting at the table with us in the flesh. 'Anthony, the sessions with David and Mandy and Edith are not working out very well and we need your help, so Anthony, are you with us please?'

Again silence, and again nothing, and then without any kind of warning the upturned wineglass move smoothly over to the card with the "yes" word written on it. It was a single fluid movement and although Beth gasped and Julian audibly gulped, neither of them, to give them credit, took their fingers from the glass.

All the hairs on the back of my neck were standing on end. I was not a spiritualist medium and yet if this were a genuine phenomenon, here I was making direct, premeditated contact with the world of spirit for the first time. I wasn't climbing into Harry's shoes, but this was a far cry from sixth senses associated with palmistry and the Tarot cards

I tried to keep my voice calm and steady, but I would be the first to admit that it wasn't all that easy. 'Anthony, if this really is you, where are you exactly?'

Smoothly, but seemingly with great deliberation the glass moved to a series of letters around the circle.

I A M H I E R.

'Anthony, we're having great difficulty with the mediums. Is there anything you can do to help?'

Again, slowly but with fluid and smooth deliberation the glass moved around a sequence of letters. I was damn sure I wasn't pushing the glass and I just hoped to God that neither of the others were doing it either.

C O N T U T R I T R U S T S P A R O W.

It took the better part of three or four minutes for the glass to spell out this seemingly meaningless jumble of letters.

On the face of it this seemed like nonsense, so we needed some focus. 'Anthony, if this is you present at this table give us the first letter of your last name.'

Immediately the glass moved up to the letter Z and Beth's indrawn breath counterpointed perfectly with her half brother's sigh of exhilaration.

'Okay children,' I said, talking directly now to my physical companions in the room. 'Time for the true test. Please take your fingers from the glass!'

Looking at me in some wonderment, both Beth and Julian withdrew their fingers, as I withdrew my own, leaving the upturned wineglass isolated and untouched in the middle of the table.

'Again, Anthony,' I said, reaching out for Julian's left hand and Beth's right, 'we ask you to confirm your presence. Are you really here?'

For three seconds and four heartbeats nothing happened, and then, much more slowly and rather more laboriously than before, the wineglass, untouched by human hand, moved around the table. H I E R W I T D U K E. As the glass chose its last couple of letters a small ecstatic moan escaped from Beth's lips.

'Daddy's really here,' she whispered to herself. 'Oh God, he's really really here!' She began to cry softly and I didn't think I could hold the link for any length of time longer if she was going to do that.

'Thank you Anthony, we will talk to you again tomorrow,' I said, and I was about to utter words of closing ritual, but again, without any physical contact the glass proceeded to move around the letters, albeit even more slowly than before. N O T O M – it spelt out and then – X D A Y .

'Oh God,' Beth cried out in emotionalism rubbed to the raw, her face wet with tears of pain and pure delight, 'that was definitely definitely my father!'

I stood by the open window, uncorking a bottle of wine and listening to the subtle sounds of the night. The river – always the river, the whispering of reeds the bending of trees, three mad and out of season cicadas and a couple of bullfrogs. In the near distance the erratic tinkle of goat bells, and much further afield the occasional premature detonation of a pre-Christmas firework from the other side of the mountain. Some half smashed juvenile in the back streets of Jimena thinking it would be a good idea to throw a banger at the nearest lonely cat. And then there were the smells, mud, greenery, fresh earth, clean rain, wild flowers... Spain's unique aroma that tugged at heart strings and opened the doors to different senses, unmeasured by science but duly noted by the heart and soul of a man in love with this wild exotic land.

I poured the wine – a very expensive Ygay – with a reassuring glugg into three large glasses, then keeping one for myself, passed the other two over to Beth and Julian. The Australian sat impassively watching his would be lover and half sister as she scribbled swiftly on a small pad of paper. You could see that Beth was all fired up by what she was doing. There was that certain obsessive glint in the woman's eye that bode ill for anyone who might disagree with the conclusions she was about to jump to.

'This all makes sense!' Beth exclaimed with enthusiastic passion. 'First of all we asked if Anthony was here and the glass moved to the "yes" – we all saw that, didn't we? And then we asked where he was and the glass spelt out I A M H I E R which could either mean, if we read it phonetically, that he is "here" or that he is "higher". Then we asked if he could give us any help with the mediums and the glass spelt out C O N T U T R I T R U S T S P A R O W – and although I suppose that could mean any number of things if you break the letters down into groups, the first section C O N T U T R I obviously means "continue to try" and in the last bit of that pattern, we can take it quite literally that he's saying "trust sparrow" – although I'd be the first to admit that I haven't a clue what that means exactly…'

She looked at me hopefully, but I could give her no enlightenment. 'Carry on,' I said. 'Let's see what else we've got.'

'Okay,' she said. 'Now, this is where we get some real evidence, because if you remember, this was the point when we took our fingers off the glass and we asked him if he was really here and the glass spelt out H I E R W I T D U K E, and if we take H I E R to mean here or higher, all we have to do is explain W I T D U K E and that's so incredibly easy because Daddy had an old gun dog called Duke that was a family pet for years and years and we all cried buckets when he finally died of old age, so Daddy's simply saying "I'm here with Duke!"'

Her eyes shone with triumph and I could see that Julian was equally excited. Me? Well I was still being Yorkshire Cautious and prepared to play Devil's Advocate at the drop of a hat.

'Okay, so far so good, but what about the rest? What does the last bit mean?'

'Well, you said that we would talk to him again tomorrow and the glass spelt out N O T O M X D A Y and I think that could mean "not tomorrow", and then either "the next day or Christmas day".'

'Which would be exactly the bloody same,' Julian cut in pointedly.

And if Beth was right, Julian was right as well.

223

If Beth was right.

I sat down on the sofa next to her, studied her notes and tried to come up with a better interpretation of letters than she had managed to come up with – and because my mind doesn't work like that (look, I can't even do the simplest of crossword puzzles and I always lose at scrabble when the scrabble board is being used for what it's supposed to be used for) – I came up with nothing and therefore had to accept that Beth's conclusions were likely to be far more accurate than anything I might consider feasible.

'So if nothing is going to come through tomorrow, is there any point in even trying to get our dollar's worth out of our three top bloody mediums?' Julian asked grumpily, and I grinned into my glass, because as sure as God made little green apples, he did have a point, didn't he? But something else was nagging at the back of my mind.

'Before we deal with that one, can we back track a bit? Anyone got any idea what Anthony might have meant by "trust sparrow'?'

Blank looks from the pair of them, and even when I asked them to think about it there was still a totally negative response... But oh dear, at the back of my psychic mind the church bells were ringing loudly and clamorously even though there was nobody pulling the ropes! It all hinged around the word "sparrow" and I struggled for a mental connection that would clarify what I was looking for. The only thing I could come up with was that in some obscure tracts of Greek mythology flocks of sparrows were regarded as the carrying force that took the spirit of the newly dead to the otherworld, but instinctively I knew that this was not the connection. Apart from that, if we were to take Anthony Zander's communication literally, he had said "sparrow" and not sparrows. In fact, come to think of it, he hadn't said sparrow either but "sparow". Did that mean the same thing or was there something different happening here with this spelling of the word?

So we came back to Messrs. Breck, Doubleday and Schiff and I was not feeling charitable.

'Look Beth,' I said. 'At the end of the day, this has got to be your call, but if you want my opinion, I don't have much faith in any of these three people, especially not Mandy or David. Edith is another matter, because I can't forget that she brought some very accurate stuff through for me, although she got nothing really specific for you and Julian, and in no case did she, just like Mandy and David, get anything through at all that might connect with Anthony.'

I stroked my empty pipe thoughtfully. This made Julian look nervous so I reached out and helped myself to one of Beth's Marlboro Lights. 'So,' I pondered out loud, 'if you were to ask me for my opinion, which I know you haven't done, but if you were to, what I'd suggest would be this. Given that Anthony's message seems to indicate that Christmas day is the optimum time for communication, let's give ourselves and our visiting friends a full free day off tomorrow. Let's go and do Christmas in Spain. Then, on Christmas day, we'll have another group séance and let our friends know that (a) we are expecting a damn sight more from them that we've had and (b) we are looking to hear from somebody in particular. Now if they come through with some evidence and proof, that's fine and we'll take it from there. If they don't then we can send them home early on Boxing Day, get them out of our hair, and decide where we go from there.'

'Can't we just pack 'em off now?' Julian asked.

'Nope, not really, because apart from anything else we might find that they still have some role to play and also, trying to find seats on flights on either the 24th or 25th of December would be like looking for gold dust in the middle of the Sahara dessert... But it wouldn't hurt to make a few phone calls tomorrow morning, just to make sure we can get seats for them on the 26th no matter how much it costs us – sorry, costs you – and then we're rid of them.'

'Don't you feel like pulling out too?' Beth asked her loaded question very quietly, and I was amazed and dismayed that she had to ask it.

Christ knows I was missing my wife and I was missing my home and I was feeling as guilty as sin about being here in Spain when my lady was left holding the fort back in York – but this business with Zander was of such critical importance to me that I could not walk away from it.

'No,' I said emphatically. 'Not just yet. Not until we know. We've proved tonight that we can make some kind of contact without Tom Dick and Harry and as a last resort, if we have to, we'll prepare our own session with the ouija board. The fact that the glass moved tonight without any of us touching it proves that Anthony is here to be talked to, and if our three stars can't get through, but we can, without their professional help, well, this gives me great hopes that all is not yet lost, and one way or another we'll bust a gut to make contact before this Christmas is over.'

Ooh, these were brave words, based on hope and good wine, and almost as they fell out of my mouth, I began to worry about having said them.

'James,' Julian got up from the sofa, grabbed my hand and pumped it up and down like a back room bar tap, 'you really are The Man.'

Beth sinuously uncoiled and wrapped her arms around me, hugging me very tightly to her excessively slim but-never-the-less sensually feline body, 'James, thank you so much. You're an absolute darling.'

I reveled in the attention I was getting.

And I worried.

Twenty: *Christmas Eve, Jimena 2003*

One of these days I'm going to write a book called "Sofas I Have Known and Loved". Over the years I've spent more nights on sofas than you can imagine, some of them good and some of them not. Beth's sofa fell somewhere in the middle, and after two nights, (well, one and a half, really) I decided that going back to my own bed at El Anon had to be a very good idea. We agreed to meet up for lunch the following day, and as the town hall clock clanged out its midnight chime heralding the arrival of Christmas Eve, I drove back into the village and parked at the bottom of Calle Consuelo.

I sat for a minute with the window open, soaking up the atmosphere and allowing my mind to freewheel around the events of the day. I felt incredibly tired – not just tired but drained of energy; all my get up and go had got up and gone, and I spared a passing moment's thought for people like Harry Andrews, Michael Kingscoate, Micky Reed, Jane Jackson and Steve Holbrook.

These were the working mediums with whom I'd either had or still did have professional associations with and I wondered how on earth they did it? Night after night on the road, giving devastatingly accurate demonstrations of clairvoyance, frequently on stage for more than two hours and then usually with a long drive home afterwards and a stupidly early start the following morning. This had been their routine now for many years and yef their energy seemed infinite. Okay there was a huge discrepancy in our ages, but even so...

I found my pipe and shoved it in my mouth, and then took it out again. It tasted awful. I'd over-smoked it and had burned my palate in the process. And yet the smoker's need for tobacco chewed in my chest, and with a sigh, I climbed out of the car and trudged up the hill to the hotel. The Anon bar was full of Jimena's youth, tight arsed boys and big breasted girls, all with animated voices and flashing Spanish eyes, all sharing the undercurrent of sexual excitement and exuding pheromones of expectation. The new Andalucian Rock was blasting out of the sound system, kind of like Black Sabbath crossed with flamenco with a curtsey of acknowledgement to Freddy Mercury, Queen and Montserrat Caballe.

I forced my way through to the bar counter, got a brandy and coke and a packet of LM's, then fought my way out on to the terrace. It was a mild night and the terrace was as busy as the bar but I managed to find a quiet corner under an oleander and perched on the parapet wall. It was a good place to see without being seen, to watch and observe, to pry and imagine and play the part of the voyeur. I drank my drink and smoked a couple of cigarettes, letting the festive ambience wash over me. I noted with interest that David Doubleday and Mandy Breck were huddled in deep canoodling conversation over on the far side of the terrace; they were so into themselves that I don't think they'd have noticed me if I'd stood right in front of them and had blown smoke in their faces.

I felt a stab of unreasonable resentment. Damn it all they weren't here to exchange TV anecdotes and enjoy the te ta te of sexual flirtation – they were here to contact Anthony Zander, which so far they had singularly failed to do! The chances of them doing so in the future were, in my opinion, minus zero, but they were being paid a lot of money for this outing and the least they could do was to try. Rather than dissipating their energies on the love's young dream thing, they'd have been better off resting and getting their psychic acts together...

And then I realized that I was reacting this way because I was envious and jealous.

Here on the hotel terrace bar everyone was with someone else. Boys with their girls, girls with their boys, Mandy with David, David with Mandy, and as usual, Charlie Muggins was all on his own with a belly full of booze, a chest full of smoke and a head full of negative thoughts. Well I'd been here a few times in my life, and listen, I'm the guy who actually designed that bloody tea shirt – but it didn't make it any easier.

I thought of my wife and wished she were here with me – then experienced a surge of negativity because the bottom line was, of course, that she wasn't. But in the script of life, she was supposed to be, wasn't she? Oh I knew that there were good solid genuine reasons why she could not be with me, but acknowledgement of those reasons did not appease the selfish little boy who still dwelt within the framework of my psyche, and for two pins I'd have another few drinks and then I'd have a tantrum!

I grinned at my own degree of cynical self assessment, then as I slid a few inches down the slippery slope of self deprecation, the grin became more of a grimace. Two thoughts did battle for supremacy in my mind. One involved the times that I had looked at beautiful sunsets and golden dawns in distant magical lands, wishing with all my heart that instead of standing there in solitude there might be someone special and wonderful in my life who would stand there with me and appreciate the beauty of that which I was seeing with my single pair of eyes. God, taking mercy on the lonely, fulfilled the wish and provided me with the someone special and wonderful, and then being the perverse bastard that He is, He removed the sunsets and the dawns, drew a veil across the distant magical lands, and gave me North Yorkshire instead. Which just goes to show that try as you might, you can never have everything!

The second thought, more of a memory really, centred around a psychic reading someone had done for me in Gibraltar; it would have been late in 1988 at a time when I was feeling particularly alone and vulnerable and couldn't see what was in my life the following month let alone the following year. The reader had been good and accurate, but her bedside manner needed some work and as for tact and diplomacy, well, she didn't have any. "You're looking for love," she'd said as her parting shot, "and although one day you might find it, you'll always be on your own. Men like you are always on their own." It had not been a cheering thought, but I'd known even then that she was right.

Sod it. I went to my room, had a long shower, then went to bed. My mind wouldn't let me sleep 'till I'd re-run the session with the ouija board a couple of times... In some ways I was amazed at my own bottle because I've never liked the idea of the planchette and have actively avoided it for most of my working life, and yet born of desperation and frustration, and I suppose, if I am to tell the absolute truth, a deep and burning desire to impress Beth and Julian, I'd turned to it as a last resort – and something had certainly come through. Beth had been convinced that it had been Anthony, and although I thought that it was probably Zander and most assuredly wanted it to be Zander, I'd need more than a glass moving to a few scrabble letters, even if the damned glass had moved of its own accord, before I could allow myself to be convinced.

When sleep did come it was born on the wings of a sparrow that asked me to trust it.

I was up early, having a Christmas Eve breakfast on the newly scrubbed and hosed terrace long before nine o'clock. I'd slept well and had woken to a glorious blue day. Gabriel was on duty that morning and I discreetly asked him if an English/American couple had booked in the previous night, and he confirmed that they had, around ten o'clock, and they had been lucky to pick up a cancellation. When I asked if they'd checked out as yet, he told me no, and that they were still sleeping. Which was good, because I wanted to be long gone before they put in an appearance.

I lingered over my coffee and very mindful of Edith Schiff's words, put a call through to Mrs. Christie. She picked up immediately and we were able to have a long and warm conversation. It may have been an expensive call but it was a very important one, being the first time we'd actually had any length of conversation since I'd been away. After about ten minutes chatting I wished her a happy anniversary for the second or third time and told her that I would be back for her birthday on January 2nd at the very latest, and maybe even before that, depending what happened here over Christmas. When she asked me how things were going, I became hesitant.

'Not brilliantly well, I'm afraid. We've had no major successes or contacts so far and quite frankly if our three clairvoyants don't come up with something half way spectacular tomorrow, the chances are we'll be packing them home on Boxing day, then I'll need a another few days maybe to tidy us some loose ends, and I'll be home as quick as I can.'

'Aren't they very good then?' she asked in all innocence.

'Put it this way, they're supposed to be the best in the world – although God knows by what criteria, and quite frankly none of 'em can hold a candle to half a dozen of the people we've got in our own back yard.'

She laughed. "I'll tell someone you said that."

We talked for a bit longer then broke the connection, and for my part I felt better than I'd felt for days. The dark mood of the previous night had dissipated and a load had been lifted from my mind. I hadn't realized just how much I was going to miss Jo and nor had I realized how dependent my mood in Spain had been upon her mood in the UK. In some ways it's nice to be missed, but being missed carries with it some weight of responsibility.

I drained the dregs of my coffee and deciding that another cup wouldn't do any harm, turned to see if I could catch Gabriel's eye, and to my horror saw that Mandy and David had sat down for breakfast at a table less than twenty feet away. Twenty feet was twenty feet but with the acoustics on the Anon terrace they must have heard every word I'd said. I cringed with embarrassment, kicking myself for not getting away from the hotel before making my telephone call.

The showman took over and I put on my brightest two faced smile.

'Good morning you two!' I waved cheerfully. 'You're up bright and early. Have a good night?'

The way they were looking at me I might have been talking to a pair of granite gargoyles. Maybe they were miffed because I'd caught them post indiscretion or maybe they were hopping mad because they'd heard me doing them down over the 'phone. On the one hand, the very last thing I was looking for was any kind of confrontation, but on the other hand if there was any air to be cleared it was better done now than later. So taking the bull by the horns, I pushed my chair back and sauntered over to their table... I felt like bolting for the stairs, but Jimena brings out the courage in a man.

'Have you had chance to talk to Beth Hammond yet?' I maintained my cheerful tone. 'I think she's decided we're all having a day off today and we're going to try another group sitting tomorrow.'

'I don't know why we should bother,' Mandy retorted, her voice dripping with scorn and sarcasm, 'considering you think our last effort was so poor.'

Three ways to play this.

I chose the middle ground.

'Nobody is saying it was a poor effort,' I said mildly, 'only that the results were rather poor and I think that rather more was expected from three people who, reputedly, are right at the top of the tree.'

'More?' Mandy snapped. 'For God's sake, you idiot, I got three strong links there at that séance, and one of them was with Elvis, for crying out loud!'

I don't take kindly to being called an idiot.

Two ways to play this.

I chose the less contentious pathway.

'The trouble is, The Hammond Foundation needs some hard evidence, so can you prove, for example, that you were in contact with Elvis Presley?'

'Proof?' I won't say that Mandy snarled at me but it came pretty damn close. 'You heard me talking to the man, so what more fucking proof do you need?'

So now she was using that lovely F word.

Only one way to go, and although I really didn't want to go there, this lady was leaving me no choice. I was probably screwing the deal up for Beth and Julian and Anthony, but to tell you the truth, by now I was really pissed off.

'No.' I said gently. 'I heard you doing a second rate Elvis impersonation, and if you find that comment offensive I do genuinely apologise, but you'll have one last opportunity tomorrow to prove me wrong.'

Mandy jumped to her feet, her face now ugly with naked aggression. 'Why don't I simply tell you to piss off?' she wanted to know, and then, more to David than to me, 'David, we don't have to take this crap, do we? Why can't we just split from this shitty little place and catch a plane home whenever we damn well feel like it. I sure as hell didn't come all this way to be insulted by this asshole!'

Ummm. Now I was more than an idiot. I was an asshole.

I beamed beatifically at Doubleday. 'Will you tell her Dave, or shall I?'

'Tell me what?' Mandy looked crossly at me, then at David, and then back at me. I looked at Doubleday and raised an eyebrow.

'If we pull out prematurely we will be in breach of contract,' he said tiredly, 'and therefore we loose our fees. Also, Mr. Christie here is at liberty to write anything he damn well likes about us and if we don't like what he writes, our only recourse is to sue the bastard, and it will come down to a case of his word against ours. You and me have got each other, but Mr. Christie seems to have the Hammond people behind him, and so it would be a bit of a fight.'

Mandy looked uncertain. A range of conflicting and contradictory emotions crossed her face and I got the feeling that while one half of her wanted to kick my teeth in another part of her was more than willing to back off. Preservation of fees and reputations were very persuasive reasons for reconciliation.

I took the initiative out of her hands. 'There aren't going to be any court cases,' I said, 'and I promise you that I am not going to make up anything about either of you. But…' here I let some steel creep into my voice, 'you've both been paid very large sums of money to be here and on the strength of your reputations of being among the world's very best mediums, I'm telling you straight, we want a bit more for our money than we've had so far. So what is going to happen is this. Tomorrow you will both sit in a group séance with Edith, Beth, Julian and myself, and you will do your level best to try and make that sitting a success. If the sitting is a success, you will get all the credit due to you. If it isn't a success, it will go down on record that we tried our hardest to make it so, but sadly we failed this time round. But if either of you bright buggers don't even try, or you walk through it trying to get away with that Elvis crap, then you can argue with The Hammond Foundation about your fees, and you can argue with me about your precious reputations, because I'll take it on board as a grail quest to tell the truth about what did and didn't happen when two media mediums couldn't even raise a hair on the back of my head let alone the spirit of a man who died in the very house they're staying in less than half a bloody week before they arrived!'

And that kind of let that cat out of the bag.

'And that's kind of let the cat out of the bag,' I admitted, 'but we'd decided to tell you anyway, tomorrow before the sitting, that there is one very specific person we are seeking to contact, but as you, David, had already gathered as much, we didn't think it would come as any great surprise.'

'What about Edith,' David asked, sidestepping the issue neatly. 'Is she being packed off as well if she doesn't tell you what you want to hear?'

'Damn right she is,' I retorted.

The mobile shrilled. I would have ignored it except that I was looking for an out from this conversation and I saw that it was Julian calling, so figured it might be important.

'Yep?' I snapped into mouthpiece.

'Oh morning Mr. C, just a quickie to let you know that we've booked Edith, David and Mandy onto flights out of Malaga on Boxing Day afternoon for London Gatwick, with a transfer on to LA for Mandy. Beth says that she wants rid of the lot of 'em asap and as far as she's concerned she'll go through the motions of tomorrow's sitting but she's got more faith in our do-it-yourself system, and she's hoping we can do something together as soon as the coast is clear on the 26th... That sound okay?'

'Fine.' I told him. And then, 'Actually that sounds better than fine.'

'You still on for lunch and drinks at Cuenca's? Only reason I ask is that it looks like we might have the old lady with us. Mandy and David seem to have gone walk about, so God knows where the hell they are. Doing their own thing, I s'pose.'

'Probably,' I said. 'See you later.'

I brought my attention back to Breck and Doubleday. 'Have a think about what I've told you,' I suggested. 'Have a nice Christmas. Have some fun. And if I don't see you before, I'll expect to see you at the house tomorrow afternoon.'

So now there was open antagonism between us. Not good. But it was better than the hypocrisy of concealed contempt.

I left the terrace feeling sad but not at all bad. Mandy and David knew where they stood, and what happened next would depend, not on me, but on them.

I spent a good hour walking round the village, soaking up the sunshine and breathing in the clear clean mountain air. I'd done all my proper Christmas shopping back in Yorkshire before I'd left, but I thought it might be nice to get a couple of little somethings for Beth and Julian and used this as an excuse to nip in and out of various shops and getting into the Christmas spirit. For Julian I found a lovely thick leather belt with a heavy brass buckle and for Beth I came up with a beautifully framed miniature oil painting of Jimena's castle in the last rays of the evening. Well pleased with my purchases I headed back down to Pepe's bar for the first drink of the day.

La Tasca was full even at that relatively early hour, mostly the ex-pat community doing their own Christmas thing, but I managed to find a seat just outside the door, and sat in the sunshine sipping at a tinto verano – red wine, lemonade and a shot of lime juice over ice – and despite my best efforts not to, found myself thinking back to the recent conversation with David and Mandy. In the Christie jigsaw theory their "pieces" didn't fit into the Jimena picture; I bore them no real ill will but on Beth and Julian's behalf, their presence and cavalier manner angered and annoyed me. I didn't know how much they were being paid, but I did know that it would be considerably more than my own fee – and God knows that was more than fair and generous. And what had they done to earn it so far? They'd each done three questionable readings and they'd sat in one mockery of a séance. In my opinion it wasn't enough and it wasn't good enough, and yet they obviously thought otherwise. How they could think this was beyond me and when I dwelt upon it I found myself getting angry for Anthony Zander as well as for his children.

And then I heard Zander's voice whispering in my ear... *"Be charitable, James. Be charitable!"*

Yeah, well that was easy to say, but not so easy to do when the charity bucket was almost empty. But his voice in my thoughts did at least make me try, and when I thought about it a bit more, I suppose I did find some glimmer of enlightenment.

Take two people who have some degree of psychic awareness and clairvoyant ability, give them credit where credit was due for having distinct and camera friendly personalities, place them in a time when the media was opening up in a very big way to the idea of clairvoyance being a viable (and very inexpensive to produce) audience grabbing TV commodity, and it was inevitable and natural that people like Mandy and David would find their niches. No programme producer would be interested in featuring little wizened old ladies with tea cups and crystal balls (too witchy, too pagan, too occult) and nor would they be interested in finding the genuine clairvoyants that quietly stood their ground in the spiritualist churches (too ordinary too parochial and no media charisma) ... No, they didn't just need mediums, they needed mediums who could double as entertainers and presenters who were confident in front of the red eye and who could sell themselves as the real McCoy to their avid, if largely uneducated audiences out there in TV land.

And if the TV mediums weren't so great, well, hey look guys, don't worry, we'll edit out the crap bits and the no-hit sequences, we'll spend six hours filming to get twenty good minutes, and if we have to do a little cross-editing as well, just to make sure you look good, and the programme looks good, and the channel looks good, well that's absolutely fine!

Cut to the second strand of the problem.

You're up there on the TV screen on the receiving end of national and sometimes international acclaim and those lovely fat fees are getting shoved into your bank account every month. It is not too long before you start believing in your own publicity and recognize that you've got to make the most of what you're getting

235

while you're getting it. Spiritual integrity departs on the wings of Mamon.

Cut to the third strand of the problem.

You're dying and you haven't got an infinite amount of time. You've got good money to spend or hiring the best mediums in the world. You yourself are highly placed within the media, so where, other than within the media, do you go to find your three psychic superstars? Especially if you are in a wee bit of a hurry?

I sighed, realising that I might have got it all wrong, but at least beginning to see how the cock-up with Breck and Doubleday could have occurred. Perhaps it was not fair to blame them after all, and in the circumstances could you really blame Zander?

The noise from within La Tasca was becoming raucous so I finished my drink and walked up into the square. Here the sun struck through the branches of the sentinel orange trees that stood guard around the periphery causing a dappled light to cascade across the paving stones like a sea of sensual shape and form; the gentlest of breezes tugged at the leaves causing the shadows to dance in time to the faint rustling of leaf against branch. When I'd first come to Jimena these trees had not been here. They'd been planted in my first year of residence and had grown swiftly into verdant bushes and then even more rapidly into these healthy specimens of Seville orange. In an odd way they marked the passing of my time in this place, and I was content to sit on the perimeter wall for a while, watching the light dance its shadowy ballet, and delighting in the fact that here we were on December 24th, and for all the world this could have been the best day of a good English summer. I lit my pipe and grinned at the thought.

I watched as Barney entered the square from Calle Sevilla. He was walking slowly, ambling really, but using his Malacca cane. The straw Panama was pulled well down over his eyes, eyes that seemed to be looking down rather than straight ahead. He cut his usual dapper figure but on this day he seemed to be surrounded by an air of sadness. This impression was enhanced when he came to a halt by the wall some fifty feet away to my left, and simply stood there, still and ramrod straight, staring out along the valley.

Impulsively I shifted my rear end off its perch and strolled on over.

'Morning Barney. Happy Christmas to you!'

He turned at my greeting and his rheumy old eyes lit up with pleasure. 'James, my dear dear boy! And a very happy Christmas to you too!'

I glanced at my watch. It was still only twenty minutes to twelve. 'Do you fancy a quick Christmas drink?' I asked, nodding in the direction of La Tasca .

'That's extremely kind of you, but no, thank you. For one thing I suspect La Tasca will be full of the rowdy brigade, and for another, if I start drinking this early in the day, I shall be quite ruined by tea time, and that won't do at all! I shall of course get very ruined this evening in a bid to make absolutely certain I don't wake up until Boxing Day and that will be another Christmas dealt with in my usual way1'

I laughed dryly. 'I gather that you don't like Christmas very much either?'

'Don't you like it?'

'No, not really... Leastways not in England. Out here it's not so bad. Christmas is still a religious thing for most people, and the present giving and commercial stuff is held back 'till "Three Kings" on January 6th, which makes a lot of sense. It's become unbearable in the UK with all the hype.'

'Oh I quite agree.' And then, with an unexpected degree of passion. "I detest Christmas! You can forget about Easter and St Georges Day and Remembrance Sunday and you can conveniently forget about birthdays, but Christmas is so in your face that you can't just remove it either from your consciousness or the calendar, and so it beckons every twelve months like the ticking of some God awful time bomb reminding you that you are yet another year older and that therefore you've got another year less before the time bomb explodes and one morning, without any warning if you're lucky, you wake up dead – and then The Great Accounting begins. And that is something that I do not look forward to!'

He broke eye contact and turned his lovely wizened old face back towards the valley. His voice took on a wistful tone. 'I am eighty nine years old. I want to live to be a hundred and three. But with every turning year I find myself asking "Well Barney my lad, will this be your last one or not?" and that is not a healthy state of mind to be in, I'm sure you will agree. And the other thing about Christmas, is of course, that it makes you feel so bloody lonely! Oh it's wonderful if you're surrounded by laughing children and a loving family, but if you're not, well...' he shrugged his shoulders, not needing to take the conversation a single word further. He'd said it all.

I felt an epiphany of compassion and acting purely on impulse insisted that he join us for lunch at Cuenca's bar.

'But my dear boy, I couldn't possibly. I mean, it's very kind of you, but I don't really know these people.'

'You know me,' I said tartly, 'and as a matter of fact you have met Elizabeth and Julian before, up at Corrie's bar the other night. So you won't be among strangers, and besides,' I started getting a bit puffy and pompous, 'I absolutely insist, and so that's the end of our discussion.'

'In that case,' the walls of his reserve began to crumble, 'I accept your kind offer most gladly. You really are a champion young man.'

A curious turn of phrase for I was nobody's champion, and although nowhere near Barney's age, I was certainly not young.

Like everywhere else, Cuenca's was busy and boisterous, but we found a space at the end of the bar, and while we waited for Beth & Co. to arrive we enjoyed a glass of wine and I deliberately steered Barney into talking about his musical career. It seemed I'd been able to lift him out of his Christmas blues and he chatted away animatedly about Errol Garner's right hand reach and left hand technique until, over his shoulder I saw Beth put her head through the door, and gave her a wave. With Julian and Edith in tow she walked into the bar, and I patted Barney's arm to let him know that our lunch companions had arrived.

Barney turned from the bar... I saw him peer forwards... Watched all the colour drain from his face... Watched him take one hesitant step forwards... Watched the wine glass drop from his hands to fall forgotten to the floor... Wondered what the hell was going on? Was he having a heart attack or had he seen a ghost? And then got part of my answer when I heard him murmur with disbelief and incredulity – 'Edith?' And then in a louder voice, still questioning and loaded with emotion –

'Edith? Is this really you...?'

I switched my attention to Edith Schiff who was stood stock still six feet away. She was wearing her plain black skirt with the high collar, and her hair was pulled back into its usual uncompromising bun. She was staring at Barney with the same degree of shock and disbelief.

'Barney?' she croaked, angling her head to one side and squinting. 'Barney? Mein Gott! Mein Gott! Gott in himmel! Barney! Barney!'

She was weeping and opening her arms and Barney, oblivious to the world was falling into them and they were embracing like a pair of young lovers. They were laughing and crying, talking to each other in German (for God's sake I'd never known that Barney could even speak German) while the rest of the bar looked on with bemusement and amusement. With Beth and Julian in cohort, I watched the drama of the reunion play out before my eyes and my mind was thinking some very strange things about jigsaw puzzle pieces and the impossible powerflukes of fate and destiny and synchronicity.

It took some time, but we got the semblance of a story out of them, some of it told by Barney, some of it told by Edith, some of it told by both of them talking over each other at the same time. In brief, they'd first met in 1939 when they were working together for the War Office in London. They'd fallen in love and had had an affair that had lasted through until 1940 when they had been separated by the fortunes of war. They'd met again in 1945 and had resumed their affair until 1947, at which time they'd either separated or had been separated; they'd stayed in touch by letter for a few years, but then contact had been lost. Addresses had been changed. Letters to and from both had been returned marked "return to sender" in two languages. But over fifty six years they had never forgotten each other, and now after fifty six years, they were reunited once again in the Andalucian hill village of Jimena de la Frontera, and wasn't it amazing! Wasn't it unbelievable? Wasn't it a fantastic coincidence? Wasn't it just wonderful?

They ate little more than a few token mouthfuls but they drank copiously. Beth, Julian and I, we ate more, drank almost as much and shared in the joy of their moment. We asked questions – few of which were actually answered. We joined in the excitement and the animation of their conversation. But my head was way off on another tangent completely.

After fifty six years an unexpected reunion was amazing but it had to be believable rather than unbelievable, for in the final analysis, it had actually happened, hadn't it? But was it a fantastic coincidence or was there some other energy at play in this strange scenario? Jimena is not exactly the crossroads of the world, but a small hill village unmarked on most maps, so what was it about this little township that caused such catalysts in so many peoples' lives – people who had never even heard of Jimena until they arrived in the place? Was this just wonderful, or could it be more accurately described as wondrous?

I tried tuning in to their conversation on an alpha level, trying to pick anything up on a psychic vibration, while at the same time studying their body language – and the only thing I came away with was a thought fragment that suggested that although Edith had been genuinely been surprised to see Barney she was not quite as surprised as Barney had been to see her. Improvable, totally subjective, no more than a nuance of an impression, but that thought nagged and barbed and wouldn't go away.

And now I have a problem, for obviously there is a story here longing to be told... A love story wrapped in espionage and spanning more than six decades. This story, if told, would see Barney in the role of an SIS controller and Edith as his remarkably successful SIS operative who wormed her way to the very top of the Nazi hierarchy before being exposed as a spy. It would be a story about seerism and clairvoyance, of the occult, of great hope, great fear and great endurance. It would be a story of the concentration camps and the huge determination of spirit to survive the darkest days of the holocaust. It would be a story of healing and a story of how some things can never be healed despite the passing of however many years God might provide. It would be Edith and Barney's story – but their story has no part to play in this book other than to draw our attention to the strange energies that are seemingly so unique to the village of Jimena de la Frontera. This is Anthony Zander's book, and page counts, publishing deadlines and a promise force me to leave Edith and Barney's story for another book at another time.

After an hour or so we left them to it. To say that they had a lot of catching up to do was probably the understatement of the year.

Through lack of any better idea we retreated to La Casa Blanca and I told Beth and Julian of my run in with Mandy and David that morning and we talked at some length about what we were going to do next. Just as Julian had indicated, Beth was feeling no more charitable than I had been feeling earlier on and she had come to some very definite conclusions.

'It's quite straight forward,' she said vehemently. 'Either they come up with something tangible tomorrow afternoon or they're all going home on Boxing Day. I've had enough of this shilly shallying around, and to echo your sentiments, James,' she gave me a passing nod, 'I want something for my money. If they do manage to get something for us, and I quite agree that at this stage in the game they might as well know that we want contact with someone specific, although I'm damned if we're going to tell them who, then we can reassess and see where we go from there.

'I think that Mandy and David are little more than a pair of clever con artists, and quite frankly I shall be glad to the back of the pair of them. Although the jury is out on Edith, the truth of the matter is that we've had less from her than the other two.'

'That's not strictly true,' I said quietly. 'You and Julian got bugger all, but she sure as hell impressed me, even if there was not one single thing that was relevant to Anthony.'

'Fine,' Beth retorted. 'But Anthony is what this is all about, and the fact of the matter that the only one who has forged any kind of link with him is you with the glass and the letters.'

'That wasn't me,' I said. 'That was us.'

'Whatever. I'm not interested in semantics. But the fact remains we achieved more on our own than with our three experts put together. If we can do it once, surely we can do it twice?'

'Indeed, we can certainly try, and in principle, maybe with a little more preparation and a little more focus, we can do a lot better than we did last time... But if it comes to it, I wouldn't want to do it until our guests are well out of the way and we've done something to remove their energies from the house as well as their physical presences.'

'How long will that take?' she asked, facing me with her legs parted and her fists bunched into her waist.

I shrugged. 'A few hours maybe, I...'

'Good!' she snapped. 'If they're going they'll be gone by ten o'clock. I'm damned if we're going to drive them to the airport so

241

I've got a taxi on standby.   That means we could start at lunchtime!'

'Yes we could start at lunchtime,' I said, 'on condition that you are feeling calm and centred and totally serene.'

'But I am not feeling calm and serene!'

'That's the whole point, love – you need some calm and serenity before you go into something like this, and Julian, that goes for you to!'

'I'll do my best, man.'

Beth's bottom lip was trembling with petulance, then she saw the way that I was looking at her, and she couldn't stop the smile from tugging at the corner of her mouth.

'You're teasing me,' she complained.

'Maybe just a bit,' I admitted.

We talked for another half an hour about Edith and Barney, marveling at the coincidence which I didn't think was just coincidence and wondering what they were up at that moment. For Julian's money they were shacked up in a geriatric sexual tryst back at Barney's apartment…

'Don't be so disgusting,' Beth shuddered. 'They're far too old for that sort of thing!'

Which showed how little she knew about the sexual habits of crinklies.

…And for her money they were holding hands in a dimly lit corner talking about old times and breaking into occasional floods of tears at the tragedy of fifty six years having passed them by.

I thought they were both wrong and was going to keep my money's worth to myself – but both Beth and Julian pushed for an opinion to such an extent that I had the choice of either making one up or committing myself to what I really thought.

'I think they're probably still at Cuenca's,' I said slowly. 'And Beth, you might be right about them holding hands, but I don't think they're talking about themselves particularly. I think they're talking about us. And I think maybe they're talking about the war.'

'The war?' Julian wondered out loud.

'Yeah, that little historical blip that occurred between 1939 and 1945.'

'Why the war?' Beth asked.

'Because if you read between the lines of what we've been told and what we know about Edith from the file you put together about her, it was probably the war that made them and then broke them.'

'I don't understand,' said Julian. 'They broke up in 1947 didn't they? And that was two years after the war was over.'

And he was right about that but he wasn't taking into account the three years Edith had spent in Belsen or what she might have had to do to survive those three years. And he wasn't taking into account the way in which that kind of experience can indelibly scar a person for life, scarring not just their bodies and their minds, but also scarring their very souls. Edith may have loved Barney to death but if, in her mind, he was in any way associated with the horrors she must have experienced, it was inevitable that as part of the process of expunging those horrors Barney's presence in her life would also have to be expunged.

As if by tacit agreement we allowed the conversation to veer away from the reunited friends. Their history was their history, and we, peripherally caught up in the slipstream of their reunion had neither the right to pry nor even to speculate.

We ran out of conversation so to while away the afternoon we watched "Titanic" on Canal Sur (dubbed into Spanish with the most unlikely voices) and drank a bottle of wine.

By five o'clock I was restless and decided to head back to the village. I got mixed signals from my friends. They wanted me to go so that they could be alone but they wanted me to stay so that they could not be alone. I told them I'd be at El Anon if they wanted me and did a scarper.

By the time I got back to the Anon Jimena had fallen into Christmas Proper mode. Apart from La Tasca and Corrie's that had stayed open a while longer than most to serve the ex-pat community, all the bars and shops were shut and the Spanish population had retreated behind doors to do the family thing. Despite the profusion of decorative lights and festive bunting the streets were deserted and the village had become something akin to a small ghost town.

I showered and changed and then because I needed air and space, I walked the familiar streets for a couple of hours, soaking up and being touched by the calmness of the atmosphere. My head was full of disconnected thoughts that needed to be plugged in and turned

243

on, except that in some cases I had the plugs and no sockets and in others I had the sockets and no plugs! Square pegs in round holes!

I realized that despite my earlier bravado I was troubled by the turn of events with Mandy and David. Unintentionally I'd made a couple of enemies there and as I had enough of those already I could have done without making two more. This scenario couldn't have been in Zander's script, but then, I wondered, had Zander even had a script in the first place or had he been a tool of some agent energy that was pushing the puzzle pieces across the board as part of some private spiritual agenda to which we mere mortals were not privy?

And then there was the business with Edith Schiff and Barney, which if you took it at its face value was a bizarre coincidence. Was it any less bizarre to think that this was not a coincidence at all but a pre-destined twist of fate that had needed Zander's input to be fulfilled? If Zander had not invited Edith to Jimena she would never have made the fifty six year old connection with Barney Lavell – so was Edith part of Zander's puzzle or was Zander part of her's?

There were other thoughts along these lines that demanded my attention, not so pressing but in their own way just as niggling – that wrapped themselves around the emotional link between Beth and Julian. If Zander had not been diagnosed with a terminal illness would Beth have given up her law practice to look after him and would Julian have remained by his father's side had Zander been hale and well? Without Zander would Julian and Beth ever have made their mental connection, and now that they had, would they be allowed by someone's law to consummate it on a physical level? In these modern times buggery is quite legal between consenting adults and tipping the velvet has even made it onto our TV screens, but as far as I knew, in English law at least, it's still incestuous and therefore illegal to have carnal knowledge of one's half sister or brother!

Beth more so than Julian had this issue to deal with for it must inevitably be she who finally decided the outcome of the situation, and I did not envy her the role she was being asked to play. In the face of it there was only one way it could go, for despite all her beauty and vivacity Beth Hammond was still a conservative lady with traditional values – but what if Zander's fated presence in her life had less to do with being her father and more to do with presenting her with the personal challenge of overthrowing and rising above some stupid pre-birth control Victorian law which was totally out of sympathy with personal emotions and the need of two pure hearts?

And then, of course, somewhere in the midst of this matrix, there was me. What was my role in all of this? What was I supposed to be doing? Who or what was shoving my pieces around the board? Was it my task simply to record and narrate these events in an honest attempt to earn my fee or was I being used by a Higher Authority to celebrate Jimena's presence in the world, and within the fullness of time, to bring other needy souls in search of healing to this sanctuary in the Spanish mountains?

It was a grandiose and ego pleasing notion, but I'd been playing the "what if" game for more than an hour and saw no harm in pushing it a little bit further.

So, what if I'd been brought in to write a book about Anthony Zander but the real agenda was that I should write a book about Jimena de la Frontera with Zander's involvement being only peripheral to that priority? That would make some psychic sense of why Zander chose me for the task, for Jimena, both the reality and the idea of the place, was so deeply ingrained within my consciousness and sub-conscious that my failings as a writer might be made up for by my dedication to and obsession over this magical hill village in the middle of nowhere important.

You!

You're sitting there reading this in Middlesborough, Manchester or Medway. Your lover has left you! You're bankrupt! Your spirit is sick and your body is ill. You are emotionally drained and intellectually destitute. You are devastated! You are empty and need to be filled. You are cold and long to be warm. You are desperate to cry but tears refuse to fall. Life has slammed its oh so selective bloody door in your face and now you need somewhere to hide but there is nowhere to hide. You need to run but there is nowhere to run to!

But you are reading this!

And now you know about Jimena de la Frontera. It is not Lourdes. There are no miracle cures. But it is an honest place and its magic, especially its healing magic, is beautiful. Its ability to bring calm to the troubled soul is genuine. It is a spiritual safe haven and its incredible synergy offers succour and sanctuary. Your life may have gone wrong and you may be feeling suicidal, but what if you have within you the skill and the knowledge to cure cancer? Please don't put your head in the oven or jump off the roof. Far better you come to Jimena for a while and find the cure.

I ended up sitting mournfully alone by the remnants of the log fire in the El Anon bar trying to work out the answers to the meaning of life and everything and getting nowhere very fast. The room was filled with shadows and the exotic aroma of woodsmoke and red wine and the senses of a tired mind opened themselves up to a host of evocative memories...

A younger me stoned out of my mind trying to dance the flamenco on a creaking table top, Garth Odell offering me a Bloody Mary for breakfast on the premise that if that was what he was having for *his* breakfast it should be damn well good enough for me! I remembered Garth and Suzana's two beautiful kids, Alex and Sammi, dressed in their pyjamas and argueing over the bar counter with the ferocity of eight year olds who was going to have the last drop of milk on their corn flakes, and then there was the wicked mischievous smile of my old friend Sam Sellers who could shock you at the drop of a hat but whose words seldom, if ever, caused any real offence.

My eye lit upon the old black telephone on the corner of the bar and I remembered the times when I'd paced up and down willing it to ring with an expected call from home. Occasionally it had rung and even though the call had been for me, I had never heard what I had needed to here.

Among the shadows I remembered the dancing lightmotes of mid-summer sunbeams, the laughter and the late nights of a long passed season when I had been a blank canvas and an empty vessel; now the canvas was covered in vibrant oil and the vessel was full to overflowing, but still I remembered well the days when I had been The Magician and now resented more than ever my new role as The Hermit.

Twenty One: *Christmas Day 2003 – The third séance*

Neither Edith nor Mandy and David returned to La Casa Blanca on Christmas Eve but they did arrive en masse after lunch on the 25th in Eloy's aging taxi and we were ready and waiting for them. Beth and Julian ushered Mandy and David into the kitchen where Miguel and Maria had prepared a light Spanish buffet – it was all smiles and Happy Christmas and "Oh Gaaaard we're so sorry we dipped out on you guys last night but we kinda got this thing going and..." Personally, I didn't care to know where David was dipping his thing, but what I did want was a private word with Edith.

I steered her into the reception room. 'Are you all right?' I asked

All right? The bloody woman was positively glowing! 'Jah, I'm fine. Vhy do you ask?'

'Well, you didn't come home last night and we were all a little bit worried, and...'

'Vhere I vas last night is my own damn business, jah?' she retorted brusquely, but there was a merry twinkle of fun in her eyes. 'Now, vhat you vant to ask?'

'Will you lead the séance?'

'You haff no faith in ze American?'

'None whatsoever, and none in Mr. Doubleday either."

'Ach, vell I never had any faith in zem either, even right from ze beginning. But no, it is not for me to lead ze séance.'

'The time is not yet right?' I queried sardonically.

'Who knows, but it iz not right for me to lead. I zink you should do it anyvay.'

'There doesn't seem to be a lot of choice, does there?'

'You could alvays just forget about it.'

'No Edith, that is something we can't do.'

'Jah,' she pulled out one of her Caporals. 'I know zat.'

She eyed me quizzically, blowing out a plume of thick French smoke. 'But if nozzing 'appens today, zen vhat? Ve all go home viz our tails between our legs?'

'That's what it looks like,' I admitted.

'Zen ve must hope zat somezing does 'appen.'

She patted my arms and turned to go, and I had no choice but to follow.

Emulating Mandy's efforts we had worked hard to prepare the room. Flowers, candles, a few quiet prayers and some nice sandalwood incense... Even so, as we filed in to take our places around the table the atmosphere left much to be desired. There was a tension that plucked at the synapses – I had to accept that it might have been just me because, oddly, I was feeling nervous and uncomfortable with the role that had been dumped on my shoulders – but at the same time I sensed that none of the six of us wanted to be here, and me least of all. Mandy wanted to be alone with David, David wanted to be alone with Mandy, Edith, I suspected, wanted to be back in the village with Barney, Beth wanted to be alone with me, and Julian wanted to be wherever Beth wanted to be.

When I'm in this kind of situation, one where I really don't know what I'm doing, I resort to the old theatre technique of acting the part. So I took a big breath and started acting.

'Ladies and gentlemen this is to be our last attempt to bring something through in a séance sitting that can prove, to the Hammond Foundation's satisfaction, that there is life after death. In all fairness I must inform you that there is one particular person that we desire to have contact with, and this is a gentleman who died in this very house less than a week ago. It was he, who, before his passing, formulated the nature of these experiments and put certain controls in place that we are duty bound to adhere to. As far as he is concerned, he is waiting on the other side to make contact.

'I am not a medium and neither are Beth and Julian, but you, our guests, *are* mediums and therefore, armed with the knowledge that there is a spirit waiting to come through, we are hoping that you will be able to facilitate some kind of link. If we do manage to get through today, then the Hammond Foundation will be happy to take these proceedings one stage further, but if not then we will close down the experiments today and cut our losses.'

'Have you any idea how iumpossible this task is?' David asked from his side of the table. 'Trying to identify one specific spirit is like trying to identify one single grain of rice in the middle of a paddy field' He wasn't complaining exactly, just telling it like he thought it was.

'In one sense you're right,' I agreed, 'except that this one spirit is there waiting to be identified. The gentleman has a very strong affiliation and love link with Beth and Julian and he has a strong psychic link with me. In his earthly incarnation he was a profoundly

248

spiritual man, a very advanced spirit, who, we believe, is well capable of coming through in séance if we can connect the correct phone lines and light the right beacons.' Too many metaphors, but I knew what I meant and so did they. 'During the last year of his life this gentleman trained and prepared himself rigourously for this endeavor and with your help we believe we can be successful.'

Mandy, in a conciliatory tone: 'Do you actually have anything of his, you know, a personal belonging that we can handle and work from?'

'This whole house was his,' Beth said softly from beside me. 'It was a place that he was highly in tune with. A place that he loved very much.'

'It would have been much better if you'd be open with us about this from the start,' Mandy observed with a faint trace of scold in her voice.

'Yeah, but that would have screwed up any kind of objectivity, wouldn't it?' Julian countered, matching her scold with scorn. 'And besides, you guys are supposed to be straight out of the top drawer, so we figured we shouldn't need to tell you. That you'd already kinda know, if you know what I mean.'

'Ach Julian, I am very sorry but it does not alvays vork like zat,' Edith put in. I don't think she was trying to defend the others, just offering her own opinion based on her own experience.

'Either way,' I was eager to ease the friction that was beginning to build up around the table. 'Now you know what we're trying to achieve. You also need to know that is of paramount importance to the Hammond Foundation, and if necessary we'll sit here all day and all night until something comes through, but for the sake of the integrity of the experiment we cannot give you any more information. It's up to you to tell us. I don't know how you want to go about it, but we're in your hands and we're happy to take our lead from you.'

Both Mandy and David looked at Edith but Edith remained silent and impassive. In the meantime Beth and Julian were looking at me expectantly.

'All right,' I sighed, 'as long as you remember that I do not have a lot of practical experience in this particular field. So, let's join hands, chill out, relax and find some calm, and let's try thinking about a lovely spirit waiting on the other side to make contact with us, just a little bit out of sight and a little bit out of reach.'

So we joined hands, we chilled out, we relaxed and found some calm.

And nothing happened.

And forty five minutes later still nothing had happened.

So we called a halt, had a tea break, and then went back and tried again.

And still nothing happened.

Not a mutter, not a murmur, not a whisper, not a creak, not a groan. Not a rocking table, not a floating trumpet, not a dimming of light or dropping of temperature. Not even a message from Elvis! Three mediums, one psychic and two willing recipients, and between us we didn't even get one lousy dog's bollock!

After almost an hour into the second half of the session, Edith broke the circle. 'I am zorry but ve are vasting our time. Zere is nossing here. Maybe ve all vant somezing to be here, but zere is nosing here.'

'She's right,' Mandy exclaimed with a degree of relief. 'I'm not getting a single thing either.'

'Me neither,' David piped up.

And although I hated to admit it, I wasn't getting any kind of psychic vibe either. The room was as flat as a pancake and Marley's ghost had more life in it than anything we had going for us here.

'That's that then.' Beth stood up, stiffly formal, and behind her cold eyes, forlorn with mute disappointment. 'I'd like to thank you all very much for your time and effort, but as of now I am declaring these experiments over and done with. Your fees are quite secure and you are welcome to remain at Casa Blanca until tomorrow, but you will kindly note that a taxi has been ordered for ten o'clock in the morning to take you to Malaga airport and flights have been booked to London Gatwick with connections to LA for Mandy and Zurich for Edith. There is still plenty of food in the kitchen for anyone who would like it, and for anyone who needs a lift back up to the village, please have a word with Julian. I'm sure he won't mind driving you up in the Jeep. James,' she turned to me, 'I'd be grateful if you could spare me a few moments in private, please.'

'Of course,' I muttered, only too glad to be getting out of this room but not knowing quite what might be in store for me "in private".

I followed her through the house to her study. She closed the door behind us with an angry slam, and then glowered at me. It was a very dark look and I found myself thinking that if ever I got into any serious trouble with the law, I hoped that Beth Hammond would be defending me and not prosecuting.

'It didn't work, did it! It didn't bloody work!'

'No Beth, I'm sorry love, but it didn't.'

'James, why for God's sake, didn't he come through? We were all there. We were all waiting. So why didn't he come through?'

'Beth, I don't know. Under normal circumstances I'd say go and ask one of our mediums but it seems pretty damn obvious they don't know either.'

She snorted. 'They don't know their arses from their elbows! My God, what a waste of time and money! I thought these people were supposed to be good at what they did, but they haven't given us a damn thing. Not one damn thing!'

And then the damn broke and she burst into tears, not little sniffles but body wrenching sobs that were long overdue for release. I wrapped her in my arms and drew her body up against my chest, smoothing her hair and patting her back, whispering what I hoped might be encouraging words into her ear. Then I sat her down on the sofa and rocked her gently like a baby while she cried herself out. In the distance I heard the sound of the Jeep starting up and then the crunch of tyres as Julian started out for the village. Then it was quiet and she fell asleep for a while

At one point she stirred. 'James, you'll get through to Daddy, won't you?'

'I don't know love, and that's the truth. But I promise you that I'll try.'

'Tonight? Can we do it tonight?'

'No,' I patted her shoulder. 'We'll do it tomorrow.'

Then she fell asleep properly and I held her until the sun dropped behind the mountain and I heard the sound of the returning Jeep.

I met him in the kitchen.

'Where's Beth?' he asked.

'She's sleeping. In the study. She was a bit upset earlier on.'

'Not surprised. Reckon she could do with a cuppa?'

'No, I'd let her sleep if I were you. How did you get on, by the way?'

'Dropped 'em in the square. The old guy Barney saw us coming and he was out from behind the trees like a shot, helping Auntie Edith out of the car like she was royalty. Jeez, talk about love's young dream!' He chortled, and then, more soberly, 'actually it was really kinda sweet.'

'What about the other two?'

'Said they'd be back in the morning – they'd obviously shoved some stuff into an overnight bag – and they buggered off. Thought I might as well have a. beer, but I couldn't find anywhere open, and Lord knows I looked. Guess I could have got one at the Anon but I figured that was where DoubleBreck would be, so I cam back here, and here I am, wondering what the hell we do next.'

I pulled a couple of San Miguels out of the fridge. 'How are you feeling?' I asked.

'How d'ya mean?'

'Do you feel like washing you hair, watching Christmas TV and then getting an early night, or do you feel like going down to the coast, finding somewhere that's open and having a good old blow out?'

'Oh man, I'm up for that Mr. C, but what about Beth?'

'It's Beth I'm thinking about most. She needs to get out of the village for a while and she needs to let her hair down. Frankly she could do with getting completely rat arsed, but I'd settle on seeing her just a little bit merry.'

'Hey, y'do know its Christmas night, don't you? Not going to be much open even down on the coast, is there?'

'Depends on how much of a Christian you are.'

Beth woke up around seven o'clock. She did not want to go out but Julian and I bullied her into it, so she got into some clean jeans and we piled into the Jeep.

'Where am I going?' Julian asked from behind the wheel as we pulled out of the village.

'Get down onto the 340 then head east towards Malaga.'

'Christ, we're not going to Malaga are we? Its bloody miles away!'

'Nowhere near,' I reassured him. 'We'll be where we're going within twenty five minutes, so you can entertain us on route with some nice Australian Christmas carols.'

'Hell man,' he glanced at me dubiously, 'for one thing I can't sing, and for another there aren't any nice Australian Christmas carols.'

'It is Christmas and we are going to sing Christmas carols,' I announced with unswervable determination.

So we sang "Away In A Manger" and then "Oh Come All Ye Faithful" and on to "Good King Wenceslas." We lost the plot completely around verse six of "Twelve Days of Christmas" and as we by-passed Sotogrande "We Saw Three Ships Come Sailing In." We found ourselves driving into the deserted coastal hamlet of Torre Guardiaro desperately trying to remember the third line of "Oh Little Town Of Bethlehem."

First impressions suggested that Torre Guardiaro was shut but I directed Julian off the 340 and down through a couple of narrow back streets until we were virtually on the beach, and there, tucked away behind a row of small fishing boats was the little Moroccan restaurant I remembered well from an earlier chapter in Christie's history of Andalucia. The restaurant, little more than a beach café really, was old world basic with plastic table cloths in a red and white check; filigreed lattice screens offered most of the tables a degree of privacy and the ubiquitous bottled candles provided half the available light while the rest came from Arabic wall sconces and a couple of draped strands of green and red fairy lights. It smelt of tobacco and salt, sea, sand and fish, and while it was healthily busy with an exclusively Moroccan clientele, it was by no means overcrowded and we had no difficulty in finding a small table, half in the café and half out on the wooden boardwalk. This was a place of smugglers, pimps and drug dealers, but I saw no reason to cause Beth any undue concern, so mentioned nothing of El Marok's chequered past.

I picked up the dog-eared menu. 'We've got three choices,' I smiled. 'We can have fish, fish, or fish!'

'In that case I think I'll have the fish,' Beth said with a flicker of amusement.

'Nah,' Julian interjected. 'I've got a much better idea! Why don't we all have the fish?'

And then we were laughing. Not rolling in the aisles exactly, but enjoying the humour and appreciating the camaraderie.

We ordered swordfish steaks with olives and a green salad with a communal bowl of cous cous. None of us felt like wine so we ended up drinking Stella from ice cold bottles. Beth asked for a glass, one came, and after giving it a brief glance she went back to the bottle top. It was that kind of place, not very salubrious but reeking with atmosphere, and as our dinner progressed at a leisurely North African pace the tension of the past few days started to dissipate and we began to relax – not to the extent that we were doing the jolly Christmas party thing, but certainly enough to register and be noted. Gentle strains of Moroccan folk music, so generically close to Flamenco, harmonized with the sibilant swish of the sea as small waves broke with hypnotic repetition upon the shingle beach. A teasing tantalizing breeze blew off the ocean, sparkling with ozone and carrying with it a hint of warm spice from the not so distant African shores.

This part of the coast was sufficiently far away from the tourist trade to retain its ethnicity. You could still buy a small house for around forty grand; you wouldn't be getting much for your money, but you'd still be here on the beach with this ambience. If discos and McDonalds were your thing you'd hate it, but if, like me you recoiled from the notion of brash music and fast food, well you'd do just fine.

Thinking of houses drew my attention back to Beth and Julian and I wondered what they intended doing with La Casa Blanca.

When I broached the subject they both looked thoughtful. 'I really don't know,' Beth admitted. 'It's difficult, isn't it? On the one hand the house is filled with sadness, but on the other hand we have our memories of Anthony's last days locked within those walls.'

'Apart from that,' Julian added, 'we've got the old bugger buried in the back garden, haven't we! Anyway Mr. C, why do you ask?'

'Ummm,' I mused, scrabbling for my pipe, not because I wanted to smoke it particularly but because I needed a minute to gather my thoughts. *And I wasn't at all sure where these thoughtsd were coming from.* 'I was just thinking that this isn't a bad place to live. People tend to take you at your face value. They're not so much interested in what you are, but who you are. They're not too interested in histories. They don't ask questions. And then you've got this...' I waved my hand towards the moored boats, the beach, the lapping ocean. 'You don't find much of this in London or LA, do you?

'Obviously, you've got a problem with La Casa Blanca. How could you sell it, but on the other hand how could either of you live there? So maybe what you could do is buy somewhere else, you know, not so big but big enough for the two of you, and then turn La Casa Blanca into a small hotel or maybe even some sort of healing sanctuary... That way it would remain yours but you'd be out of its every day life. If you did go the healing sanctuary route that would be a fitting tribute to Anthony's memory... Anyway, think about it. It was just an idea...'

Beth was looking at me very oddly and I wondered if she was remembering our conversation back at Cuenca's bar that day we had met to talk about the book. Julian had his head cocked to one side, and I wasn't sure whether he had picked up the underlying message of my comments, but Beth had.

'You are a wonderful man, Mr. Christie,' she said, reaching out across the table to touch my hand. 'I think Mrs. Christie must be a very lucky lady!'

That stabbed and wounded, because God knew I was missing the aforementioned Mrs. Christie, and I would have loved for her to be here with me in this moment, sharing this time and this mosaic of experience. I'd played gooseberry enough times in the past to know how the script went, line by bloody line, so I could cope well enough with this threesome, but Beth's comment still caused me a small problem. My wife would be in North Yorkshire in the bussom of a family festive season with turkey, TV, Christmas trees, noisy children and dozing parents. Presents would have been exchanged, party games played, there would have been the usual tears before bedtime from her niece and nephew. It was one kind of Christmas, but this Spanish Christmas was a different kind of experience and one that I infinitely preferred to all the false bonhomie and greedy commercialism that went with the British version. Not that I didn't love my family, because I truly did. I just wished that they could all see some sense and move to Spain en masse.

I deliberately steered the conversation away from me and my lot and encouraged Beth to recount some of the Christmases she had spent with her father; we drank a lot more beer and then foolishly went on to brandy and by midnight we were on our way to being quietly plastered.

I paid the bill and drove the Jeep back to Jimena. Julian and Beth fell asleep in the back. I thought that the Jeep was great and decided that I wanted one.

I hoped I hadn't done the wrong thing by pointing a way forward to the sleeping couple behind me. But then, I wondered, had that been me, or another energy simply using me as a channel to convey a message either from Anthony, or if not Antrhony, some other caring soul from the world of spirit? I would be the very first admit that I am no kind of chaneller, but as I have discovered, spirit works in some strange ways sometimes and if it cannot get its message across in one way, it'll keep on trying again and again and again until the connection is made and the message gets through.

The impression that I got was that Julian and Beth had been so wrapped up in Anthony's demise and departure that they hadn't given much constructive thought to what they were going to do after the event. Now that time was here and whether they liked it or not they had some decisions to make. Glancing at their reflection in the rear view mirror, Beth's head resting on Julian's brawny shoulder, his cheek resting on her hair, they looked very good together. No, more than good. They looked *natural*.

I am no lover of stupidity and I resolved there and then that whether my hand was being pushed by spirit or my own determination to see love triumph over restriction and some out dated man made law, I was going to help these two people find their happiness any way I damn well could!

They woke as we left the tarmac and started down the riverbank and I smiled to myself in the darkness secure in the knowledge that at least someone had made a decision, in this case me, and that it was a very good decision indeed.

The Citroen CV6 is a remarkable motor car. I'd done 90,000 miles in the one I'd owned when I was going through my "green" period. It's a bit like a pram on wheels and is probably the least safe vehicle on the roads of Europe, but to give it its due, it does have character and it tends to come in all different colour schemes with all manner of personal modifications peculiar to the personality of the owner.

Barney Lavell's CV6 came in a faded rust streaked yellow with green wings. With Barney leaning over the wheel and peering through the windscreen with and acute case of chronic myopia, it chugged and creaked into the drive and came to a stalling halt next to my hire car. Barney and Mandy and David got out – but there was no sign of Edith, which was a bit concerning because coming up the drive behind Barney there was Señor Eloy with his Fiat taxi

I stayed out of the way and let Beth handle it. Apparently Edith had decided to stay on in the village for a few days, and would travel back to Switzerland at her own expense later on. She'd sent Barney to pick up her things, and he was happy to provide Mandy and David with a lift. I have to say that none of this came as any great surprise. I'd hardly have expected Edith to go home after her emotional and unexpected reunion. On the other hand it seemed that David and Mandy were anxious to leave, and they were gone with old Eloy in the space of five minutes. As soon as the taxi was out of the drive I wandered down from the study to have a word with Barney and to do the CV6 thing.

The car was a wreck, but that's the thing about CV's. They just keep on going! I was peering in through the door, trying to work out the mileage when Barney came up behind me with Julian in tow, carrying Edith's suit case.

'Wonderful old girl, isn't she?' he exclaimed with enthusiasm.

'You talking about the car Barney,' I straightened up, 'or about Edith?'

'Both, dear boy! Both!' – there was such an air of excitement about him that I was reminded of some young fickle teenager who'd discovered love and the joys of sex for the first time. I was amused by the scenario and felt happy for the old man. Maybe his life would now take on a new sense of meaning, and it didn't need much psychic intuition to figure out that if Edith didn't visit Spain very often, Barney may well start traveling to Switzerland on a regular basis.

'Is she okay?'

'Yes I think so… It's been a rather emotional time.'

'I'll bet. And what about you?'

'Me? My dear boy I don't have the words to tell you. Seeing Edith yesterday after all those long long years, and of all places, here in Jimena! That's the most incredible thing, isn't it?'

I smiled and nodded and gave the old man a brief hug before he got back into the car. 'Just you make sure that Edith comes and sees us before she leaves,' I told him.

'I will, but, I, er, don't think she's leaving for some little while yet.' Barney blushed behind his lines and liver spots and I gave him a wave as he put putted down the drive.

With Miguel and Maria's help we blitzed the house cramming a major spring clean into one midwinter lunch time. The day was clear and bright but also a little cool, never-the-less I insisted that all the windows be opened as wide as they would go. You could accuse me of being a prima donna, but neither Beth nor Julian thought so. Like me they wanted all vestiges of the Doubleday/Breck/Schiff energy to removed; there was need for a fresh energy and a different mental approach. All the psychic waters had been muddied here over the past three days and at the risk of sounding melodramatic, they needed to be cleansed. In a perfect world I would have preferred not to have got the Ouija board out until the following day but I knew that if I made that suggestion Beth would be having none of it. There was almost a manic glint of determination in her eyes as she went round with her mop and duster, and while some of it might have been accumulated tiredness and stress, she was a woman working to an agenda and a timetable. Julian, like most errant men in a similar situation, went along with it and let her get on with it in her own sweet way.

We were done by three o'clock. Had some coffee and sandwiches and walked along the river for an hour just to clear our heads. The eucalyptus trees rustled above our heads and the reeds whispered by our feet while shards of sunlight stabbed down through the branches and although I felt nervous about the forthcoming session with the ouija board, I also felt resigned and relaxed. Either we'd get through or we wouldn't. If we didn't, then I'd be home before New Year's Eve, but if we did get through to Anthony, well, put it this way, I'd want more than a few letters from a moving glass before I'd be sufficiently convinced to call the séance a success.

I felt that we did have some chance of making the link for despite the lack of contact through Mandy, David and Edith, I sensed that Zander's presence was still here in this place and that his inability to make contact had not been his fault. This may have been fanciful wishful thinking, but as I say, it wasn't so much a thought as a sixth sense.

Back at the house I took a siesta for an hour, coming to Beth's study a little before six o'clock. She and Julian had already laid the scrabble pieces out on the coffee table with our upturned wine glass in the center. The tape recorder was on the sideboard and Julian had set up his videocam on a small tripod.

And now, for some reason, I felt *very* nervous. So much rested on this session and I knew I was ill equipped to do things properly. All we could do was open the portal, and if anything were to happen, it would be Anthony that made it happen, not us.

I sat down, opened my mouth to say something, then shut it again. From somewhere outside, towards the front of the house, there came the unmistakable putter putt putter of a CV6. And suddenly I knew that everything was going to be okay

By the time we got there Barney was helping Edith out of the car. She was wearing the same severe black dress she had worn when she first arrived, but now her hair was out of the bun and fell in long silver tresses half way down her back. She looked a little like The Witch of Endor.

'Er, I'm sorry to disturb and all that, but Edith insisted that I bring her out to you... Er, I don't know why...'

I locked eyes with the old lady. 'I do,' I said quietly.

'Jah James. Now iz ze right time for me to do my vork.'

We left Barney in the kitchen with a glass of wine and took Edith through to the study. She looked around, nodding approvingly, then her eyes lit upon the ouija board. 'Ve shall not be needing zat,' she chuckled scornfully, 'but zis is a good room.'

'Would it have made a difference if you'd seen this room before?' I asked.

'No of course not. Zer time vas not right.'

'But now the time *is* right?' I suggested. 'When did you know this?'

'Half an hour ago. I vas about to drink schnapps and eat a chicken sandvich vhen I vas told to be here. Zo here I haff come.'

'Who told you that you had to be here?' Beth queried. She was quivering with suppressed excitement and all thoughts of a ouija board session had gone right out of the window.

'My dear, I haff no idea, but vhen my voices speak zen I listen. All zer time I haff been here my voices haff been silent, but now zey are talking, all very loudly, so I come vhere zey send me.'

'Well it's nice to see you love,' Julian said. 'Get you a beer or a nice little cuppa?'

'No Julian, iz very kind, but nosing zank you. Vhat you can do is take letters from ze table and maybe light some candles. I vant lots of light, but I vant it soft light, jah?'

Julian busied himself with the chores he had been set and we sat down on the sofa. 'Your presence here this evening couldn't have anything to do with the fact that Mandy and David left this morning, could it?' I wanted to know.

'I don't know but I do know zat I did not like zose two people very much. Zey are very clever and very professional but I zink zat zeir spirits are in zeir vallets and not in zeir hearts.'

Beth, in an uncharacteristic move, put her arm around Edith's narrow shoulders and gave her a hug. 'Edith, thank you so much for coming back to help us.'

Edith gave her a strange look, glanced at me, then turned her attention back to Beth. 'He knew,' she jerked her thumb in my direction, 'zat I vould not go until I had done ze vork.'

Beth raised a questioning eyebrow and I shrugged. 'I'm sorry, but I had no idea.'

'Of course you did,' Edith scoffed, and then more thoughtfully, "or if you did not, zhen you are a very stupid man and you should haff known! You of all people!'

I honestly didn't know what she meant by those remarks. I didn't know then and I still don't *know* now. Today I could make an educated guess, which is a lot more than I could do at the time.

Julian finished lighting half a dozen lovely pink candles and then came and sat at the coffee table next to Beth, facing Edith and myself. 'Okay Auntie Edie, we're all yours, so go for it.'

'I am not your Auntie Edie, but go for it ve most certainly shall. Now all ve do is hold hands and ve vait – maybe ve vait for half an hour maybe ve vait for a few minutes, but I don't zink zis is going to take very long. Von zing is very important. Please do not qvestion me while in ze séance. Zere vill be time for qvestions later, jah? Good! Now ve vait.'

We waited.

About twenty seconds.

Then Edith closed her eyes and her breathing changed.

And the atmosphere within Beth's cosey study also began to change, somehow becoming more sentient and intense. And that's not all that changed, because when Edith started speaking a few seconds later, it was still Edith Schiff's voice, but all of the accent had gone and she was using straight English.

'I have the gentleman here that you want to speak with and who has been waiting to speak with you. He is very pleased to be with you at last and he apologises about the timing. He has many things to say to you, but his first message is for James...'

I tensed .

'The message for James is that you were right about the movie set and that there are no watches or clocks in the spirit world!

'The gentleman that I have with me is of medium height and build, he has grey hair and blue eyes, and he speaks with an American accent. He is about sixty years old, I think – no forgive me, he is showing me the number sixty two so I think he was sixty two years old when he died, and now he is showing me a date on the calendar of December. He is writing a big red circle around the number seventeen, and is telling me that he passed over at twelve o'clock. He is not saying whether this is morning or night only that it was twelve o'clock... No, I am sorry, not exactly twelve o'clock but just *after* twelve o'clock.'

Edith fell silent for a brief moment and I became aware of the fact that the atmosphere in the study had shifted again and was now crackling with prescient energy; the hairs on the back of my neck were standing on end and the flames from the candles seemed to be burning extraordinarily brightly.

'I have a name,' Edith said definitely and without drama. 'Our guest is telling me that his first name is Anthony and that his second name is Sander... No, not Sander, but Zander He is also making a

261

point of telling me that he has never been called Tony, and this seems to be a private joke that I am not I sure I understand...'

'I...' Beth opened her mouth to interrupt but I lightly kicked her ankle and shot her a warning look.

'Anthony is telling me that he has seen Susan but it will be a little while before they will meet again because he has a lot of work to do first. Susan has been looking after The Duke... and this is another joke because The Duke is a dog, not a member of a royal family...'

In the circumstances Beth's gasp of delight and amazement was allowable.

'He has a message specifically for his son Julian, and he is making a point of stressing that Julian is his son. Julian, he wants you to know that although he has not seen her yet, he has an appointment with Margaret, and he assures me that you will understand what this means.'

'Yes I absolutely do,' Julian said soberly before I could reach his ankle with my foot. It didn't seem to put Edith off her stride so maybe I shouldn't have worried.

'Anthony would like you all to know that since his passing he has been free of all pain but that it has taken him... I'm not sure how to say this, but it has taken him some time to get the drugs out of his system? He is telling me that he was on a lot of drugs prior to his death and that he did not like to take them for although they helped him deal with the pain they also clouded his mind. He is telling me that he died of cancer that started low in the stomach – I can see him patting his stomach – and then spread very quickly throughout the rest of his body.'

Again Edith fell silent for a while; her hand was firm in my hand but her breathing had become quite a lot more shallow and her head seemed to have tilted a little more forwards. Bathed in the unearthly glow of the pink candles the lady looked radiant and for a brief second I had a clear impression of what she might have looked like all those years ago when she had first met Barney Lavell. Incredibly beautiful and totally stunning!

'I am being told that Anthony is buried here, within the grounds of this house. He is laughing very loudly at the incident with the coffin, so there is another joke here? Something about the coffin being too short or his legs being too long, and he is saying that he never liked that particular pair of shoes anyway. I do not understand what I am being told here but again he assures me that

262

you will. He also wishes me to thank you for the gifts you gave him. He thanks Julian for the Saint Christopher medallion, he thanks Beth for the statue of Oscar, even though it was never his, and he thanks James for the book of poems. He strives to say that his knowledge of these gifts must be of great importance to you but again he is not telling me why...'

In a millisecond Julian, Beth and I exchanged a quick glance, that one brief look confirming the identity of the coffin gifts. All of us had wet cheeks but across Beth's face there was a look of sheer bliss. Julian looked stunned, and I'm not sure how I looked, being more aware of how I felt. There seemed to be a space of several inches between my bottom and the leather cushion of the sofa.

'I have more messages. He thanks Julian for the tree and he thanks James for the poem – not the poems but the *poem* – and he thanks Beth for being the most beautiful daughter a father could wish for. He says to James to do it yourself and he says to Julian and Beth that he wants you to be together. There are messages within these messages but I do not know what they mean.'

We did, though.

Edith's breathing was becoming very shallow now and I was aware that her grip on my hand had tightened.

'He wants us all to know that he is not sorry to be where he is. That at the very moment of his passing he knew he had done the correct thing. He wants us to know that... That on the other side it is what we expect it to be... There is no pain and there is no sorrow, but there is reparation and that there is work to be done. He says that he watched you while you ate Moroccan food last night and that he was amused by Beth's reaction to a dirty glass. He is also saying that he was pleased with James' idea...'

The length of the candle flames was quite extraordinary – they reached up almost to the ceiling, and from somewhere all around me wind chimes were tinkling playfully – none of which concerned me as much as the feeling that I was now well off the sofa and levitating on a cushion of air. I don't *know* that I was, but that is what it felt like. The room weas warm with a scent of incense and perfume, and it seemed, to my eyes, to be suffused with a rosey glow.

'The energy for this link is passing so I must be quick and tell you all that Anthony considers the experiment to be a success, that his reason for inviting the four people he invited were sound, and that he will visit you again....

'Jah jah,' Edith's voice clicked back into Germanic Swiss, 'he vill visit you again vhen ze time is right, and zhat zer times vill be almost zer same for James and Beth but vill be different, jah, later for Julian....

'And now I vish to break zis circle, and viz your permission, I must sleep for a vhile...'

Edith straightened her head, let go of our hands, and smiled at us hopefully. 'Zat helped, jah? Zat proved somezing?' She saw what I suppose were the stunned looks upon our faces. 'Good, I hoped somezing vould come through, and it did vhen zer time vas right. Now you,' she turned directly to me, 'get up and let zis lady sleep for half an hour, zhen I shall go back to ze village to be viz my Barney.'

I got up of the sofa, very relieved that I was able to, and Edith promptly stretched out full length. 'Go and talk to Barney or go and talk to yourselves and come back for me in zirty minutes.'

We stood in the corridor, the three of us wrapped in each others arms like a miniature rugby scrum. Later we would talk about the séance and go through it line by line, but at this early moment we just needed each others physical presence; I don't think any of us could have spoken coherently anyway. This was the contact we had been waiting and hoping for, and in our own minds there was absolutely no shadow of doubt that Anthony Zander had made contact. His every criteria for a correct identification had been fulfilled and he had rounded things off with a number of small personal details – Beth's dirty glass at the El Marok, for example and the business of the undersized coffin – that clearly indicated that he'd had sentient awareness of our realm even after having left it! Certainly, there had not been much detail of what it was "like" over there, but maybe that would come later. Even so, there had been some clue in that ambiguous but in some ways very reassuring line "the other side is what we expect it to be."

And I had some thoughts about that!

We convened around the kitchen table. Barney had enjoyed his glass of wine, and a couple more for good measure. Edith looked tired but serene, while Beth looked totally exultant! The Hammond/Boyd "thankyou" bit became effusive, so I backed off to the fridge and pulled out some drinks – cold beers and a bottle of mediocre schnapps from the village supermercado. Barney looked hopeful, so I yanked a bottle of red out of the wine rack.

'Are you aware of Edith's gift?' I asked quietly below the hubbub of conversation from the other side of the room.

'The spooky thing? Oh yes dear boy, of course. Always known about it, right from the beginning. That's what made Edith of such great interest to us back in the old days.'

'Us?' I raised a questioning eyebrow.

'Not supposed to talk about it, but, oh it was such a long time ago. Sixty years! Can you believe it?'

'Tell me about "us" or that bottle of Rioja is going straight back into the rack!'

'British intelligence. Edith was a gift from the gods, she was young and beautiful, she spoke half a dozen languages quite fluently, she could quite easily pass for a German, and of course she had this spooky thing going for her that the Germans, certain high ranking Germans anyway, were incredibly interested in. Anyway...'

'Barney!' Edith's voice cracked across the kitchen like a pistol shot.

'Oh fuck it,' said Barney mournfully. 'Now I'm going to catch it.'

It wasn't what he said but the way that he said it that elicited the huge laugh of good humour from me. The words were alien and incongruous coming from the lips of such a genteel and gentlemanly gentleman. I put my arm around his shoulder and propelled him over to his paramour. 'Barney was just telling me, because I asked him, how you two first met. Sorry if I've got him into trouble.'

'Barney vas alvays getting into trouble, and vorse, getting me into even more trouble, but zank God, zose days are gone...'

Funny the way she said that. I got the impression that rather than thanking God that those days were gone, she was cursing him and that given half a chance she'd have them back again in a trice.

'I have a few questions,' I said.

'Jah,' she sat down at the table, and we took seats around her. 'I zought you might haff... Is zat a bottle of schnapps you haff got in your hand? Good, I shall haff a very large glass, and Barney vhere are my cigarettes?'

Schnapps and Caporals in hand she invited me to ask my questions, with the codicil that she might not have the answers.

'My first question is this – did you have any idea of Anthony Zander's presence in this house before making contact with him this evening?'

'No.'

'Were you aware that during you time of contact you're voice changed... That you spoke with no trace of an accent?'

'No I vas not avair of zat but I am not surprised. It is somezing zat has 'appened before.'

'Do you have any memory of the conversation you had with Anthony Zander?'

'Jah, I remember everyzing, but it iz like a distant memory, not somezing vhich 'appened only an hour ago.'

'Please can I ask a question?' Beth cut in eagerly.

We nodded and she got up from the table, went over to one of the kitchen draws and came back with a small framed photograph of her father. 'Edith, is this the man you were speaking with during the séance?'

Edith smiled, took the picture and nodded slowly. 'Jah, leibling, zis is ze man. Your father, Jah? I zink he misses you very much but he vas so pleased to visit wis you tonight, and no, before you even ask it, I don't zink it vould be a good idea to try and have regular conversations viz him. Now he vill come through to you personally vhen he is able to... And you also Julian, If you vant to have anozzer séance, maybe do it vonce a year. Not vonce a veek or vonce a month.'

'But how will he come through without you?' Beth sounded distressed.

'He vill find zer vay, leibling. He vill find zer vay.'

Edith sounded tired now, but I had one more question.

'I have one more question,' I said.

'Jah vhat is zer qvestion?'

'Does the word or the name "sparrow" mean anything to you?'

That got her attention. Her eyes narrowed and she shot a questioning look at Barney.

The old musician cum whatever with the SIS held up his hands in defense. 'Edith, my darling, I promise I didn't mention it or breathe a word!'

'Vhen I vorked for Barney and his friends in ze var "sparrow" vas my code name. Vhy is zis important to you James?'

I told her about our session with the ouija board and the letters than had come through saying T R U S T S P A R O W and this seemed to mollify her; by now though she was anxious to leave and we had little choice other than to let her go. She did promise to see me within the next two days to answer any more questions I might have and I was more than satisfied with that.

Twenty three: *La Casa Blanca - December 27th*

I met Edith Schiff at eleven o'clock on the morning of 27th December. It was a two hour interview conducted, for the better part, in front of the log fire in the corner of the Anon bar, which was pleasantly quiet after the Christmas rush. She was happy to answer what questions she could and seemed to retain a clear memory of the séance she had been so successful in leading. While she was erudite and direct with many of her answers, she found some of my questions confusing, and therefore had to find her way through to an answer that I could understand.

For example, when I asked her what Zander had been wearing she told me that she hadn't the slightest idea – that she had been aware of his spiritual presence but had taken little notice of his attire. She was puzzled by the point of the question until I explained that I was trying to form a picture of Zander's physical location.

'All I can tell you James iz zat it vas bright and calm and full of love and humour. If it zounds like cliché zen it is a cliché, but your Mr. Zander vas delighted to be vhere he vas.'

So she had not "seen" a picture of Elysian fields, beautiful gardens etc, and had not been graced by visions of angels or old men with long white beards sitting on noble thrones surrounded by cherubim and seraphim?

'Acht, of course not, stupid man! Only a fool or a very small child carries zat vision of heaven!'

So what was her vision of heaven?

That question made her reach for her Caporals. 'James, ze vay you mean it, I do not haff one. Ze place of spirit is a place of light, a place of healing, a place wizzout barriers and borders but at ze same time a place vhich has countless dimensions of existence. You are asking me to explain somezing zat is inexplicable! Like asking me to describe ze vind vhen all I can do is describe ze effects of ze vind…' She puffed furiously at the cigarette. 'You are asking me to describe ze colour of red to a man who has been blind since ze day he vas born!'

You might, she suggested, tell the blind man that red was the colour of heat, and therefore if he was feeling heat he would, were his eyes to be opened, be seeing the colour red – but this was subjective to the individual's perception of heat. Extreme heat and extreme cold, she reminded me, feel pretty much the same when brought into contact with human flesh. In short, a little like Harry Andrews et al, Edith had no vision of heaven, only an impression, and again I was mindful of other clairvoyants with significantly less talent who seemed to have an AA road map to the afterlife: did they have some secret knowledge that the likes of Edith were ignorant of, or did they just have incredibly fertile imaginations?

I asked her again about the phenomenon of her changing voice during the delivery of her messages in the séance, but again she seemed to pay it very little heed.

'Zis is just somezing zat 'appens vhen my spirit guide iz vorking viz me. If we were vorking in German zhen it vould not 'appen because it vould not need to 'appen, even in French, it vould not 'appen because it is a second tongue. I speak English, jah of course I do, but English is not quite zame. It is a language I have learned razzer zan haffing been born viz, so zometimes my guide, she comes in and gives some help. You zay I used anozzer voice, but surely James, it vas my own voice, but only vizzout ze accent, jah?'

'That's perfectly true,' I admitted.

'Good, vell zink on zis. I haff heard you speak Spanish. Sometimes you speak just okay Spanish and sometimes you speak very bad Spanish, and it is only vhen you haff had some drinks and haff lost your shyness zat your Spanish becomes okay. Zer rest of ze time it iz awful.'

I didn't quite see the analogy, and trying hard not to get the hump, I steered the conversation into talking about her spirit guides and she corrected me immediately. There were no guides, only a single guide, who she recognized as being female, a lady who had lived a number of different lives in a number of different times, which explained why she appeared to Edith in different guises, sometimes as a nun, sometimes as a priestess figure from an earlier civilization, occasionally as some mediaevally reclusive wise woman, and sometimes simply as silvery-blue orb of feminine energy...

'I zink she had had many names in many different lives... As ze nun, I feel I vant to call her Brigitte or Sister Brigitte, and because in all forms she needs a name am happy to call her Sister, and vhy not? She has been my sister in spirit since I vas twelve years old...'

'Was it then that you discovered your clairvoyant abilities?' I asked, immediately seeing the parallel timelines that so frequently link puberty with precognition.

'Jah, I suppose zat vould be right, but it vas not until maybe two years later zhat I started to do any vork vis the gift... Even in zose days you had to be careful vhat you said and who you said it to...'

I encouraged Edith to talk about her childhood and her formative years, but she was uneasy about this and shied away from the subject, so I turned the talk back to her Sister Guide, and the concept of reincarnation and the living of more than one life. I pointed out that this was an idea that many people, even committed spiritualists, had some difficulty with.

'Zen zey haff not zought about it or zey haff not examined it! Of course ve live more zan von life! How could ve learn all zere is to learn in just von life? Anyvone who zinks ve could do zat is eizzer ignorant or arrogant in ze extreme!'

She looked at me very narrowly. 'You do not believe zere is only von life do you?'

'No Edith, I don't.'

'Zat is good...' She leaned across the table and touched the back of my hand. 'Do you know vhy you love Spain so much?'

'I could give you lots of reasons,' I smiled.

'Jah, I am sure you could, but I vill give you just von. You hate ze cold. You hate ze cold. And vhy do you hate ze cold so much, and vhy are you so attracted to aeroplanes, and vhy do you sometimes haff problems vis your shit, and vhy do you haff many problems sleeping in ze night but no problems sleeping in ze day?'

This was electrifying because I knew the answers to these questions – or at least, I thought I did. The question was, did Edith?

'Go on,' I said cautiously.

'No, zere is more yet! Haff you ever vondered vhy zis life has been so very turbulent for you? No, vell, I vill tell you! I zink in your last life you vould haff been a flyer in ze var, bombing Germany from fifteen sousand feet, freezing freezing cold and shitting your pants like everyvone else did on zose night raids. I zink you vere very young vhen you vere killed vhen your plane vas shot down, and like all young spirits who die violently before zeir time, you vere reincarnated and turned around quickly to finish your vork. People who are born in zese circumstances alvays haff troubled lives. Vhen vere you born? 1946? !947? Eizzer vhay, you vere probably killed in '44 or '45 tovards ze end of it all.'

As far as I was concerned Edith was telling me something that I already believed to be true. The inquisitor might ask why I believed that to be true, and in good conscience that would make the subject of another book. Suffice to say my belief and curiosity in the concept of reincarnation had led me along some long and protracted pathways of research over the better part of four decades and I was secure in myself about the depth and integrity of that research. In part the research had led to a passionate interest in the whole of the history of the second world war in general and an obsession with WWII military aircraft in particular. The sceptic might suggest that Edith had read my mind, but if that had been the case it must have been a very clever trick (or gift in its own right) for I had not been thinking of anything to do with my past lives while I had been talking to Edith about the subject.

'Zen, of course,' Edith finished, 'in ozzer lives zere vould, I zink have been links vis Russia, maybe if you haff been to Russia in zis life you found some of it very familiar, jah?'

Oh jah, damn right about that Edith!

'Also, almost certainly you vould haff had a past life living here in Spain as a Spaniard!'

And damn right about that too and I had the PLR tapes, all four hours of them, to prove it.

'Edith, I am very impressed,' I said it humbly and with profound sincerity.

'Jah, so you should be!' she smirked, but it was a teasing smiling smirk. 'Vhen ze time is right, I am pretty good, jah?'

I asked her if she wanted to talk to me about Aleister Crowley, and she didn't. The only thing she did say was that she had gone to learn from him and had ended up teaching him a few things. She did not elaborate either on the detail or the context of her remark and would not be pushed. This was hardly surprising.

So I asked her if she wanted to talk about Barney and her time as The Sparrow.

'Vhy?' she wanted to know. 'Are you just curious or do you zink of writing a book?'

'Both,' I told her truthfully. 'But I understand a book has already been written – by your son?'

'Jah Richard wrote a book, but it vas a long time ago and it did not sell many copies and it did not meet vis my approval. Zere vere

271

zings he vanted to know vhich I could not tell him so he wrote vhat he sought vas ze truce. Vhat he didn't know for sure he guessed but so often got it wrong.'

'Anthony Zander read that book and he thought it was excellent. It was one of the reasons why he insisted Beth should track you down.'

'I did not know zat.'

'So will you tell me?'

'About Barney and ze var?'

'Yes.'

'I zink zo, but first ve must ask Barney.'

So we asked Barney, who'd been waiting in the restaurant.

After some preliminary ground rules had been put in place, Barney said yes, and for the second half of my interview with Edith Schiff we talked, not about Anthony Zander but about the second world war, the SIS and an agent called Sparrow. One of the ground rules was, that if ever I did write a book, I would not publish it until both Barney and Edith had had passed over.

'Zat vay ve can vatch vhat you say about us and make sure you get it right!'

'Can that be done?' I asked.

'Jah, it happens all ze time. Didn't you know?'

The session ended with me inviting the pair of them, on Beth's behalf, to join us for dinner that night. They both accepted on condition "zat ve eat anyvhere but zat cold vhite block house down by ze river and ve talk about anyzink you like but nozzing do do viz clairvoyance or séances or sparrows."

Beth wasn't going to like that, but I said it would be perfectly fine.

I knew that Beth and Julian would be waiting for me at La Casa Blanca expecting a full report of the interview with Edith – indeed they'd wanted to come along and be part of it but I'd denied them access on that one, so I only spent a few minutes in my room sorting out the Dictaphone tapes and making a few salient notes before getting into the hire car and heading down to the river. I didn't think that Beth would be too pleased about the ban on clairvoyant conversation – she was absolutely itching to go over the whole thing again and pick Edith clean of any scrap of extra information she could get, and if I decided to tell her, I didn't think she'd be too pleased to hear that Edith thought La Casa Blanca to be a cold white blockhouse down on the river. Maybe I would have to find some tact and diplomacy to sort that one out!

As expected I found the siblings waiting for me, and they hung on to my every word as I reported on my conversation with Edith; I kept it to the subject of their father, for anything to do with anything else was between me and Edith and Barney. Fortunately neither of them was too dismayed at the idea of going out for dinner rather than eating in...

'If we are going out, then I know where I'd love to go!' Beth said.

'Yeah, likewise,' Julian put in.

'El Marok?' I queried, and getting a double affirmative, sighed at the idea of eating fish again. Still, it was supposed to be good for you, right?

Beth was less happy about the conversational restraints, but when I pointed out that after a few glasses of wine and a couple of hard hits of schnapps the ground rules might be relaxed, and she became more philosophical.

The morning had been cloudy but with the spreading of the afternoon the sun broke through and shoved the temperature up to a very pleasant high sixties. There wasn't a great deal for us to do so we sat on the terrace sipping at San Miguels and chatting again about the stunning events of the previous evening. They wanted my considered opinion, and with no disrespect to my good and talented friends elsewhere, I told them that it had been the most convincing demonstration of clairvoyance I had ever seen.

Julian raised, what for him, was obviously a naggng thought. 'Edith couldn't have found out anything about Anthony while she was up in the village – you know, in that time between when she left here, and then came back because all of a sudden "the time was right"?'

It would have been easy to fob him off, but I could see that Beth was interested to hear what I thought, so I put a case together for the defence. 'Certainly David and Mandy could have mouthed off and got some response that filtered it's way back into Edith's ears,' I conceded, 'and yes, there is a little man in the town hall who is richer now than he was a month ago because of the permiso he provided us with, and yes, there's that wretched little priest Father Sebastian who knows that a blaspheming unclean non-Catholic has been buried in unhallowed ground, and it is quite feasible he's been shooting *his* mouth off... So Edith might have heard something on the grapevine. But even if she did, which I have to say I don't think is very probable or likely, consider the evidence she gave us! Anthony's name, his profession, his illness, the time line of that illness, the business with the coffin, the confirmation of what he did just before he died, what we put into the coffin. Then there were the personal messages with regard to Duke, Susan and Maggie, the fact that he was joking about the "Tony" aspect of his name, the fact that he saw you, Beth, reject that dirty glass... These things are things that Edith could never have known about, and if you take that into consideration it rubbishes the idea that she might have picked up some gossip n the village. That's what I think, anyway.'

The next item that cropped up on our very loose agenda were the three manila envelopes that Anthony had given us on the day that he had died. Oddly, we had not compared notes on the envelopes before, but we did so now. Julian's envelope had his name written on it and the spidery instruction "not to be opened until 2004" whereas Beth's envelope and my envelope said the same thing; "not to be opened until after 27th December."

'Well, today is the 27th of December,' Julian said, 'so let's open 'em up and see what's inside.'

I felt uneasy about that for some reason, and was gratified by Beth's hesitation. 'It says not until after the 27th of December,' she pointed out.

'It's only one day,' he protested, 'and apart from that in Australia it is almost the 27th, isn't it?'

'But we're not in Australia,' I pointed out mildly, and then – and I don't know what made me do this – I slid my envelope over to Beth. 'Here love,' I said. "You hang on to this for me, and we'll open them together at breakfast time tomorrow.'

We talked some more, mostly, as I remember, about York and Yorkshire and about cats and Joanna, and I let it be known that I was intending to try and get back to the UK on either the 29th or the 30th. Beth seemed disappointed and pointed out that I could stay for as long as I wanted, and Julian suggested that I 'phone my wife and tell her to come out for a holiday. It was a tempting thought, but they were ignorant of the family commitments and emotional stresses and although I would have loved to have stayed on for a few more days, a few more weeks even, and although I would have loved to see Mrs. Christie jumping on a plane and flying out to join me, I knew that I couldn't do the first and Jo couldn't do the second.

Maria appeared with a plate full of fried chicken in garlic and a bottle of red wine. Catching me at the height of my appetite I ate and drank with gusto, and then inevitably felt tired and drowsy afterwards. The temptation was to go and find a bed or a sofa and to enjoy a long languishing siesta, but for once I fought the temptation, and took myself off for a brisk walk down by the river.

The brisk walk turned out to be more of an ambling stroll and I got no further than that special little area beneath the trees and amid the reeds where I had sought and found refuge on the day of Zander's death. As on that day, a scant ten days ago although it seemed more like ten weeks, I sat on the boulder and watched the river dance by in the sunlight. Now, as then, despite the séance with Edith, I was filled with a deep sadness, but for very different reasons.

As I had grieved for Anthony and his family on the 17th of December, I now sat here and grieved for Spain. In a couple of days I would be back in the arms of my beautiful wife but in the oh so very unbeautiful North of England and I had a sneaky feeling that I would not be seeing Spain again for a while. Maybe I would never see Spain again... So I opened my mouth and breathed it in – the freshness, the light, the flowers, the very earth of Al Andaluz – taking strange and eerie solace from the thought that one day I would come to rest permanently in this place, not much more than an arrow's flight from where Anthony slept in his grave within his oaken grove.

This was not good. This frame of mind, although valid, was unwelcome. I fought against it, suppressing my feelings as all Englishmen do, and walked more purposefully back to the house. From my angle of approach I could see that Beth and Julian were still sitting on the terrace, so I deliberately cut away from them, giving them a friendly wave, and went and sat in the garden. I chose a spot by the small eucalyptus tree from which Anthony had plucked his leaf – "is this a leaf or a 1957 Corvette Stingray with a 5.7 litre engine?" – and stuffed my pipe full with the wondrous red Amphora. I could see one of Anthony's oak trees over on my right, while to my left, if I worked at it, I could see Beth's knees and Julian's trouser bottoms and the legs of the coffee table. They were close enough for me to hear the sound of their voices, but not so close that I could hear what they were saying.

I took out my notebook and started jotting down a few creative lines (well, I hoped that they were creative) and let the scents of a Spanish garden sooth an angry soul. I was aware of the breeze caressing the leaves, and from somewhere close came the buzzing drone of a bee and the impossible song of an insomniac cicada. The cijada's song became stronger, which was even more impossible for cijadas are seasonal creatures and do not dwell in the realms of Andalucia during mid-winter. Then there was a new and strange tang to the familiar scents of the garden, something dry and spicy with a hint of cinnamon… The garlic chicken and the red wine were having their inevitable effect and I felt myself drifting into that beautiful haze of afternoon siesta sleep, dreaming of…

…Except that I was neither sleeping nor dreaming… There was a sandy knoll, two impossibly tall palm trees, cobalt blue skies that were so blue that they were almost black despite a blazing sun, and above all, dominating the landscape for almost as far and wide as the eye could see, was the towering edifice of the Temple of Karnak – not in the ruined state it had been when I'd seen it on my holiday, but as it might have been when freshly built and newly constructed.

The heat that clung to me was a baking hard summer heat. There was a warm wind blowing off the desert, carrying the dry aroma of hot sand that coalesced with the more earthy pungency of mud that rose up from the eternal River Nile…

And, of course, there was Zander, waiting for me, between the two palm trees, wearing his white Billy Connolly shirt, and beaming at me like a schoolboy enjoying a wild prank. This was a much younger Anthony Zander. His hair was blond, not silver, and the pallid colour of his skin had been replaced by a first class suntan. Aching with health and vitality, he looked about forty…

Incadescant light, not as a halo, but as striating and interweaving shards of sunbeams that made the atmosphere ripple, emanated like a heat haze from within the very air… There was a tremendous sense of movement in the ether and an awareness of energies that playfully swept around us, tugging at clothes and ruffling hair.

And yet to visual intents and purposes Zander and I stood alone beneath the two palm trees.

276

He raised a hand in greeting. 'Hi James. How're you doing?'

His lips moved and he spoke the words but I heard the words in my head, not in my ears.

'Hey Anthony, I'm doing fine...' I nodded over his shoulder. 'I see you picked a nice spot for a vacation – or are you here permanently?'

'Don't quite know what you mean,' he grinned. 'No time frame over here you see... I come and go as I please and right now it seems to be right to be here in Karnak.'

I glanced again at the lovely new buildings. 'When are you there? In Karnak?'

'Told you James, no time line, so as far as I'm concerned I'm here now, but damned if I know when now is.'

'Where were you before?'

'With you. In Jimena.'

'And before that?'

'Sleeping.'

A thought crossed my mind. 'You do know you're dead, don't you?'

'Yes, of course I do! And damn glad of it too! I couldn't have gone on much longer like I was back there...'

'Why did it take so long to get through in the séances?' I asked.

'It didn't,' he retorted. 'Mrs. Schiff lit the beacon and I just homed on to it straight away.'

'What about our session with the ouija board?'

'That was difficult. Didn't know what you were doing or what was happening. I was waiting for the signal but I wasn't getting it. Don't remember too much about that now, but I dare say it will come back to me later.'

An echo of female laughter washed across my face.

'We're not alone here, are we?' I asked.

'Hell no, you nearly got knocked over by a little girl with pigtails and a red dress.'

'Why couldn't I see her?'

He laughed. 'You're not passed over, James, you're just visiting, and I know you've got millions of questions, but they're all going to have to wait... I just wanted to make contact now while I can, to say thank you for all your hard work, and to ask you to give my love to Beth and Julian, especially to Beth. In some ways she's as

277

tough as old boots, but in others she's far too sensitive for her own good... Just tell her I popped in to say goodbye...'

I started to get a panicky feeling. "You can't go yet!'

'Yes I can."

'You're our only link! You've got to stay with us.'

'Always with you.'

'No, we need communication Anthony. We need to know!'

'Actually James, no, you don't. Just tell Beth that I love her, and I guess, if you want to, you can open your envelopes now... And maybe you want to remember that nothing is ever an accident and even the biggest mistakes are made for the best of reasons...'

His voice and form were fading and I was flying through a flurry of tears overpowered by the taste of salt and the unmistakable smell of eucalyptus. There was a sense of incredible urgency – I had to talk to Beth now and tell her what had happened, and in my head I heard myself shouting her name, over and over again...

I have to write this next passage very very carefully, for it is written from Beth's experience and not my own.

While I had been dozing beneath my eucalyptus tree Beth and Julian had been soaking up the rays on the terrace. Julian had disappeared to visit the bathroom and Beth had found herself falling into that lovely half state between sleep and wakefulness.

She tells me that first of all she heard her father's voice calling her name, which was enough to jolt her back into a state of alertness, at which time she heard her name being called again, this time, however, it was my voice shouting from the eucalyptus tree, and not her father's! Then she heard her name called again, simultaneously, by both voices.

Acting purely on instinct she immediately got up from her chair and followed the direction of the voice – which brought her to the eucalyptus tree. She saw me sitting there with my back to the bole, seemingly asleep, while all around me and the base of the tree was the lovely golden light. Standing in the middle of the light, superimposed upon my form, her father stood smiling.

'Hi there baby,' he said. 'Just popped in to say hello and goodbye, that I love you very much and I'll be watching over you...'

Then the light had swiftly faded and I had started calling her name in my own voice, and telling her to get the bloody envelopes.

A very short time later, with Julian looking on in some bewilderment and with tear streaks down our cheeks, we opened the two manila envelopes that Anthony had given us on his deathbed. In mine there was a single sheet of paper, and in Zander's spidery hand, there was the single word: *Karnak*. I felt weak at the knees and sat down, watching while Beth, with a less than steady hand, opened her own envelope.

'What does it say?' Julian asked, beside himself with impatience.

'It says "I'll see you again to say goodbye",' she said.

And a little bit more time later, when we were sitting with Edith and Barney in El Marok – a different night, a different atmosphere, with waves pounding rather than lapping on the shingle beach and with spits of rain and spray carried on a cool wind off the sea – we had to breach Edith's ban on the subject of clairvoyance as we told her of the afternoon's occurrences.

Edith did not seem overly impressed. 'Ach, it iz quite natural for somezing like zat to 'appen. I am sure it vill 'appen again. Anthony is now in a different vorld and ve must let him rest zere. If it iz necessary he vill find a vay to come to you, and sometimes you vill know he is zere and sometimes you vill not. It depends on your own sense of avareness. Vhat you must do is learn how to live your lives vizzout his physical presence and personality, alvays remembering zat he iz viz you in spirit and alvays remembering zat vhen it is your time to go to ze vorld of spirit, he vill be zere to velcome you.'

'But I want to be able to talk to him every day!' Beth exclaimed.

'Zen leibling, talk to him every day! I am sure he vill hear you, but please do not alvays expect an answer. Vhere he is now he has ozzer vork to do.'

I guess that's about it. I arrived back home in time for New Year's Eve and my wife's birthday and then got thrown in at the deep end with new work regimes for our 2004 tour dates. In the few stolen hours that were available I began sifting through the three A4 notebooks I had managed to fill and started transcribing about seven hours of Dictaphone tape recordings.

In those early weeks of the New Year I felt strangely dislocated and despite the ever calming presence of the Prozac, my mood swings were enormous and I was in an ongoing state of emotional discomfort. The time in Spain and the experience with Zander had affected me deeply, and although we kept in touch by telephone, I found myself missing the company of Julian Boyd and Beth Hammond.

The only time when I did feel marginally grounded and focused was during the long late hours of the night when I would sit at the PC trying to put this story together.

Reading through it as I have done during the last few days, I realize (as you will too if you have stayed with me this far) that it is an enormous mish-mash of a tale and is probably unpublishable by any normal means. That's what Mr. Mage at Mage Publishing thinks, anyway.

I went to Spain to write about some experiments with clairvoyance and to try and establish hard proof of life after death, but somewhere along the line those notions got shanghaied and instead we seem to have a book about a funny little hill village called Jimena in Southern Andalucia!

Also we have three interweaving love stories. One is of a man's love for a country, another is of a man's love for his children, and a third is of those children's love for each other.

I suppose too that it is about the process of ageing and the psychological distress this process can bring if you haven't learned how to grow old gracefully. But then, when I think of Edith Schiff and Barney Lavell, maybe also it is about the endurance of friendship, the serendipity of fate, and the fact that you do not have to be young to be in love.

I don't know what this book is exactly, but I do know that it is not a novel, and therefore there are many unresolved issues and lots of loose ends and dangling strings that no novelist worth his salt would leave untied. In many respects truth can be stranger than fiction and in real life there are *always* dangling strings and loose ends.

As I read through this file I realize that I have many unanswered questions and that things occurred that I either do not fully understand or I do not understand at all!

I don't, for example, know what happened to me when I saw Zander at Karnak – but see him there and talk to him there I most certainly did, and in a way that seemed totally real; nothing like a dream or a vision or a trance. It was the first experience of this nature that I've ever had, and if anyone is up there listening, I'd welcome a repeat performance! Nor do I, for the record, have any idea as to how Anthony Zander chose the word "Karnak" for his coded link with me.

While I think I understand why Zander chose me, and I clearly understand why he chose Edith Schiff, I do not know why he chose Mandy Breck and David Doubleday to take part in his great experiment. Potentially David has great talent but he is a confused soul and is a victim of his own celebrity. Mandy is a cynically disciplined cold reader and is into her profession for fiscal and egotistical gain rather than anything of a spiritual nature. And yet Zander had inferred that their selection had neither been a mistake nor an accident! Enlightenment on this point would be gratefully received from anyone who knows more than I do!

Throughout this story there appears to be a constant stream of coincidence and odd connections, which in isolation would be enough to arouse curious comment, but when placed all together become something of a challenge to deal with.

There is the dual link with Jimena between myself and Anthony Zander. There is the Karnak poem connection and that obscure movie "Somewhere In Time" with Christopher Reeve and Jane Seymour. There is the weak, but intriguing (at least from my point of view) link between myself and Stephen King. There is the Schiff-Zander-Lavell link that in its own right is fairly mind boggling.

And these things are to name but a few!

Then there is the ongoing numerological significance of the dates and times involved in the whole experience. I first heard from Zander on November 11th (11 + 11 = 4) and found myself flying to Spain on December 8th. Zander popped the pill which ended his life at 12.05 on December 17th and he was 62 years old to the hour.

281

Play the numerology game with Julian's birthdate and you get 6. Play the same game with Beth's birthdate and you get 2. Together they make 8. My key significator numbers are jointly 4 and 8... And in my opinion this is stretching the law of numerological coincidence beyond breaking point!

What was intended to be an objective report has become a deeply personal account and for that I can make no apology. I suspect (although cannot prove) that this was Zander's intention all along. I apologise to anyone I have upset by this writing, and there must be loads of you because I seem to be upsetting everyone these days. One of my editors feels that I am in great need of some professional counseling, and he may well be right.

As I said earlier, I have had a number of phone conversations with Beth and 2004 has been a busy year for both she and Julian. They have been sensible and discreet and have moved to Spain as was suggested to them. La Casa Blanca has been rented out to close personal friends and there are plans in the wind to turn the house into a healing center sometime before or around 2006. I think that Julian and Beth have been very brave. They have insisted that I use their real names – but to be fair, these are not *quite* the names they are using at this point in time up in their mountain retreat. Both of them have read this manuscript and it is published with their full approval... which gives me some small hope that it might also meet with Zander's approval. If he's listening in, and I'm sure that he is... *Done my best for you Anthony, done my best!*

I'm delighted to tell you that Edith and Barney got married on Barney's 90th birthday – I would have loved to have been able to go the wedding, but it was in the middle of a very busy touring period so I sent flowers and best wishes, and rejoiced for them quietly.

A key question that must be addressed is – was Anthony Zander's experiment with death successful?

I believe that it was although not perhaps in the way that he had intended. On the one hand the performance of two of his mediums was a great disappointment and therefore there can be no objective triangulation of evidence. Edith, however, came through for us with an unprecedented degree of detail and accuracy and we do have all of her evidence on audio and video tape – which at this stage is still sitting securely locked in Beth Hammond's safe. We, Julian Beth and myself, have had *our* hard proof courtesy of Edith, but again one is left with the age old problem, namely that it is our proof and not necessarily yours unless you are prepared to accept this report and find your faith second hand.

I have changed David Doubleday's name to avoid a legal conflict and to remain true to the promise I made to Beth. I have not changed Mandy Breck's name and she must defend her own position in whatever way she chooses. And of course, I have not changed Edith's name, for in my opinion she deserves all the credit and accolades she can get for being a truly phenomenal medium whose powers I have never seen the likes of before.

This book has to end somewhere, so I'll end it by telling you about Julian's manila envelope. You will remember that Beth's envelope and mine had an open after December 27th instruction, while Julian was told he should wait until 2004? At the beginning of January Julian had returned to Australia to tidy up his affairs there before moving permanently to Europe. In the flurry and the fuss the envelope was temporarily forgotten, but then one morning, as he'd opened a file, it had fallen onto the breakfast table, almost splashing into his corn flakes... Julian being Julian didn't hesitate for a minute. He ripped it open and found a short cryptic message in his father's hand.

"My Dearest Julian – there can be no proof for you until you believe. Suggest you phone James – Love Anthony."

So again, Julian being Julian, he picked up the phone straight away and put a call through to me in North Yorkshire, where it was something like midnight. I'd been sat at the computer in a really dazed state writing up the notes of my long interview with Zander the day we had walked around the garden. I'd been at it for several hours, and my head was full of images of Spain and the whole Zander story. When the telephone buzzed on my desk I picked it up and without thinking, said 'Anthony Zander, can I help you?'

Julian's voice was incredulous. 'Anthony? Dad?'

I was very tired and had no idea who was speaking.

'James Christie Productions. Can I help you?"

'James, it's Julian! What's going on?' He sounded very confused. 'You just spoke my father's name, and for God's sake, you did it in his voice?'

In Anthony Zander's voice?

Did I?

I might have done.

I wasn't sure.

By the same Author

"The Light In The Darkness"
Mage Publishing ISBN 0952710919 biography

"Out Of This World"
Mage Publishing ISBN 0952710927 biography

"The Spanish Wizard"
Mage Publishing ISBN 0952710900 poetry

"Analucia Moon"
Mage Publishing ISBN 0952710935 poetry (illustrated)

All titles may be ordered through leading book shops or direct from Mage Publishing at 27 Clifford Moor Road, Boston Spa, Wetherby LS23 6NU or order online from

www.pebooks.co.uk